Ancestors
& Angels

Ancestors & Angels

JANE CRANMER

British Library Cataloguing in Publication Data

A catalogue record for this book is available from the British Library.

ISBN 978-1-7391481-1-9

I have been extremely blessed in my life, by the family I was born into, the family I married into and the children of this union. I am also fortunate in having the closest of dear friends who are truly kindred spirits. This book, I hope, will immortalize my loved ones on both sides of the veil.

You are never more than a thought away.

In remembrance of Sidney William Berry 1935-2010

I know how much you were looking forward to reading this Dad - the first copy is winging its way to Heaven – enjoy! xxx

Acknowledgements

To Mark, for supporting me financially and emotionally through this extremely long process – did I really say it would "probably only take about three months to complete"? Thank you for believing in me enough to let me follow my dreams, even if you're not sure you can believe what I'm actually writing about!

To Matt, for your meticulous help in formatting, copy editing, and assisting with and finalising the cover design. I received a book on grammar and punctuation for Christmas and I promise I'll try harder next time!

To AJ, for long hours spent deliberating over the size of butterflies and what angle they should fly at, and helping set up websites, and showing me how to copy and paste… and turn the computer on, you're so talented!

To Dan, for designing the Ghostwriter logo and not grumbling too much when you had to keep readjusting the size over and over again. Lots of like, Nun.

To Jess, for telling me to "go for it" in the first instance, and for helping with the re-type after the lap top was stolen. Big hugs Madam Mim.

To Lee, for being a good sport and giving me free reign to tell it like it was – hope it makes you smile – Big Sis. x

To Lou, for allowing me to include your email and being good enough to "tell the tale" in your own words,

To Kate (the doctor) Milnes, for proof reading the enormous first draft, after that all those dissertations must seem a doddle! Thanks for getting the ball rolling.

To Carol Ward, for the first edit, thank you so much for taking time out of your busy schedule to read my book, what a pal!

To Reuben Davison at Bank House Books, thank you for helping me decipher the finer points of publishing and pointing me in the right direction. It has been much appreciated!

To Jacky Newcomb, "The Angel Lady", thank you so much for your wonderful inspiring emails, for your kind endorsement, and for helping me to believe I could do it when the going got tough!

To Uncle Lou and Janet for assistance in recalling some of the details from times long past.

To Aunty Margery, for all the sandwiches, cake and copious cups of tea that kept Matt and I from flagging with exhaustion on many an afternoon.

There are so many family and friends who have helped me in this endeavour and I would like to thank you all. A writer's journey is often a lonely one but I have found that no matter how arduous the task became at times, someone would pop up at just the right moment with a bit of inspiration to spur me onwards.

For those of you who may be wondering how you managed to evade the pages of this book, I have two more in the pipeline and I needed to hold a few tales back… your turn will come, there's no escape!

xxx

Contents

Prologue

Sometimes they come back...

A sudden cough, a splutter, and she was back again. Only exactly where was back?

Throwing off the cover and sitting suddenly bolt upright; the old lady was alerted to another presence in the room by a gasp of consternation. Peering imperiously over the top of the sheet, her eyes settled on a small man with a startled face, wearing rather grubby overalls.

"You," she demanded. "Come here!"

Eyes wide like a rabbit caught in the headlights of an oncoming vehicle, the man hesitantly approached her. He had a small feathery moustache, a spattering of freckles over his nose, and a pronounced twitch in one eye.

"Where am I?" She demanded.

"I'm really sorry missus; there must have been a mistake..." He stuttered.

"Mistake?" Somewhere at the back of her mind a memory stirred. She had been on a journey.

"They said it was fish poisoning took you over... You've been gone three hours or more now."

Why was the wretched little fellow squirming around as if he needed to make water, wringing his hands, perspiration all over his brow? "I better get someone." He scurried off.

Bemused she looked down, there was a considerable draft coming from somewhere. Horrified she discovered the sheet was barely all that seemed to be covering her dignity. She wrapped it closer around her, became aware of her long silver hair hanging loose down her back, unthinkable, how absolutely terrible to be seen in such a dishevelled state!

Footsteps up ahead, clattering hastily down the corridor, the twitchy fellow was back, followed by a stout chap with curling grey whiskers and lavish sideburns, the hair on his pate she noticed was slightly less lavish.

"Good heavens it's true!" His balding head flushed a florid shade of red. "Madam my abject apologies!"

Still clutching the sheet in one hand she raised the other as if expecting him to fall to his knees and kiss it; instead he clutched it to him, gazed at it bemusedly as if she had grown an extra digit.

"Enough of all this silliness," she exclaimed, brushing him aside and swinging her legs around to sit up. "Where are my family? They have allowed me to return, I need to say farewell," she declared, exasperated.

The two men exchanged an inscrutable look.

"Who have allowed you to return missus?" Ferret face asked.

A whiff of summer flowers, children's laughter, golden sunlight shining in some far off place, the feeling of forever…

"I can't remember who exactly," she scowled. "But I have only two weeks and lots and lots to arrange."

Shaking his head in consternation the whiskered chap clutched her hand again. "Of course, of course, we'll send for your family to fetch you."

"At once!" She commanded. They scuttled off, casting wary glances over their shoulders as they retreated.

Curious she looked around further, what on Earth had she been lying on, it was hard and unyielding beneath her fragile aching limbs. A cold grey slab appeared to be her resting place.

"Mary, Mother of Jesus, I'm in the mortuary!"

The year was 1931, forty four years before a gentleman name Raymond Moody would study and write a book *Life After Life* about a phenomenon known as NDE (Near Death Experience) in which hundreds of cases of people returning from the dead were examined. This meant nothing to the family of my great grandmother, Mary Holdcroft, they simply rejoiced to have her safely back amongst the living and took her home again, for what, as she also foretold, was to be a brief period only.

This tale, with many others, passed into family legend, re-told by word of mouth down the years, until here we are, ready to revisit the past, examine the present, and speculate about the future… it is time to open the closet door and take a peek into Narnia.

Introduction

I have some good news for you. You are not going to die – not ever.

Now that I've got your attention you are probably wondering how I know this. It is an awfully bold, presumptive statement for a complete stranger to be making to you, isn't it? You are right, and I don't have any short answers. I have been on an amazing journey of discovery that so far has spanned forty-four years, and was in fact begun with my ancestors long before I arrived. It won't be a brief tale, so I hope to goodness you're sitting comfortably, and any of you wearing seat belts might be advised to fasten them, and if you're not… well, just hold on tight!

The answers to life, the universe and everything are somewhere just along the road, or maybe somewhere over the rainbow, so climb aboard your broomsticks, click the heels of your ruby slippers together, and repeat after me, "I do believe in fairies". Ok, you don't have to, but the ride will be sooo much more fun if you keep an open mind.

One more word of warning before we proceed, everything in this book is absolutely true, most of it defies logic, and some bits of it defy gravity, it is best read as it was written, with an open mind, your tongue in your cheek, and a large glass of something at hand to steady your nerves…

See you on the other side!

Part One

'Tis all a chequer board of nights and days
Where destiny with men for pieces plays
Hither and thither moves, and mates and slays
And one by one back in the closet lays.

The Rubaiyat of Omar Khayyam

Chapter One
Beyond the veil and back again

Following the thread

Hard though it is for me to believe, there was a time when I did not exist in the physical realm.

My predecessors lived and died oblivious to my soon-to-be existence, yet were it not for them, I should not be who I am today. Their genes are my genes; their blood runs through my veins, all their gifts are mine. In order to understand why I am who I am, and where the thread begins, as far back as I am able to trace it at least, it is necessary for us to take a journey back into the past.

Once upon a time…

Mist. There is always mist. The mists that envelop the moors near where my family grew up. The mists that edge the boundaries between the etheric and material worlds. The mists of time now rolled back a century and more to the beginning of my story. The mists beneath the hedgerows, where my ancestor used to forage and sometimes sleep.

Jane Nut – Gypsy Jane, Romany, my great great grandmother, the woman whose name I bear, and yet know so little about. But, as far as I know, this is where the tale begins.

My Nana Elsie, herself the granddaughter of Jane Nut, used to tell me tales of the brightly painted gypsy caravans, sleeping out under the stars, the campfires, the singing, dancing, and the mysterious gift of the fortune teller. To my knowledge, my Nana had never experienced this lifestyle first-hand, but amongst other gypsy blessings passed down across the generations was the art of the storyteller.

Traditionally gypsies did not learn to read and write but passed on their lore by word of mouth. My Nana was an entertaining and talented conjurer of words; she would lull me to sleep with her stories, both real and imaginary. I slept many nights beneath that painted caravan myself, transported back in time to a place long before I was born…

Who can now say when or where or how it happened, but somehow Jane Nut broke with tradition and settled down with a local lad, William Buckley. They went on to produce several children, one of them being Mary (later known as Polly), my great-grandmother. Mary in her turn made good by marrying George Holdcroft, the impoverished heir of a once wealthy family, their fortune long gone, but his breeding impeccable.

The Holdcrofts' had been rich and powerful landowners, however, following the tragically early demise of his beautiful, and much loved, wife, the then heir to the estate (Elijah Holdcroft) turned for solace to drinking and gambling and, within a short time, had squandered the fortune left to him by his forebears.

By the time George Holdcroft and his new wife Mary (Polly) came into their inheritance, there was precious little left except the stance and demeanour borne of the upper middle classes and a few pieces of fine furniture.

Mary (Polly), I am told, was the undoubted matriarch of her family. She had strong, bold features, piercing black eyes and dark brown hair. There was a swarthiness to her skin that presumably came from her mother's Romany origins – at some point the family had been Huguenots, fleeing religious persecution from France and, apparently, Mary was thought to be very "Frenchified" in her look, her ways and her turn of phrase.

Where the gypsy blood met the French lineage is a riddle I have yet to solve, but it blended beautifully in the persona of Mary Holdcroft. From an early life of high expectations (I believe the Buckleys' were reasonably well off in those days, otherwise, Mary would not have been deemed a suitable match for a Holdcroft… no matter how financially embarrassed) to what should have been a fortuitous marriage, my great grandmother found herself reduced to the servitude and poverty of the working classes.

If it bothered her (and lets assume, from what is known of her nature, it did) she was far too well bred to let it show. She kept her chin up, her head held high, and, like her mother before her, accepted her lot, and just "got on with it".

So there she was, forced by drastically reduced circumstances to leave behind the Staffordshire village where she grew up to set up home in a modest terrace house, out in the wilds of Yorkshire.

For many years, the growing family lived in and around the mining district of Wakefield. They were surrounded by people in cloth caps with bewildering accents and strange turns of phrase, a penchant for whippets and brown sauce with everything, cobbled streets and buildings with rooms crammed to overflowing with large extended families and sometimes the odd lodger too.

Nonetheless, she made her home there, shouldered her lot uncomplainingly, stood by her gallant but penniless husband, and in time they had eight children, one of whom was my Nana, Elsie.

From their mother, they inherited dark hair and eyes, a haughty carriage and certain "Frenchness" from their father they inherited, well, let's be honest, not a lot, the poor fellow found by the time his children came along there was nothing left!

Ideas above her station

My Nana, Elsie, was amongst the youngest of these eight children. George was the eldest followed by William, the twins Harry and Olive, Elsie herself, Leah, Tom and Horace, the baby of the family.

With eight children in the house, this meant that there were ten people, and occasionally a lodger to help with finances, living in one small terraced house. Despite her humble beginnings, Elsie held herself with a demeanour befitting the upper classes, which you may imagine was wildly at variance with the people she grew up living amongst.

The manners, high ideals, airs and graces of my great grandmother were passed down through the generations. A working-class family with an upper-middle-class mentality! (I daresay the gypsy heritage was greatly played down). Nonetheless, they were extremely poor and whilst the boys were now forced to work in the pits, very like those their grandfather had once owned, the girls in turn went into "service".

9

Elsie's first foray into service was to be short-lived, she found her first position aged just fourteen, sent several miles from home to work as a maid for a wealthy family.

Seven days a week, with just one afternoon off (and nowhere to go as a young single girl on her own), Elsie worked. Up at six to clean and light all the fires, prepare, cook and serve a lavish breakfast for the household, then scurry off to the kitchen out of sight.

Elsie's breakfast was one small banana, and that was expected to sustain her through till lunch (mid-afternoon) which generally consisted of bread and dripping.

Although she did her best to keep her head down and worked her fingers to the bone (almost literally, her hands permanently chapped and sore from the various household tasks), Elsie still managed to get herself noticed, on the one hand favourably by the master of the house who, having engaged her in conversation one time, was pleasantly surprised to find she spoke in a genteel and articulate manner, and thereafter would often find occasion to speak with her.

On the other hand, the mistress of the house found her most disagreeable for the self-same reason: she did not feel Elsie spoke in a tone befitting her station in life.

Matters came to a head one day, when unable to bite her tongue, Elsie had the audacity to answer back to an unfair comment thrown her way by the mistress of the house, in fact, she found that once she gave vent to her feelings it was somewhat hard to stop until she had eloquently, and fluently, pointed out all the shortcomings of her vacuous mistress and her pampered, spoilt way of life.

You could say Elsie returned home in disgrace, although fortunately, the master of the house considered it his responsibility to see her deposited safely on the train home, with an extra two weeks' wages tucked into her hand, just to see her family right in the meantime.

Elsie returned again to the world of the servant class, cooking and cleaning being the main occupations available for a girl of her age and station.

It could be perilous just taking a job in those days. Once she was chased for miles across fields when she took a wrong turn on her way to a new position. Her pursuer, a large man in an overcoat and knee-high boots, was only scared off when another young chap appeared out of nowhere, seemingly on a morning stroll across the fields.

"Must have been my guardian angel," Nana mused to me years later. "He saw me safe into the nearest village, then vanished before I had the chance to thank him!"

Nonetheless, she swore never to seek work in that town again. "Beware of Huddersfield!" she told me superstitiously.

On another occasion, it was a warning voice in her own head that made her turn down a prospective job offer.

She had arrived at the "big house" and was waiting in the hallway whilst the housekeeper looked over her references. Suddenly, something inside told her instinctively not to take the position, and much to the housekeeper's bemusement she told her there had been a mistake, took back her references and hastened out of the door.

She began to walk home, remonstrating with herself for her foolishness. It wasn't as if the family were so well off that they could afford her picking and choosing where to work, good positions were hard to find.

As she dithered indecisively, wondering whether she dare go back again, (for surely the housekeeper wouldn't entertain her now, anyway), she bumped into an old lady she knew.

"I hope tha's not goin for a job up at yon house Elsie," her companion advised. "Master's a bit too fond of the young maids, and Mistress turns a blind eye, if tha knows what I mean." She gave a knowing nod in the direction of the house.

Elsie thanked her for the tip-off and hurried home; pondering on how she'd sensed that something just wasn't right there.

It wasn't the first time she'd been proved right by intuition, and it certainly wouldn't be the last.

War is declared

Elsie Mae Holdcroft, aged sixteen, was petite, with enormous brown eyes, waist-length chestnut brown hair and the manners of an aristocrat, but when pushed had the tongue and fists of a navvy.

It was around this time that she met and fell in love with my Granddad, James Webster (usually known as Jim). James was tall whereas Elsie was small; he towered over her at six foot to her five foot two. He was blonde and blue-eyed with a big booming laugh, from hard-working northern stock. James had a quick temper that was more than matched by Elsie's feistiness, but they were equally bright, learned and humorous, so decided to get engaged, and therefore embarked on a love/hate relationship that would span over seventy years!

Not long after they became engaged the First World War broke out, in 1914. James lied about his age, being just sixteen, in order to enlist. With his height and broad shoulders he was accepted unquestioningly and, along with thousands of young patriots like him, was soon fighting in the trenches of some foreign field.

Back at home, Elsie became a land girl, working on a local farm, where she felt drawn to the horses, perhaps by something gypsy in the blood or, as she always believed, a familiarity borne out of a previous incarnation as a cowboy!

James was one of the fortunate few that survived the hell that that war quickly became and, apart from a sojourn in hospital with trench foot, returned home physically unscathed. I don't know for certain if it was the horrors he witnessed during those four years of service, but my Granddad was a lifelong Atheist; I suppose it would have been hard for him to believe in a God that could look on whilst such atrocities were committed.

As soon as they were able after the end of the war James and Elsie were married.

James got work down the pits, and Elsie played the traditional role of housewife, keeping their little home spotless, and creating culinary delights out of nothing; for truly in those days, nothing was about the extent of what they had after the rent was paid. Fortunately, Elsie's numerous relatives lived round and about, and they all muddled through to help and support each other in whatever way they could.

There was a strong sense of community back then, and although people had little enough to give, they were always willing to share with someone less fortunate.

A young family

It was in March of 1923 that Elsie and James's first child was born, a daughter they named Mary (for Elsie's mother, presumably). Fortunately, she survived childhood, holding on to life with tenacity despite the poverty and deprivation of her early years.

Mary's earliest memory was Christmas Day 1925 when she was not yet two years old. She was awakened by her father to see her "present" and he carried her into the bedroom next door where her mother, Elsie, sat cradling a tiny bundle.

"Look, Mary, here's your new brother Jim." (Named for his father, as was often the tradition with the first boy).

From that moment on Mary put on the mantle of responsibility as the eldest child, determined to care for and tend for her younger siblings as each arrived in turn.

In April 1929 Mary, now five, and Jim, three, gained another addition to the family, Horace, named after Elsie's youngest brother.

Mary took on the role of "little mother" to her two brothers, as Elsie was swept up in the endless daily rounds of cooking, cleaning and laundering, and had scant time or attention to pay to three children under six.

Their dad was out working long hours down the pit and would return home exhausted and black with coal dust from head to foot. It would be fair to say Elsie had a full-time job trying to keep the coal dust out of the house, and off of the furnishings.

Each evening before tea could even be contemplated hot water had to be boiled and a tin bath set behind a screen before the fire so that Jim could scrub and scrub until he was clean. A proud man, tired and hungry as he was, he would not sit down at the table still in dirty work clothes.

This then was the world inhabited by my grandparents and my Aunty Mary, Uncle Jim and Uncle Horace. Extremely poor, extremely proud, closely knit, family and community-minded folk. Times were hard, but they were happy nonetheless.

Fond farewells, tobacco and peppermints

By the time Mary was born, there was barely any trace of the former wealth that had once been in my family. My great grandmother however still retained a strict and aristocratic air about her. Once a week Mary would be allowed to visit her grandparents, along with her mother. It was actually quite scary, she confided to me many years later.

My great-grandmother always wore a starched black gown with a small white lace collar. She had a beautifully carved straightback chair that she sat upon, but everyone else was required to stand.

Her room also contained a sumptuous gilt mirror. On the one occasion Mary had strayed to take a peek in it my great-grandmother had admonished her mother, Elsie, to "Tell her to come away from that mirror, with such vanity she is bound to see the Devil inside it!"

Mary didn't need telling twice. In fact, she found it was generally best to stand with downcast eyes, and speak only when spoken to.

From what I can gather my great-grandmother was a rather cold and imperious woman, who had been forced to live a life she considered far beneath her.

The only time Mary was ever encouraged to be childlike was in the company of her granddad, a complete contrast to his stern and imperious spouse.

Her granddad's pet name for her was "My Little Wench." She would often meet him on his way home from work and they would stop off at the village store.

He always bought a stick of liquorice each for Mary and her brothers, a bag of peppermint drops (his favourites) and a pouch of tobacco. The latter he would stash away in his waistcoat pocket with a wink to Mary, "Don't tell your Granny!" The rest of his wage was given straight over to his wife for housekeeping.

Sadly, Mary's beloved granddad passed away when she was about eight years old.

Before the funeral, the coffin stayed at his former home, in the parlour (the best room in the house, naturally), in pride of place as was the custom in those days. Mary was very upset, and so it was not totally surprising that the night before his funeral her granddad appeared to her in a dream. He said not to cry, that he was alright, and very happy where he was, Aunty Mary told me many years later, but then he leant closer and said, "I need you to do me a favour though, my wench."

Mary asked what this favour might be.

"Well," said her granddad. "Your Granny has left my peppermint drops on the sideboard, and my tobacco is still in my other waistcoat!"

The morning of the funeral dawned, and the adults were quite startled as Mary rushed unceremoniously into her grandmother's parlour.

"Don't fasten up the coffin yet!" She declared.

"Why Mary, whatever's the matter with you?" Her mother asked, taken aback by this sudden rude behaviour.

"Granddad told me in a dream that you have forgotten to put his tobacco and peppermint drops in the coffin with him," Mary declared.

"It was only a dream pet, of course we wouldn't forget a thing like that," soothed her mother, Elsie. "He asked me especially before he died." But she checked anyway, and they weren't there.

"Oh my goodness, with all the preparation for the funeral I must have forgotten, I could have sworn I'd put them in, wherever can they be?"

Fortunately, Mary knew exactly where to look. There on the sideboard were the peppermint drops, and in the waistcoat of his everyday suit was his pouch of tobacco. (He was of course being buried in his "Sunday Best"). Mary put them lovingly into the coffin with her granddad.

"I wasn't sad after that," she told me many years later. "I knew he would be ok as long as he had his peppermints and tobacco pouch with him."

I'll go when I'm ready!

Mary, Jim and Horace were now left with one remaining grand-parent on their Mother's side; the somewhat remote, Frenchified, strict grandmother, who still ruled over her family with a will of iron.

Mary's weekly visits remained a secret torment, somehow no matter how she tried, she never stood straight enough, or was clean enough or her hair tidy enough, to meet with her grand-mother's approval. Dutifully she still went to see her, but in her heart of hearts she would have loved to decline.

The older the granddame became, the more imperious she was, the harder to please. There was something decidedly strange and other-worldly about her too, but of course no-one would ever dare to remark on it.

Just when it seemed she was destined to live forever, Mary's grandmother suddenly was taken severely ill, with what the doc-tor diagnosed as "fish poisoning" and died.

She was in the mortuary for several hours, laid out on a cold slab, when, to the consternation of the local undertaker and his assistant, "the corpse" was seen to move.

With a cough and a splutter the old lady threw off her sheet and sat up!

The family were summoned and duly took her home, elated. My great grandmother called the eldest family members to her.

"I've come back," she announced. "Because I told them I needed to say "Au revoir", but I will not be able to stay with you for long, I have been allowed only two weeks."

Of course everyone remonstrated with her that it had all been a terrible mistake, and she would be back with them for a long time yet, they felt sure.

Two weeks later Mary, who was nine, and her cousin, also called Mary (Wainwright, her Aunty Olive's daughter) who was eleven, were out in the street playing hopscotch when suddenly, the older of the two Marys stopped.

"I've got to go, Grandmother is calling me," she announced.

Mary was perplexed. She had heard nothing, and grandmother's house was streets away, but still she hastened after her cousin to see what was going on.

By the time they got to their grandmother's house it was crammed full of family members, several of which had also heard her "call" or felt a sudden impulse just to go to her.

Mary's grandmother was sitting up in bed, dressed immaculately, and holding court.

One by one she called each family member to her to tell them something. Mary went forward with her mother, who was heavily pregnant with her fourth child at the time. Her grandmother put her hand on Elsie's bump.

"My time has come now," she said decidedly, then added, "This is a boy – and you are to name him Louis – spelt the French way. "

Startled, Elsie agreed.

"You must remember," the old lady impressed upon Elsie, "this is merely "Au revoir", not goodbye, until we meet again."

That was it. A quick kiss was permitted and Mary and Elsie were dismissed.

Once everyone had been seen, contented that all her affairs had now been satisfactorily put in order, my great grandmother settled back, closed her eyes and breathed her last.

A few days before the funeral, in the middle of the night, Mary awakened with a dreadful toothache, crying for her mother Elsie. Unfortunately, her mother was otherwise disposed as Mary's younger brothers, Jim and Horace, were both ill with some childhood infection and she was trying to tend to them, whilst fighting her own sadness and exhaustion.

Mary was suddenly aware of her Granny sitting next to her, at the side of the bed. She looked lovely, younger somehow, luminous and dressed all in white, with the most serene and beautiful smile on her face, a countenance not often presented in life.

"Hush child, your mother cannot come to you just now," she was heard to say, and then she placed her hand on Mary's inflamed cheek. Instantly the toothache disappeared and Mary fell into a deep and peaceful sleep.

The next morning her mother looked in on Mary and apologised for not being able to come through the night.

"It's alright, Granny was here and she made it better," Mary told her. Her mother went quite pale.

"Mary, your Granny has died," she reminded her.

It seemed her grandmother could not resist showing them she was alive and well on the other side of the veil. Perhaps unsurprisingly, several weeks later, when Elsie's fourth child made an appearance it was a boy. He was named Louis, spelt the "French" way, of course!

Someone to watch over me

When my relatives were little more than children and my own mother not yet born, Louis was the baby of the family.

If ever there was a case to be made for someone having a Guardian Angel, Louis certainly put his to the test as a child!

One particularly harsh winter the snow had piled up against the house four feet deep. My nana told me later that they could barely see through the windows for the ice.

James, my granddad, discovered the front door open, and a strange little hole tunnelling away from the house. A quick head count revealed the baby, Louis, who was only two at the time, had disappeared. James and Jim, as the oldest boy, had to go in search.

They frantically dug their way out of the house and found the place Louis had exited his escape tunnel. They also discovered a pile of discarded clothes in the snow, not only was little Louis out in below zero temperatures, alone at two years old, he was naked! Both shivering unbearably, they tracked the little mite through the snow, eventually finding him ploughing his way through the drifts to his Aunty Olives' house in search of a biscuit, totally unperturbed by the cold.

Another time, several years later, when Louis was about six, Jim, Horace and Louis found a disused flour mill. They went inside and were chasing each other around as boys do. Horace and Louis found a stairwell to a higher floor, and came out on a ledge encircling the upper level. Jim looked up from below to see them running along above him; Louis backwards to taunt Horace who was trying to catch him.

With a sick feeling Jim realised seconds too late that Louis was backing towards a part of the ledge that had broken away.

"Louis watch out!" He screamed as Louis took a step out into nothing and plummeted thirty feet to the ground.

"Did it hurt?" I asked him, sixty years later.

"A bit," he recalled.

Amazingly, apart from the odd bruise, he was unscathed from a fall that should really have killed him. Jim and Horace were in a worse state from witnessing it happen.

Someone, somewhere, must have been watching over him his mother Elsie mused. His father, who didn't believe in such things, was lost for a logical explanation. "Bloody lucky!" seemed to be his theory.

"She's waiting to take me"

When Mary was about eleven she was especially fond of her little cousin Jeffrey. He was only two and very sweet, but sadly the little mite contracted pneumonia. Mary would visit him to try and cheer him up. She found him lying in bed limp and pale, but smiling to see her all the same. Mary knew he was seriously ill, and found herself crying suddenly. Then little Jeffrey took hold of her hand.

"Don't cry Mary," he lisped in his childish voice. "I'm going to Jesus soon, and my grandmother is waiting to take me."

Years later Aunty Mary recalled she had never seen anyone so happy or so fearless. True to his word the little lad passed over a few days later.

"It was strange," Aunty Mary told me, recounting the memory. "When he told me he seemed so calm and certain, and so much older than his years, and when he spoke of our grandmother he looked past me to a corner of the room, so I'm certain she was there, just as he said she was; waiting."

Chapter Two
Predictions and possessions

New arrivals and acquaintances

My grandparents' youngest child arrived in 1938, a baby girl christened Olive, named for Elsie's sister. This was, and is, my mum.

Born the year before war broke out once again, Olive was the adored, indulged baby of the family. Her eldest sister Mary was now fifteen, and more like a second mother than her older sibling. The two eldest boys, Jim and Horace viewed her as a little princess and protected her as such. Louis, now seven years old and suddenly ousted from his position as baby of the family, viewed her as a rival or co-conspirator against the older boys depending on the circumstances

Scarcely had the latest addition to the family arrived then it was time for Mary, the eldest, to depart. At sixteen she lied about her age in order to gain employment in a public house many miles away. This entailed a tearful departure, as she had to leave home and live away. It would be several months before she could afford the train fare required to return on a visit.

Mary had lodgings inside the pub. She found the landlord and landlady kind and hospitable and quickly became friends with their daughter Elsa, a blonde and sophisticated nineteen year old, who took Mary under her wing.

Mary's naturally pretty look of dark wavy hair and large dark brown eyes complimented her companion's blonde blue-eyed visage by contrast. Mary shy and reserved, Elsa bold and brash; they were very popular with the young male clientele, but Mary wasn't interested in romance, her primary objective was to work hard and send home as much of her pay as she possibly could.

Suddenly, war broke out, and the pub became frequented by young soldiers from the local barracks.

One evening as they were working Elsa gave Mary a surreptitious nudge.

"You see those two soldiers that have just come in?" she asked. Mary was so busy she had barely had time to look up, let alone ogle any young men entering the establishment, Elsa pointed them out.

"See the blonde one? He's mine." Mary looked at the soldier disinterestedly, he was clearly far too old for her, or Elsa for that matter.

A voice spoke decisively in her head, "I'm going to marry that man."

Mary jumped and looked around. She looked again at the soldier, curiously. What was she thinking? She knew nothing at all about this man, and had no interest in him. Let Elsa have her fun, she was much too busy.

So Elsa did her worst. She flirted outrageously, dressed provocatively, batted her lashes, and dropped hints about having no escort for the village fair. The dark-haired younger one of the two soldiers quickly took the bait and offered to take Elsa. The blonde haired stranger simply smiled, then he turned to Mary who was keeping to herself, wiping dry the glasses behind the bar.

"What about you?" he enquired. "Would you like to go to the fair?"

Mary was instantly abashed. Elsa's eyes flashed angrily at her, but the soldier was smiling coaxingly. Suddenly she felt it would appear rude to say no, so she acquiesced. Anyway, she told herself, if they went as a foursome it would give Elsa another opportunity to charm him.

The soldier extended his hand.

"My name's John, but all my friends call me Jack," he said.

As it turned out they all had a wonderful time at the fair and Elsa found she quite liked the dark-haired chap after all. As for Mary, she couldn't remember ever having laughed so much.

"How old are you?" Her new friend asked.

"Eighteen," Mary quickly responded. She didn't dare let anyone know her true age for fear of losing her job.

"I'm twenty-seven," Jack told her.

He had been in the boy soldiers from fourteen, and then the regular army where he had worked his way up to sergeant. Mary found she liked his good humoured, polite manner very much.

For several weeks Mary and Jack went out on her afternoon off. They got on extremely well, despite the age difference (an even greater difference than Jack realised), and Mary found herself looking forward to Wednesdays each week. Then one day when Jack called to collect her he seemed quieter and more preoccupied than usual.

"I've got my orders at last" he told her. "I'm being posted abroad by the end of the week."

Mary had barely time to take this in before he blurted out, "I wondered if you would consider getting engaged, then we would be able to stay in contact, I would be allowed letters from my fiancée and I could write back."

A little stunned, Mary found herself saying yes before she'd barely had time to think.

Jack pulled a small brown box out of his top pocket; a pretty three stoned ring twinkled there which fit Mary's dainty finger perfectly!

"I'm so glad you said yes," Jack confided. "As I've already taken the liberty of telegraphing your parents to say you are engaged and coming home. It won't be safe to stay here so near the garrison in the next few weeks, and your family will need you with them, I expect."

So, a somewhat dazed and astounded Mary found herself saying goodbye to her new friends and even newer fiancé and climbing aboard the train home, her ticket paid for by Jack, who seemed to have thought of everything except whether she had an opinion on the matter!

Mary's parents were less than pleased to have her return home engaged to a soldier who was unknown to them and eleven years her senior.

Fortunately, her mother's displeasure was soon diverted when Mary's father, James, enlisted for the army again, voluntarily.

Now in his late thirties he was old enough to be excused service, but to James it was simply a matter of honour; his country needed every able bodied man to fight against Hitler and he was going.

Elsie was furious that he was going to risk his life unnecessarily a second time, leaving her and five children to fend for themselves, but there was no changing his mind.

James was made up to sergeant in respect of his former service and proudly marched away to war a second time.

Elsie's one consolation was that as yet her sons were too young to enlist. Jim was nearly fourteen, and took on the role of "man of the house", a position that frequently rubbed up against Mary's position as eldest.

Elsie left them all to their bickering, she had more than enough to worry about. She was penniless, husbandless indefinitely, and had five children to feed, with the youngest, Olive, only just turned one year old.

Keeping the night watch

The war years were hard for everyone. Money was scarce and, even when there was money to spend, everything was rationed and there was little available to buy.

Fortunately, for Elsie she found a friend in the local grocer, who used to find ingenious ways of making her tea ration stretch further each week.

Most people have their addictions; Elsie's secret passion lay beneath a tea cosy. The family could not survive without several cups of their favourite brew each day!

Elsie's two sisters Leah and Olive were in slightly better positions financially. Being older and more settled, they kindly endeavoured to help out wherever they could.

Somehow, the women of the family pulled together to support each other and the children whilst all the men were away at a war that seemed to last forever.

Elsie took on the role of mother and father, her indomitable spirit and stubborn will to survive kept the family going. She would take on board any work she could to earn a few extra shillings a week.

One surprising source of aid came from a previously unsuspected talent she discovered for "reading tea leaves".

It had started as a parlour game to amuse herself and her sisters, but word soon got out and frequently neighbours would beat their way to her front door to request a reading.

With the men-folk away at war the local women were anxious for news, no matter how it reached them or what quarter it came from.

Elsie did not especially enjoy the task of reading the tea leaves as they did not always foretell good news. She refused to charge for the readings but was often paid in gifts of tea, sugar, bread or milk, all of which were welcome with five children to feed.

Mary, now eighteen, managed to secure work as an auxiliary nurse at the nearest hospital.

Although this was a harrowing time for a young girl to work on the wards, Mary found she had an aptitude for calming and healing the people she nursed.

Her hardest task was working on the children's wards, with younger siblings herself she was moved by the plight of many of the youngsters in her care. Mary's kind and soothing manner made her a huge hit with her young patients, but less popular with some of the older nurses whose bedside manners suffered by comparison.

"You're too soft with them!" they'd chide her, as she often stopped back after her shift was over to read bedtime stories or sing them to sleep with her lilting, mellifluous voice.

It was during one of these night time sessions that Mary encountered the ghost.

Mary and her companion had settled the children on the ward for the night, and were quietly filling out reports at the nurses' station. Unexpectedly, they heard footsteps at the far end of the ward where it led to a short corridor that finished in a dead end. Thinking one of the children must have got out of bed and was perhaps sleepwalking, Mary went to investigate, leaving her colleague in charge.

As she approached the bottom of the ward she could distinctly hear footsteps in the corridor beyond.

"Hello?" she called out softly, not wishing to startle whoever was there, but there was no reply.

Mary entered the corridor and peered into the gloom. At the

far wall where the corridor ended she could make out the appearance of a soldier, although his face was hidden by shadow, his uniform identified him.

Somewhat startled, as to get there he should have had to walk past the nurses' station, and she had not seen anyone, Mary gasped, "How did you get in here?"

When he didn't reply she drew herself up to her full height of five foot three and advanced upon him boldly.

To her surprise, as she approached, the man seemed to just melt into the wall and was gone. When she hesitantly touched the spot he'd apparently disappeared into she found it icy cold to the touch.

Shaking a little with disbelief and fright she hurried back to the nurses' station, where she informed her astounded friend what she'd witnessed.

When matron came to do her rounds Mary found herself relating the tale again.

Matron nodded thoughtfully. "There used to be a door at the end of that corridor you know, but it's been blocked up since after the First World War."

She wasn't at all surprised by Mary's tale, reassuring her that "when you have been nursing as long as I have you come across a lot of strange things – he won't harm you, don't worry."

After that, Mary heard the footsteps pacing the corridor at the bottom of the ward on several nights. She didn't bother to investigate, choosing to leave the lonely soldier to his night-time vigil.

Perhaps he was keeping watch over the slumbering children, guarding them and their nurses through the long hours of the night.

Girl with a past

Mary was not the only one to see ghostly phenomena.

Baby Olive was growing into a charming, precocious toddler. She had bright red, wavy hair, and huge brown eyes, her manner both childish and imperious by turns, depending on the persona she adopted.

One day, her mother and brothers found her struggling exasperatedly to tie a piece of ribbon round her neck.

"Olive, whatever are you doing?" Elsie asked. "You know you must never tie things round your neck; it's dangerous."

Olive looked at her mother, and then in an astonishingly patronising tone informed Elsie and her brothers, "When I was a lady, I used to wear a velvet ribbon round my neck. it had a round picture on the front."

She then went on to describe the cameo and details of the garb worn by women several centuries before, down to the smallest trimmings of her undergarments, much to the amazement and amusement of her mother and brothers. All this knowledge from a child of three!

They found it was not unusual for Olive to be like this, one moment a typical toddler, playing with her doll, Patsy, and bossing the other children around.

"Tum on tids!" She'd shout, exhorting them to follow her.

Then the next thing they knew a dreamy look would come into her eye, and she'd regale them with stories of "when I was a lady", using a vocabulary years beyond her age.

One day, when Olive was only three, she had been upstairs playing with her toys, while her mother was in the kitchen preparing tea. Wandering into the kitchen with her doll, Olive announced "I've just seen Grandma."

This stopped Elsie in her tracks.

"What do you mean?" She asked.

"She was in the bedroom just visiting," the little tot announced.

Elsie was more than a little surprised. As both of Olive's grandmothers had died many years before she was born, she had no knowledge of them as far as Elsie knew.

"What did Grandma look like?"

Olive then proceeded to give a perfect description of Elsie's mother - the style of dress, the way she wore her hair tied back in a tight bun, and her manner of speaking - until Elsie was under no illusion who it was that Olive had seen.

Olive could still recall the incident many years later. When she stumbled across one of her auntie's old photographs she recognised the grandmother who had "come to visit" instantly.

The house on the hill

During this period the family changed residence frequently. They were always weeks behind with their rent; the money just wouldn't stretch that far. Every time the rent man did his rounds, Elsie would draw the curtains and make the children hide under the kitchen table with their fingers tightly over their lips to show Olive she must also play the game and be quiet. Hiding under the table was a regular occurrence anyway, as Elsie flatly refused to go to the air raid shelters. She would rather they take their chances with the bombs than all be "buried alive underground," she declared.

So, when the sirens went off, Elsie and her four youngest would huddle together under the strong oak table until the "all clear" sounded again.

If pressed on the matter Elsie would say her claustrophobia was due to being walled up (at some point in a previous existence), and would elucidate no further on the subject.

When hiding under tables no longer seemed to hold the rent man at bay, the family would find it necessary to do a "moonlight flit".

With the help of the extended family a new lodging would be procured, and in the middle of the night the children would be raised from their beds to traverse the moonlit streets to wherever their latest home would be.

Louis would inevitably get the job of "piggy-backing" sleepy Olive from one abode to the next. At ten, he was not quite tall enough or strong enough to help carry the furniture with Horace and Jim, so it fell to him instead to be his little sister's mode of transport, and he bore the burden stoically.

One of the residences they moved to was a large imposing Victorian house on the top of a hill. It had four bedrooms and large spacious rooms, yet was being let surprisingly cheaply. There was a chance it may take months before defaulting on the rent became necessary again!

It soon became apparent that the reason the house was let so cheaply was because no-one dared to stay there. The house was eerie and reputed to be haunted. Not that this phased Elsie in the slightest.

"The dead won't hurt you if you leave them alone!" she declared. "It's the living you need to be wary of!"

By this time it was becoming obvious that the sensitivity of the older generation was largely present in the younger.

Mary, Horace, Louis and Olive were all acutely aware of energies, entities, and vibrational changes around them. Young Jim, however, was as steadfastly atheist as his father. He did not believe in religion, certainly didn't believe in God, and if he noticed anything strange or untoward around him would put it down to pure coincidence or the failings of other people's irrational minds.

In a family such as this we can suppose he found a lot of that occurring.

This same coolheaded, rationality stood Jim well educationally. With his logical approach to problem solving, keen intellect and conscientiousness he had managed to secure a scholarship at the local grammar school at the age of eleven.

There were no such aspirations for Horace and Louis.Intelligent, quick witted and amusing they certainly were, and like peas in a pod, not to look at, but in nature, despite their age difference.

They had different priorities to Jim and, caught up in a mixture of shrewd intuition and outright fantasy, they vowed not to let anything as mundane as an education get in the way of progress.

Like Tom Sawyer and Huck Finn they were off in search of adventure. While Jim would be sitting at the table, head studiously bent over a book, wrangling with trigonometry or Latin, Horace and Louis would be away over the fields, Olive trailing behind, grudgingly allowed along even though she was only a girl, and a rather small feisty one at that.

She was, however, extremely useful as a lookout.

All the land around where they currently lived belonged to a self-made man named Mazzarella, who was famous for his ice cream in those parts.

Alongside his ice cream empire he also owned some very nice orchards, which was where the two boys loved to go apple scrumping of an evening.

Horace and Louis would be up the trees, filling their pockets and jerseys full to bursting with the little sour crab apples they so craved. Olive would stand guard, on tiptoe, her head just peeping over the top of the wall, eyes scanning the distance. Any sign of movement from the nearby road or fields would have her scurrying back to her brothers, shouting at the top of her five year old voice, "Look out boys, Mazza's coming!"

Olive's reward for this service would be a share of the spoils and a ride back through the fields on Horace or Lou's shoulders.

They would find a place under a shaded tree and eat the sour apples until their stomachs churned mercilessly in protest at the bitter acid. They would return home with the rest, where Elsie would quickly turn the stolen goods into delicious pies, and they would all eat the evidence.

Necessity being the mother of invention, the children would find novel way to supplement the meagre rations. The fields were full of gooseberries and bilberries to be picked and made into pies and jam by their industrious mother.

Horace, Louis and Olive would follow the coal-man's cart for miles picking up bits of "nutty slack" that fell off the back of the wagon until they had a sack full of coal to take home to supplement their fire.

A good fire was essential. It had to be used for cooking, for heating, and to provide hot water for baths. All the children were carefully schooled to tend the grate and not let the fire go out. There was some electricity in those days, but people still used oil lamps for light and stoves for cooking on.

Of course, once the coal was brought home it had to be taken down into the cellar, but only young Jim was willing to go down there. If he shared his siblings' fertile imagination he had it well under control, which was probably just as well.

As they approached the house the three youngest were aware of the stark black windows that seemed to regard their presence like malevolent eyes.

In the hallway the feeling intensified, and Louis still recalls to this day that the worst bit was the landing at the top of the stairs. It was almost as if an invisible force lingered there, watching, and tried to physically repel them from climbing the stairs. This was overcome by Horace and Louis taking the stairs at a run, two at a time, Olive as ever clambering behind, bringing up the rear.

That house was cold. Even in summer the bright spacious rooms didn't seem to hold any warmth. No wonder the children were away in the fields from dawn till dusk when not in school.

Elsie remained unperturbed, she was afraid of nothing and nobody, and any discarnate entities had better remember that!

Perhaps then, it was not the brightest of moves, when one of her sisters suggested that they try their hand at the Ouija board. Elsie agreed and suggested they could use her parlour.

The sisters had never tried this before, but someone had suggested it may be an entertaining way to pass an evening, so one dark October night they all huddled together around a home made board, giggling like little girls, for all their maturing years.

At first, nothing much happened, then eventually the glass began to move under their fingers. The answers that came back to their questions became more and more hostile, as if speaking with an ill-tempered person and the glass began to move faster and more impatiently round the board.

By this time, all three sisters were beginning to feel uneasy. It was not the light-hearted bit of amusement they had been led to believe it would be. Suddenly, the glass shot out of their hands and flew across the room crashing in to the wall. That was enough, the sisters jumped up and dashed out of the room to the relative safety of the kitchen. Elsie thought it best not to venture into the room again until it was daylight.

The next morning she squared her shoulders and marched in courageously. When everything seemed alright she relaxed a little and set to, cleaning up the glass and the remainder of their board that had fallen when they fled the room.

A movement behind her caught her eye and, turning, she saw Gloops the family cat peering round the door at her.

Elsie made a "ch ch ch" sound at the cat. "Come on in puss," she coaxed.

Gloops was having none of it. Suddenly his hackles rose. He made a horrific hiss and then screeched off down the corridor.

Elsie, though a little unnerved remained calm and resolutely swept up to the remainder of the glass, before she too, thankfully left the room.

A week passed, and although nothing else untoward had happened, no-one seemed inclined to use the parlour anymore.

The family huddled round the kitchen table, the obvious excuse being that it was warmer there after Elsie had had the stove lit all day.

Gloops had gone into hiding. Elsie left out food and water that was always gone by morning but, much to her vexation, the darned cat could not be found anywhere, and no amount of calling would tempt him from his hiding place.

The children, too, were remarkably quiet, as if they sensed something was not quite right, but no-one spoke of it. Her sisters had also found numerous reasons to be too busy to call all week.

The following Saturday was October 31st, Hallowe'en. The day passed as usual in a flurry of cooking and cleaning as the younger children played outside, kicking up leaves and telling one another ghost stories. Jim assisted his mother with the heavier work, inbetween his endless studying.

Mary was due home from the nurses' home that night, ready for her day off on Sunday, so Elsie was preparing a large apple pie as a treat.

At dusk everyone started to arrive back home. Last in, flushed from a hurried walk across the fields before night fell, was Mary. The family gathered around the kitchen table with steaming mugs of tea to recount their day's activities. They had not been sitting there talking for long, when a strange, eerie sound arose. One by one they fell silent, all looking wide-eyed from one to the other.

"Mam, what is it?" Olive wondered, her eyes like saucers.

Elsie got to her feet, and picked up the poker from the fire. The horrible screeching, wailing sound, seemed to be coming from the direction of the parlour.

Mary and Jim huddled close in support of her. She admonished the three younger children to stay back, which they did, reluctantly, three little heads peering round the kitchen door into the darkened corridor beyond.

With her heart in her mouth Elsie edged along the corridor, Mary clutching her arm. Jim was trying to light an oil lamp, urging them to wait while he got it lit. Her hand trembling ever so slightly, Elsie pushed open the parlour door. The noise intensified, it made the breath catch in Elsie and Mary's throats.

Summoning all her courage Elsie pluckily stepped across the threshold into the room. The sight beyond the window made the hair on the back of her neck stand up.

In the pale light of a full moon she could make out the garden. Where the lawn should have been were cats, hundreds of cats, staring in through her window and wailing like banshees. This was the unearthly sound they had heard, but what on earth was going on?

A sudden movement caught her eye. Something moving so fast it seemed to be flying was circling around and around the perimeter of the room, leaping across the furniture. Elsie let out a startled shriek of terror. What was it?

Jim rushed into the room, running to his mother's aid, the oil lamp held aloft and Mary just a step behind him.

In the sudden pool of light Elsie could now see the creature was Gloops the cat, finally returned from his hiding place.

He tore around the room dementedly, then with a piercing screech leapt into the curtains and hung there screaming back at the cats outside. The cat's eyes were wide and malevolent. This was no domesticated pet, but a creature turned feral and dangerous.

With his usual calm presence of mind, Jim thrust the oil lamp into Mary's hands, dashed across the room and threw open the window. The cat regarded him with crazed, bloodshot eyes, let out an ear piercing yell, and dived out of the window. Jim slammed it shut behind him. The assembled moggies let out one last collective howl, then bounded away into the dark.

Elsie resolved never ever to mess with Ouija boards again.

Gloops the cat never returned. In fact it transpired that nearly all the cats in the village disappeared that Hallowe'en, much to the puzzlement of the neighbourhood.

Strangest of all, the house seemed to have lost its eerie presence, as if whatever had been entrapped there had gone along with the cat. Still, enough was enough, and before long the family were in search of a new residence, preferably one without a sitting tenant!

When no news is good news

Mary lived away through the week at the nurses' home. During this time a strange kind of subterfuge was being exercised.

Mary, as a nurse, was entitled to three square meals a day to keep her strength up. Nursing was back breaking work and matron wouldn't tolerate her nurses fainting on the wards. However, knowing her family were invariably going hungry, living on rations, Mary was overcome with guilt, and therefore decided to live on the most meagre portions she could while away from them.

On the other hand, Elsie and Mary's siblings did not wish Mary to see them struggling, so all week they also survived on the smallest portions they could, diligently saving the best of their rations for the weekend. Therefore, when Mary came home for Sunday dinner the plates were piled high with the richest, most luxurious food Elsie could prepare. Mary and the family all indulged in tales of how well they were all doing and how fat they were likely to become. Mary would return to the nurses' home, and the whole shenanigan would start again, with everyone starving themselves for six days out of seven, because love and pride dictated they must.

It was only years later they all confessed to this strange practise, and fell about laughing at their solidarity in starving together unnecessarily.

As the man of the house Jim was increasingly concerned for the welfare of his mother and siblings. Unbeknownst to Elsie he petitioned the assistance of her brother, his Uncle Tom, to get him some work down the mines. So, nobly leaving his promising education behind, Jim said goodbye to the grammar school and got a job down the pit at the age of fourteen. Elsie was of course furious but by the time she found out the deed was done.

Over the next couple of years Mary kept up a diligent correspondence with her fiancé, Jack.

As he was posted from place to place letters would often cross in the mail and so exchanges would frequently be out of synch. It wasn't the news that was important to Mary; as long as the letter arrived, the sender could be assumed to be safe and well.

Then, suddenly, Jack's correspondence stopped.

Mary wrote again and again, becoming increasingly frantic. When eventually a response did arrive, it was a telegram, Mary's heart skipped a beat, it was brief and to the point. Sergeant J. Tansley was missing in action.

Weeks passed with no further news, Mary was in an agony of despair, but managed to maintain her bright, cheery façade both at the hospital and on her visits home. It was on one of these visits home that Mary finally got some news.

It was the back end of the day and everyone was sleepy after another hectic week. The family had just settled down to a nice quiet cup of tea when suddenly there came a knock at the door.

Young Jim answered it to an old bedraggled gypsy woman, selling some rather weather-beaten lavender. He was about to send her away, bristling in a brusque fashion at the intrusion by this peddler, when Elsie stopped him.

Seeing the woman was elderly, cold and wet she invited her in. She had no money to buy any lavender she asserted, but the old lady was welcome to a hot drink and a warm by the fire.

The poor old dear was soaked to the skin as it had been pouring with rain all that day. Gratefully she pulled up a chair and settled herself for a much needed rest. After a time her eyes settled on Elsie and she smiled.

"I come from Romany stock, but I can see you have a gift as rare as mine yourself, though you don't choose to use it."

Elsie demurred that she didn't know what the old woman was talking about, she read the tea leaves a bit she confessed, but that was all it was.

Then the gypsy turned to Mary, who had been sitting quietly, trying not to attract attention to herself. Suddenly leaning forward the old woman clasped Mary's hands in her old gnarled ones.

"Your young man is missing!" She declared, then she shook her head thoughtfully. "He is well, do not fret, you will hear from him shortly."

With that she finished her drink, pressed some lavender into Elsie's hands.

"Take it with my blessing, for your kindness," she entreated. Pulling her shawl around her tightly, she went out once again into the blustery night.

True to the old gypsy's word, by the end of the week, not one, but an entire bundle of letters arrived for Mary.

It transpired Jack had not been missing in action at all, he had been involved in some secretive manoeuvres and there had been a mix-up by his regiment. As a result his post and Mary's had gone astray, going to the wrong place in both instances. He was safe and well, and better still within a few weeks had leave to come home.

"Make preparations for our wedding!" He advised, so they did. Elsie pressed the lavender inside the pages of a book, for luck.

Mary and Jack were married in a small quiet family ceremony.

Both Jack and Mary's dad, James, had managed to get two days' leave for the occasion. Mary was proud to see them both straight and tall in their sergeants' uniforms. With all her family around her it was the happiest day of her life.

Chapter Three
Peace and plenty at last

Flight to Bradford

In another characteristic move, made by a split-second decision, the family were now living in Bradford.

They had left Wakefield behind following an accident down the pit which left Jim unable to work as he had injured his foot when a large slab of coal fell on it. Jim was in plaster for several weeks and Elsie, brooding on the matter, decided she didn't want Jim or her younger sons (who would have inevitably followed him down the mines when they were old enough) in danger on a daily basis.

As luck would have it Elsie's niece, Rose (daughter of Elsie's sister Olive), was just about to vacate a large rented property in Bradford. So it was decided almost overnight that they were moving in there, lock, stock and barrel, and that was that! No grammar school educated son of James and Elsie was going to risk his life and squander his talent down the pits.

Bradford was a thriving industrial city, its buildings black with soot from the numerous mills thereabout, its centre a hustle and bustle of humanity, and the pavements pounding with the heartbeat of several thousand souls as they went about their daily tasks.

It was soon to become one of the largest multi-cultural societies in the north of England and people of every race, creed and colour were drawn there by the opportunities this bustling city represented.

The family soon settled in, and before long Jim was on the move again. He had been called up and joined the Royal Navy, sending regular correspondence home with loving missives to all the family and photographs showing him dashing and smart in his naval uniform.

Jim was part of the D-Day landings, serving as a radar operator on board one of the many merchant ships commandeered to collect the British soldiers from the beaches of Normandy. It was one of the proudest and most moving moments of his life, rescuing his comrades in arms, and bringing them safely home.

A sojourn abroad

Once the war was over Jack was posted abroad and Mary was now able to go with him.

They spent the first year of their married life in Germany. To her surprise, despite the recent conflict between the two countries, Mary found the German people wonderful, warm, courteous and very friendly. She quickly settled down to life as an army wife.

News from back home in England told them of how everyone was growing up and becoming readjusted to having Dad back with them safe and sound.

At the other side of the world, Mary and Jack were on the move again. This time they were posted to Singapore, where Jack was given an exalted position and Mary, used to living in cold, damp, terraced houses in the north of England, suddenly found herself in a beautiful white marbled colonial property, with both a personal maid and a housekeeper to assist her in daily tasks.

At night it was so hot she had to curl up with nothing but a sheet, and the essential mosquito net, it was hard to sleep for the humidity and the constant chirruping and whirring of insects. She loved it there, but it was all a world away from what the northern lass was used to.

While in Singapore, Mary celebrated her twenty-first birthday and without thinking she blurted out her true age to Jack, who was stunned as he had thought her two years older.

She finally had to confess her deception had been in order to work away at sixteen. Jack was not amused; a stickler for honesty he did not appreciate the way it had been necessary to keep him in the dark for the past five years. It was their first disagreement and they did not speak for a full week.

However, it was hard to stay cross at each other forever in such beautiful, convivial surroundings. They had no children but Jack bought Mary a cute little spider monkey she called Coco, and he quickly became like a baby to them both.

Coco was as cosseted and adored as any newborn and would have them both crying tears of laughter at his antics. He was as bright as a button with a naturally inquisitive nature and a mischievous streak.

Mary discovered that Coco had a sweet tooth after Jack had bought her a packet of "Spangles" (little square fruit flavoured boiled sweets that she liked). She had eaten one and the remainder were in the pocket of her cardigan. When she came to get another, however, the packet had vanished.

Thinking it must have fallen out, she looked around the room but it was nowhere to be seen. Then, glancing out of the window, she saw the guilty party. Coco was sitting in the middle of the patio table surrounded by discarded wrappers. She watched in amazement as he deftly unwrapped each Spangle with his dextrous little hands and popped sweet after sweet in his mouth.

Tiptoeing up behind him Mary suddenly said, "Coco, what are you doing?"

The little monkey swivelled round to look at her, a guilty expression on his face as he quickly popped the last of the sweets in his mouth. She burst out laughing; inside his cheeks were little pouches where he could store food, rather like a hamsters, and into these he had stuffed a full packet's worth of sweets. His tiny face was distorted with lots of little squares poking out of his cheeks, his mouth so full he couldn't even make his usual chittering sound to reply to her.

Opening his eyes wide and raising an eyebrow as if to say "What am I being accused of?" he reached up and poked one of the little squares in his cheek so that it was now in his mouth. Suddenly he bared it between his teeth to show her "look what I've got".

"Why you cheeky monkey, who's stolen Mary's sweets?" Mary, still laughing remonstrated with him. She made a mock grabbing gesture at him and he bounded away and up into the branches of a nearby tree where he made a great show of crunching loudly while leaping about victoriously in an "Aha, you can't catch me!" fashion. He stayed up the tree all day, until all the little squares had vanished from his cheeks.

Jack and Mary were so amused they would often buy a packet of the sweets he liked so much and hide them round the house. Coco would leap about searching, on a miniature treasure hunt until he'd found every last one. He made a small but extremely amusing companion for Mary whilst Jack was away at work and they both adored him.

Letters flew back and forth around the world, photos of exotic lands and golden beaches all faithfully captured on Jack's box brownie camera. The majority of the photos pictured a small monkey centre stage and Coco also played the starring role in the numerous letters Mary sent home.

After two years, however, homesickness got the better of Mary, and Jack agreed they could return to England. He arranged to take up a new position in the army pay corps where they would be billeted not far away from Mary's family.

The hardest part of leaving Singapore wasn't giving up the beautiful home and affluent lifestyle, or saying farewell to all their friends and colleagues, including Mary's faithful maidservant Maya, who had been more like a surrogate sister to her, it was of course leaving behind their little companion, Coco.

They thought that he might not survive the crossing and, even if he did, it would have to be followed by a long period of quarantine before he would be able to join them. Rather than put the little monkey through such an ordeal they thought it would be better if he stayed in Singapore with friends of theirs who also had a little spider monkey that Coco had often played with.

Mary and Jack parted tearfully from their pampered little monkey. On the bright side, they consoled themselves that after three long years away; they were heading home at last.

A life-changing decision

James Webster, now aged forty-six, father of five (Mary and her four siblings), had an annoying lump in his left nostril. It had started life as a nasal polyp, but had turned more serious lately.

"I'm afraid you have cancer Mr Webster," his doctor informed him, as a matter of fact. "You'll need to be hospitalised immediately and have it removed."

James, who had fought in two world wars and seen and done some terrible things, never flinched.

"What will that involve?" he asked.

The doctor explained that the procedure would involve removing the roof of his mouth in order to ensure the entire growth came out whole.

James thought a moment and slowly shook his head, "No."

He was a proud man, and in that moment his only thoughts were that for whatever time he may have left he intended that his wife and children would always be able to understand every word he uttered.

"Do not be silly Man!" The doctor remonstrated. "Without this operation the cancer will spread upwards into your brain. This is the best chance of survival you have, I strongly advise you take it!"

"How long do I have if I don't?" James asked.

"Six months maximum." The doctor pronounced his death sentence with an exasperated shake of the head.

"Six months it is then, good day to you doctor."

The doctor watched in amazed disbelief as his stubborn patient walked out of his office.

James Webster watched as the tumour grew, expanded to fill his entire nostril. Over time it became so large that the skin began to bulge and split open. It truly was an horrendous sight. His nose ran constantly, his left eye watered, and he even had to eat with his mouth open a little in order to breathe, but every word he spoke was clear as a bell.

In the end he lived to be eighty-eight: forty-one and a half years more than predicted. James Webster had no faith in anyone or anything other than himself, but sometimes the power of mind over matter can be enough.

As time goes by

The years kept flying by.

First Horace, then Louis, went abroad to do their National Service, both choosing the army. With the war over it was a time for adventure, an opportunity to travel and see the world at last. Like Jim before them they were regular correspondents, letters full of the sights and sounds they had witnessed.

On his return from the Royal Navy, Jim secured a stable job in an office with decent money and a pension attached.

Olive, incredibly bright and precocious as ever, won a scholarship to the local grammar school like her older brother, Jim, before her.

Olive excelled at grammar school. Having a penchant for languages she quickly mastered French, German, and Latin. She loved school and the opportunities it gave her to showcase her numerous talents.

Olive's school overlooked Bolling Hall, a gracious old stately home that had been around since before the English Civil War. It was open to the public, and on many a lunch break Olive would wander round the house and grounds, drinking in the atmosphere. Her natural sensitivity to vibrations meant that she could pick up the imprints left on the old house over centuries past; it was almost like taking a step back in time for an hour.

Just like her sister, mother, and grandmother before, Olive could feel the prickle on the back of her neck when she entered "the Ghost Room" where legend has it that the timely intervention of a ghost once prevented the slaughter of the people of Bradford.

(*During the English Civil War, in 1642 puritan Bradford was besieged by the Royalist army, under the command of the Earl of Newcastle.*

One night, in a blazing temper caused by Bradfords' continued resistance, the Earl declared as he went to bed that the following morning he would kill every man, woman and child in the city. The Earl was awoken during the night, however, by a ghost, wringing its hands and saying, "Pity poor Bradford."

We may suppose this had a huge effect on the Earl, as the next morning he revoked his decision to slaughter all of Bradford's inhabitants and, although he did attack, there were less than ten casualties who died of wounds recieved during the battle.)

Olive could often sense cold spots, and almost make out the whispers from a bygone age that clung to the fabric of the house like a residue.

Bolling Hall, she once told me, was one of her favourite places in the whole world to visit.

A kind and generous soul

Horace was the second of Elsie and Jim's children to get married. Aged just twenty, he met, courted and wed a young woman named Ivy.

Within the year he was the proud father of a son he called Louis, after his younger brother. With two Louis's in the family it was necessary to distinguish between them, therefore the new arrival became known as "Young Lou".

The elder Louis came back from his National Service and landed his first proper job just before Christmas.

On Christmas Eve he was let out early with his first ever pay-packet and headed off proudly into town to treat the family to a few surprises. He was standing at the market stall considering which turkey would supply a generous portion of meat per person for the ever increasing family.

They would all be gathered around Elsie's dining table for Christmas dinner as always, although there may need to be more than one sitting to feed everyone this year.

Louis's eyes were drawn to an elderly lady on the far side of the stall. She looked thin, worn and tired, and seemed to be wrestling with the dilemma of which of two rather scrawny looking birds to choose from. Again and again he saw her anxiously counting out the few pennies in her purse, as if deliberating just how far her money would stretch. The butcher appeared before Louis, ruddy faced and smiling, "Now lad, what's it to be then?"

Louis selected his turkey, a large 14lb bird with plenty of meat on it and the butcher bagged it up for him. Suddenly, on impulse, Louis beckoned him again and selected another smaller, but equally round and succulent turkey. The butcher was more than happy to wrap this one also. Christmas Eve and business was booming for him, he beamed from ear to ear as he passed Louis his wares.

Approaching the other side of the stall Louis observed the old lady was still counting and recounting her money, her brow furrowed into a troubled frown. A little shyly Louis tapped her gently on the shoulder.

She looked up warily.

"Here you go love, Merry Christmas!"

Louis thrust the smaller of the two birds into her hands and the old lady looked at him agape with surprise. He gave her a cheery smile and a wink, then scurried off into the crowd before she had chance to respond. Glancing back over his shoulder he saw the little woman's face had lit up with astonishment and delight.

If ever had it been said to him that "it is better to give than to receive" Louis knew in that moment that this was true. He felt a pure glow of happiness at the thought of the unexpected feast he had been able to provide for some poor family that Christmas, and it was a far better feeling than all the presents he himself was likely to receive the next day.

The ties that bind

Olive at sixteen was a rare beauty. She had waste length titian red hair, pale skin, pearly white teeth, and enormous brown almond-shaped eyes.

It went without saying that every young man in the neighbourhood came knocking at Elsie's door to see if they could have permission to take Olive to the Saturday night dance. Olive would banter wittily with them, but whether she liked them or not she always said the same thing; "You'll have to get my brothers' approval."

Jim, Horace and Louis guarded their younger sister closely. Any young chap wishing to take her to the dance would have to run the gauntlet of their inspection, and then of course Elsie and James would want to rubber stamp the decision. Any suitor was expected to be well mannered and polite, scrupulously clean and tidy and woe betide any one who didn't have her home at ten o'clock on the dot. It was a brave man who would dare to ask her for a date, and yet they were queuing up for the privilege.

Baby Louis, or Young Louis as he became known, was the apple of everyone's eye. The first grandchild, he was adored by the whole family. Blonde-haired with saucer like blue eyes he was the bonniest baby they had ever seen. When Ivy and Horace were too busy to keep an eye on the little chap, there was no shortage of doting, adoring, helpers.

Mary and Jack would often have Young Louis, their nephew, and Olive to stay at their cottage in Melton Mowbray, it was an ideal place to spend the holidays. Jack would while away his free time pottering in the garden, chatting to Young Louis, and Mary and Olive, close despite the age differences, would go out shopping and dancing together.

So the summers passed. Olive had her hair cut into a short elfin style, changed her full circle skirts for mini skirts and hipster jeans, her heels became higher, her waist even tinier and her wits and tongue even sharper.

Young Louis grew taller, his blonde hair started to darken. Like Olive he too was possessed of a rapier wit and keen sense of humour. From his early days he showed artistic promise, often to be seen with a pencil in hand, sketching a lampoon of some unsuspecting adult.

One day, running in from school, Young Louis was surprised to find his father, Horace, sitting head in hands, a letter scrunched up on the floor at his feet.

"Dad, Dad, what's the matter?" Louis gasped, running to kneel at his side. Horace looked up disconsolately.

"She's left us Louis, your Mam's gone." He gestured to the hastily scribbled note from Ivy.

Louis drew himself up to the full height of his eight years and put his hand comfortingly on his fathers shoulder.

"Don't worry, Dad," he said. "I'm here, you still have me, and we've still got each other."

Mary and Jack moved to Bradford to be with the family in this time of crisis.

Horace, his usual joyful disposition gone, was struggling with an uncustomary sense of bleakness, bordering on depression, that even the two Louis's could not help him lift.

Young Louis remained stoic and brave. If his Mum had chosen to desert them, so be it, he was there to be his Dad's right hand man. They moved in to James and Elsie's home, temporarily, for extra support.

Jim had long since moved out, he had become acquainted with a raven haired beauty named Margery whilst working at Low Moor Steelworks. Newly discharged from the WAFs, the daughter of a bank manager, she had quickly been accepted into the family, and they had married and moved into a little shared house in the Heaton district of Bradford.

The return of his eldest sister and brother-in-law, Mary and Jack, seemed to lift Horace's spirits. He and Young Louis were frequent visitors to Mary's new home, and gradually things settled down again.

A remarkable pooch

Happy though she was to be once again close enough to visit her family every day, Mary missed the pretty cottage and the garden she had left behind. The old back-to-back terrace she and Jack now rented just couldn't compete.

Anxious to see her happy, Jack provided a new distraction, a bundle of fluff which grew into a remarkable dog they named Patch, so called because of a brown mark over one eye.

Patch was intelligent and mischievous; a dog labouring under the misapprehension that he was actually human. Unlike the average mutt, happy to curl up in front of the fire on an evening, he would perch on the fender, hind legs stuck straight out in front, waggling his tongue about in peculiar contortions, looking for all the world as if he was trying to hold a conversation with the family.

On a night he would refuse to sleep downstairs and night after night he would slip away upstairs. By the time Mary and Jack went up to bed they would find him in the middle of the double bed, blanket tugged up to his chin (if a dog can be said to have a chin, they were sure that was how Patch would regard it), head on the pillow, snoring softly. No amount of coaxing or shoving would move him, so that was how they slept; Mary and Jack perched on either edge of the bed, and Patch warm and cosy in the middle, as he seemed to think was nothing more than his due.

It wasn't just his behaviour indoors which was peculiar for a small mongrel. Mary soon discovered that after taking Patch on a couple of jaunts across town to visit Elsie and James, he decided he would visit for himself whenever the mood arose.

Now, dogs wandering about freely was nothing unusual in those days and, dogs having a good sense of direction, wasn't particularly remarkable. What was odd about Patch was that he didn't walk there. He used to hop on the trolley bus, always the right one, and bag himself a lift for a few stops, hopping off again when he got near Elsie's!

Mary would often catch the bus herself, to be told by an amused clippie, "Your dog's been across town visiting your Mam again missus, he was on here not half an hour ago, just jumped on bold as brass, I'm not sure I shouldn't be charging him a fare he travels that frequently with us!"

Before long the regular drivers, conductors and inspectors all knew Patch by name. They never did charge Mary for his daily excursions, she was only thankful he hadn't worked out how to hail a cab – yet!

Every Sunday, providing it was fine, the men of the family would play cricket on the back field near Elsie's house.

Patch liked to play too: his favourite position was wicket keeper. Mary's Dad, James, also liked to play in this position, and there would be a tussle between the pair of them. James of course would pull rank, being human, and Patch would slink off, sulking, to be a fielder. Sometimes he looked so woebegone and pathetic, head down, tail between his legs, glancing back whenever he thought James was looking, that James would inevitably relent.

"Ok, go on then Patch, you can play back stump!" He'd shout.

Patch never needed telling twice, his head would shoot up, there'd be a "yip" of delight and he'd come gambolling back down the field like an overgrown pup.

"That dog has the makings of a bloody fine confidence trickster," James would declare shaking his head, but he'd give up his position with good grace, as no-one could resist the antics of the furry scoundrel for long.

There came one particularly cold, snowy winter's night when

Patch had taken himself off up to bed first, as usual. Mary and Jack drew the curtains on the wintry scene, the snow piled up on the window frame outside made them shiver just to look at it, and they followed their pooch up to bed.

When they got to the bedroom a surprising sight greeted them. Instead of being tucked up in bed fast asleep as usual, Patch was standing bolt upright in the middle of it. He regarded the door as they walked in, and as they approached the bed started to bark ferociously.

"Now then old chap, what's wrong with you? Come on Patch, shift over and let us into bed," Jack cajoled wonderingly.

But Patch would not let Jack or Mary even go near the bed, in fact he changed from barking to a low warning growl.

Jack and Mary were startled and bewildered. This was totally out of character, Patch had never behaved in such a peculiar fashion, he had a gentle, sweet temperament. After a couple of attempts they decided it would be best to retreat downstairs again, as the dog was clearly very agitated by their presence in the room.

Mary and Jack had just made it down into the kitchen, a little shaken and in need of a cup of tea whilst they decided what to do. Suddenly there was an almighty crash from upstairs. Trembling with fright they advanced on the stairwell. Jack insisted Mary stay put while he went upstairs to investigate.

What a sight greeted him as he entered the bedroom. On what used to be the bed, lay beams and slates. Jack blinked in bewilderment as he realised he could see stars twinkling above him from an enormous gaping hole where the roof should have been.

The roof had caved in under the weight of the snow that had amassed there, it had crashed down on the bed on the exact spot he had been attempting to get into barely moments before.

As the enormity of what could have happened struck him, he suddenly had a terrible thought, "Patch!"

To his relief a bouncing, wagging, wriggling, slightly snowy mutt came bounding out of the shadows to lick his hands apologetically. Jack was laughing and crying as he carried the unscathed little furry hero down to Mary.

"This dog saved our lives!" He declared in amazement, and

it was true, somehow Patch had had a sixth sense about the encroaching danger, and had averted disaster by the only means he had at his disposal, a loud bark and a show of pearly white teeth.

Julius Cheeser

That cold winter almost saw the demise of another family member.

Young Louis had befriended a little mouse that lived in a hole in the skirting board. Strangely, the little fellow seemed to live there alone, which was most un-mouse-like in itself. Young Louis managed to charm his Nan, Elsie, into allowing the little creature to stay, and would coax it out of its hole in the wall with cheese and peanuts.

Over time it became so tame and trusting that Young Lou was able to pick it up and stroke it.

The rest of the family being as doolally over animals as he was, it was soon accepted as another oddball pet, and given the name Julius Cheeser.

One cold winter evening Young Lou's granddad, James, came home from work to find the household in consternation. The two Louis's, Elsie, and Horace were all gathered round peering at the little mouse, which was cradled gently in young Lou's hands, rather stiff with cold and looking about to fade out for the final time.

Elsie had provided a fine muslin cloth for the little mouse to be warmed in, but it didn't seem to be doing much good. Horace and Louis were debating whether an application of vapour rub to the mouse's chest might warm him up.

"Give him here, let's have a look!" James demanded in his customary booming voice. Tentatively Young Louis passed the tiny creature to his granddad. James held the mouse gently in his work roughened hands.

"Now then little fella, what ails thee?" He pondered. He gave the little rodent a gentle stoke and was appeased to hear an answering squeak. "Not dead yet then," He mused.

Turning to Elsie, who was hovering nearby, to comfort Young

Louis when the inevitable happened, James declared, "I think this mouse must have got pneumonia."

Young Louis looked horrified, "Granddad what can we do?" He gasped.

James scratched his head thoughtfully, "There's only one cure I can think of for a mouse with pneumonia; Elsie, get me some whiskey and a teaspoon!"

So she did, and the whole family watched with baited breath while the gentle giant of a man carefully administered three drops of whiskey into the mouse's mouth.

That done he wrapped the mouse back up, popped him in a shoe box, and put it as close to the fire as he dared.

"We want to resuscitate the little chap, not cook him," He explained.

The next morning Julius Cheeser was as good as new, nibbling his way through out of the box, scurrying around merrily, I suspect, with nothing worse than a hangover!

Chapter Four
New beginnings, new names, new pets

Moving on

The light had come back into Horace's life again, this time in the form of an attractive, buxom, blonde by the name of Doreen. Barely had the ink dried on the divorce papers to Ivy than Horace had remarried and moved to Doreen's home town of Brighouse.

Young Louis, it was always intended, should go and live with them there, but his school, his friends, his beloved grandparents, aunts and uncles, and Patch the dog were all in Bradford.

So time passed and Young Louis stayed put, living with his Aunty Mary and Uncle Jack, from First School to Middle School, to Upper School, to College. Horace and Doreen barely had time to notice the years passing, as one by one they had three lovely daughters, Julie, Lesley and Alyson, blonde and blue-eyed, pretty little half-sisters to Young Louis.

The rest of the family were on the move again too, this time to some new "luxury" flats which had not so long since been built on the edge of a new council estate in Bradford. James and Elsie were amongst the first to get their keys.

Jim and Margery were now living in a cosy little semi on a tree-lined street about a mile down the road. They now had two young sons, Martin and Nicholas.

Martin was rosy-cheeked and smiley. Nick was a slightly more solemn intense little chap, devoted to his "imaginary friend" Susan, who he insisted had to go along with them everywhere. Olive, visiting, observed remarkable attention to detail when Nick spoke of Susan. How she looked, what she wanted, and for goodness sake, no one had better sit on her getting in and out of cars, it was, in fact, for all the world as if there really was another child in the room.

As mysteriously as she arrived, Susan dematerialised when

Nick reached about four. No one questioned where she went, or why, not even Nick.

Companions and rivals

Mary and Jack managed to secure a flat next-door-but-one on the same veranda as Elsie, James, Olive and Louis. Young Louis got a nice big bedroom of his own too. Patch the dog had sadly passed away the year before and once again Mary and Jack felt bereft without the affection a pet provided.

Jack came home one evening with something tucked in his jacket pocket. Mary let out a squeal, first of fright, and then delight, as it poked its head out for a look around. Jack had bought her a miniature Yorkshire terrier which she named Skippy.

Skippy, Skip for short, was the most pampered pooch imaginable, as vain as Patch had been intelligent, he loved nothing more than for Mary to brush and groom his long hair, and tie it up in pretty blue bows. He loved to be told how beautiful he was, and to be cuddled and cherished like a baby. He had an array of toys and teddies that he guarded jealously.

Bizarrely Skip's best friend was Louis's new pet, a large, proud, magnificent Alsatian called Simba. Simba was very family oriented, fiercely loyal, bright and well-trained. He obeyed Louis's every command absolutely. Simba was a large imposing animal, with tan and black hair, massive paws and gleaming teeth.

People would instinctively shy away when they saw him out on his lead with Louis, not that they need have worried, Simba paid them no heed. He would walk imperiously with his head held high and straight, looking ahead, hanging on to Louis's every command.

Sometimes, Jack and Louis would walk the two dogs together, the little pretty Yorkie dancing along beside the straight, soldierly Alsatian.

If the walk seemed too long it was not unheard of for the terrier to leap upon the back of the bigger dog and hitch a ride. Simba wouldn't bat an eyelid, but would retain his poise and walk on, whilst the little dog would yap cockily at other dogs out walking (I imagine it to have been a dog version of, "Come and have a go if you think you're hard enough!"). They would look up fiercely, see just who Skippy was riding on, and slink off quickly. Naturally, Skip assumed it was him the other dogs feared. Jack and Louis would laugh to see the little dog puffing himself up with pride. Simba paid no heed to the fluffy nutter riding on his back.

Into this picture of domestic bliss came a fly in the ointment, or rather a budgie in a cage. Mary named him Peter. He was chirpy and bright, a lovely shade of blue, an inveterate chatterbox, and just as vain in his own way as Skip was, but at least four times as intelligent.

How Skippy the dog hated that budgie, and how much did the budgie love to torment the little dog.

The bird was bold and fearless; he would swoop down from the cage to land on the top of the terrier's head. Skip would snap and snarl and toss his head about, but Peter would cling resiliently to the long hair with his sharp talons, like someone mastering a bucking bronco.

When Skip eventually accepted he wasn't going to unseat the bird, he would huffily lie down, glaring upwards, fluffy eyebrows raised. At this point Peter would deftly unpick the beautiful, beribboned bow on Skip's head and fly off with a triumphant squawk, as if laughing at the vain little animal. Outraged, Skippy would bark until Mary stepped in to keep the peace and tied his bow again. Peter would bide his time, then strike all over again.

Whole afternoons could pass in this way. Never had anyone witnessed such jealous rivalry between a dog and a bird!

Peter had the upper hand because he could talk, but Skip and he were equally vain. The budgie would stand for ages at a time gazing lovingly at himself in his mirror. He would make loud kissing noises at himself and declare, "Peter's soooo precious, Peter's soooo beautiful, Peter is such a clever boy!" in a perfect mimicry of Mary or Jack's voice.

On one occasion Peter's curiosity nearly cost him dearly. He saw the water in the goldfish bowl shimmering, and fluttered down to perch on the edge, presumably to nosy at the goldfish, but also to admire his own reflection in the water. This time he managed to overbalance, and fell, sploosh, head first into the fish tank. Fortunately for him, Mary was on hand to hear his fluttering and squawking, and rescued him before it was too late.

We can only imagine Skippy watching the proceedings with interest and being disappointed at the outcome.

On his return home that night, Jack was most amused to hear the day's adventures. "Silly Peter fell in the fish bowl!" he said repeatedly to the bird, who listened intently.

Before long Peter had learned the new phrase, with his own slant to it added.

"Silly Skippy fell in the fishbowl!" He would declare, or, "Silly Jacky fell in the fishbowl!"

"What?" Mary would say, "Wasn't it Peter who fell in the fishbowl?"

Peter would instantly retort back that Peter was "beautiful, clever and precious" - a bird with a truly selective memory.

When he wasn't tormenting the dog, idolising himself in the mirror, or falling in fish bowls, Peter liked nothing better than having a fight with the large salt and pepper pots on the dining table. They were metallic, and when Peter strutted up to them he could see his own distorted reflection shining back. Because they were solid he must have assumed that these were in fact two rival budgies, and would launch a full attack, pecking them repeatedly, until he had edged them to the end of the table and knocked them off, yes, you guessed it, onto Skippy who would be peering up at the table bemusedly, wondering just what that confounded bird was up to now.

Mary and Jack quickly learnt to be wary at meal times, as Peter liked to swoop down and land on their forks. On more than one occasion Jack had to pull back quickly before he got a mouthful of budgie.

One time Peter was aiming for the fork but overshot and went skidding across Jack's plate instead, covering both himself and Jack in a generous helping of gravy.

"Who fell in the gravy?" Jack would ask him; naturally the retort would come back,

"Silly Skippy fell in the gravy!" That bird never missed a trick!

Metamorphosis

Time was passing, James and Elsie were almost in their sixties, Mary approaching forty, and Olive, the baby, was nearly twenty-three.

She had been working for many years since leaving grammar school, but like her brothers she chopped and changed jobs, always searching for that something to capture her imagination. Little did Olive know it, but she was about to set off on an adventure of her own and leave the family nest for good.

James, Elsie, Louis and Olive had taken a family holiday, something that was a rare occurrence and a testimony to the newfound wealth from having several family members gainfully employed at last.

They had opted for the exotic holiday resort of Butlin's Holiday Camp at Skegness. A never-ending round of fun and games, their days filled from morning to night with frenzied activity, meals doled out at set times with military precision, a large dose of family fun had been prescribed and they embraced it wholeheartedly. To Olive, it represented the most gaiety she had witnessed in her entire life. As the week rolled on a plan formulated in her mind, she was determined to be a part of this amazing place.

On the final day of their holiday, whilst everyone was tidying up and packing cases, Olive made her way across the camp to the manager's office. Impetuous as ever, she knocked boldly on his door, and let herself in.

The manager really didn't know what had hit him, as this bright, breezy, red-headed girl bounced into his office. Sitting herself on the edge of his desk she explained how much she liked his camp, where she thought it could be improved, and why she was exactly the girl he needed to change it.

Was she saying she wanted to join his redcoats? He spluttered.

"Yes," She declared, offering him her hand to shake, "When do I start?"

Before he knew where he was, the flustered chap had offered her a job, arranged for her to return the week after next for training, and there she was signing on the dotted line.

"And what's your name Miss?" He asked, realising he had just offered a position to someone he had not even been properly introduced to.

Olive paused for a moment, then said decisively, "Jan, Jan Pamela Webster." She signed her new name on the contract with a flourish.

New life, new name, she decided. Olive was an old fashioned name and it was part of her past. Jan was the future. Now all she had to do was go back to the chalet and inform her parents and brother she was changing her job, leaving home the week after next, and oh, by the way, that she had metamorphosed from Olive into Jan.

Centre stage at last

Jan loved being a redcoat, she loved her little shared chalet and her roommate Susan, she loved her new found independence, she loved meeting new people, she loved being part of the in-camp variety entertainment evenings, appearing in the "Redcoat Shows". She was in her element and she shone.

Before long Jan was choreographing most of the dance routines and starring in a lot of the acts (she was always a consummate actress – her brothers had told her so!).

She took over as the voice of Radio Butlin's, early starts no longer phased her in fact she enjoyed being the first one up, waking the holiday makers with her cheery, "Good morning campers." She spent her days making announcements, meeting and greeting, taking part in various activities that involved lots of energy and unbridled enthusiasm. She spent her evenings under the spotlight on stage and her nights propping up the bar until the small hours. Jan's candle burnt at both ends, but she was young, fit and happy.

A year went by, then another, Jan was made chief redcoat, a position she held with pride. She still enjoyed arranging the shows and greeting the guests. It was also part of her remit to welcome visiting celebrities and make them feel comfortable too. Life was going well. She visited home from time to time, and the family holidayed at her camp when they could. It was one endless party.

Then Jan got another opportunity; she was invited to work in London. This was a position where she would meet potential celebrity clients and wine and dine them at the Post Office Tower restaurant which was run by Butlin's at that time.

Never one to let an opportunity pass her by, Jan packed her bags, hung up her blazer, and made her way to the bright lights of the city. It's fair to say Jan partied even harder now, as it was all part of the job. The famous names and faces became a blur: her only regret in later years was that she never got to meet Frank Sinatra. "I always hoped he'd fancy doing a season at Skegness," she lamented.

Jan had now worked for the Butlin's empire for quite some time, she loved the lifestyle, but gradually after three years away she found herself struck by home sickness. Enough was enough of a good thing she decided, she packed her bags a final time, and headed home at last.

Bradfordian fairy tale – Acts one and two

Back in sunny Bradford, time had moved on, but not much else had changed, except for Jan. She was glad to be home, but she was restless. She looked up some old friends, the ones not yet married and burdened down with husbands and children that is, she felt she needed a night out, so she arranged to go dancing.

Sidney William Berry, enter stage left.

The man standing before Jan was around her own age, she surmised. Unconventionally handsome, with the high flat cheekbones of an Irishman, twinkling grey eyes, and a shock of silver hair that was swirled into a rakish quiff. (It had turned prematurely grey when he was seventeen he told her later, he had not minded, as it had originally been a vibrant shade of ginger – he felt the silver was a little more sophisticated).

It was not, however, his looks that primarily attracted Jan to this young man, it was his humour, his turn of phrase, a certain joie de vivre that echoed hers. (She should not be surprised; he led a charmed life he confessed, having once kissed the "Blarney Stone"). As if enacting the story of Cinderella they danced all night with each other, turning down all other invitations. Jan knew instinctively that here at last was "the one", but contrary as ever she kept him guessing as to her true feelings for date after date. Around the third date, Jan set up a meeting for Sid with Horace and Louis. This was to be the "acid test" so to speak. They met in a bar, Sid bought everyone drinks, and within ten minutes they were all getting on like a house on fire. Definitely "the one" then, thought Jan.

Several weeks later Sid took Jan to one side, he explained that for a long time he and a close friend from work, Rex, had been lined up for a stint working for their company abroad, for six months. It would in fact be America. Sid wondered, if there was any possible chance Jan would conceive of waiting for him.

I believe the phrase was "not bloody likely!", but she may have put it more delicately than that! This placed Sid in a quandary, but the choice was clear, the girl or the career. He inveigled the advice of his older, wiser, sister Kathleen. What should he do?

Act two sees Jan and Kathleen in the Ladies toilet of the dance hall, applying lipstick, powdering noses, primping coiffeured hair. Kath tentatively explained Sid's predicament to Jan, would she change her mind perhaps? Jan's response was unequivocal; she wouldn't wait around for anyone.

Kath thought for a moment then she asked Jan the question Sid had told her to hold in reserve. If Sid should decide not to go to America, what were the chances Jan would consider becoming engaged to him?

Jan replied with a smile and an inscrutable look on her face, "To get the answer to that one, Sid would need to ask for himself!"

So Sid asked, Jan said yes, and the adventure of a lifetime was called off.

However, Sid's friend Rex did go to America on his own, met a girl out there, married her and made his fortune into the bargain. He remained friends with Sid and Jan anyway, because he liked them both, and he came back from America to be Sid's best man.

So here we are, the stage is set, and all the players are now in place. Sid and Jan are happily married and about to become parents for the first time.

It is time for me to make my entrance in this story…

Part Two

Come fill the cup, and in the fire of spring
Your winter garment of repentance fling
The bird of time has but a little way
To fly…and lo the bird is on the wing.

The Rubaiyat of Omar Khayyam

Chapter Five
Dawn of a new day

In the beginning...

Before we get started, I really ought to introduce myself, and my immediate family.

My name is Jane Cranmer, formerly Berry, and I have recently come to terms with the idea that I seem to be a psychic medium, (though recent data from the scales report I will soon be a psychic "large").

It appears to be a talent I have had my entire life, and yet, for reasons that will become apparent throughout the course of my story, for most of it I have been blithely unaware. I suppose, like most people, I have been searching for rational answers in an irrational world. It's only when you learn to embrace the illogical that the answers really reveal themselves.

I am married to Mark Cranmer, who I have reason to believe is my soul mate. He disputes this, a) because as an atheist he doesn't think he came from anywhere, and he doesn't think he's going anywhere, and b) it's far too scary to imagine he might be saddled with me for more than one lifetime. Still, he has managed to cope with my idiosyncrasies for the past thirty years; it can't have been all that bad!

Mark works for the council. He believes in regeneration, saving the planet, saving the environment, saving the whales, and anything else in danger of extinction. The saving of souls he leaves firmly in my department.

We have three children; at the time of writing Anthony, the eldest, is now twenty-three, Daniel twenty-one, and Jessica is eighteen. They would probably all describe themselves as non-religious, but still have minds open enough to take an interest in what I do (usually with an amused smile on their face it has to be said, but aren't all teenagers cynical?). They are happy to discuss anything and everything, just so long as I don't talk over "Lost" or "Kerrang" or expect them to think before lunchtime!

Of course, as the Irish comedian Dave Allan (a childhood hero of mine) once said of the Irishman giving directions, "I wouldn't start from here if I were you."

This is not where my tale begins, and I can assure you there are a fair few twists and turns to go before we get to here, so I'll have to take you for another little trip back through time.

The year is nineteen sixty-six, it is February the sixteenth, somewhere around lunchtime…

Arriving

My mother told me I "died" twice before I was born. I was a breech birth, but no-one had realised until the last moment when they couldn't get me out.

"Your heart kept stopping," Mum told me. They were running down to theatre trying to gown up, scrub up and put Mum under. In all the panic they were shouting over her

"We've lost the baby, no there it is again… no… no… the heart-beats gone… oh, no, the heartbeat's back again."

I am told it stopped four times in total, as my soul poised somewhere above, trying to decide whether I really wanted to be human again. As she disappeared into the dark hole of uncon-sciousness Mum didn't know if she was about to give birth to a live child or a dead one.

Fortunately I lived, or this would be a very short story and I'd be dictating it from the other side. I was finally delivered by cae-sarean section, and my mother didn't get to see me for quite a while afterwards.

My Nana, Elsie, remembered the day well. "I was the first one to hold you," She told me proudly. "You had the biggest blue eyes, and you looked at me as if we'd known each other a lifetime, I've never seen such a serene baby, just looking round taking everything in…I told your Aunty Mary, she's been here before."

I was named Jane after my Nana's grandmother (the gypsy).

My Mum and Dad only had a one bedroom flat when I arrived on the scene. This was fine for the first six months, but when I got to the stage where I was rattling the cot and throwing bears out all night they decided they needed a new solution.

I changed residence. Nana had space in her bedroom for a cot, as Granddad shared the room next door with Uncle Louis. My Aunty Mary and Uncle Jack and cousin Lou (Young Lou) lived in the flat next-door-but-one. So I started life as part of my large extended family, three flats, nine people, three dogs and a cat.

By this time my Nana, Elsie, and my Granddad, James, were both about sixty-eight years old.

My earliest memories of my Nana are sharing a room with her. (I would have been about two, I can remember a very long way back!). Each morning I'd wake up to the same scenario, Nana would be first up and getting ready to start the day. Getting ready seemed to take ages. She had layer after layer of undergarments to put on, strange contraptions with hundreds of hooks and eyes to wriggle into, vests and petticoats, voluminous knickers, stockings, garters; it all looked very complex. She would sit on the edge of the bed, her back turned to me modestly, and somehow manage to wriggle into all of these encumbering garments from under the tent-like folds of a flower sprigged nightgown.

All of this would take the better part of twenty minutes, which would be interspersed with the occasional sigh, tut, or curse muttered under her breath if one of the dreaded hooks and eyes had been fastened out of sequence, which meant the entire corset had to be redone again.

If Nana realised I was awake she would burst out singing or whistling nonchalantly, presumably to stop any further lapses into muffled cursing, as she would never intentionally let anything stronger than a "Hell's Bells!" out when there were children present.

She followed her morning regime beneath the cover of her nightdress, as meticulously as a Knight donning his suit of armour, and probably with more difficulty judging by the time it took.

Once dressed as far as her petticoat, she and I would venture to the bathroom: I would be seated on the side of the bath and subjected to a thorough soaping with a flannel; I can still recall the shock of icy cold water being washed in and around every fold of each ear. Nana admonishing me for having "so much muck in there you could grow taters in them". She meant potatoes, I learnt later.

She would dig under my nails with a small metal file, telling me that germs lurked beneath them. I knew all about germs, Granddad had fought against them in two World Wars: they couldn't have put up much resistance if they were small enough to hide under my nails, I reasoned!

Once I was clean enough to pass inspection, Nana would attend to her own ablutions. She would lather her face, neck and arms with a strongly scented carbolic soap, that made me wrinkle my nose, whatever she used on me smelt much sweeter by comparison, then after drying off she would comb her hair, which by this time was dark brown interspersed with streaks of steely grey. It was lovely soft hair as I remember, shoulder length, set in neat pin curls that she would shake loose and brush out.

Nana always looked very fresh, clean and smart, but at the same time warm and homely. She was the sort of grandmother you wanted to curl up on, in her lap, and hear a story or listen to her sing a lullaby. Smiling and infinitely loveable, she was at the same time a no-nonsense sort of a woman, who did not suffer fools gladly, and would certainly tell them so.

Breakfast would be taken in the living room, boiled eggs and soldiers set out on shiny crockery laid on a crisp white tablecloth.

Granddad would join us for breakfast. He was still a tall, strapping, giant of a man, with a large booming voice. He was always in trouble. Nan was forever admonishing him to lower his voice, for fear he would "frighten the children," "disturb the neighbours," "wake the dead," or something.

Granddad would just laugh and shout all the louder. I suspect the German artillery fire had damaged his eardrums and left him a little deaf.

"What's that y'say Else?" He'd boom.

She'd roll her eyes in exasperation, and I knew she was biting her tongue just because I was in the room with them. He was sure to get it in the neck later!

Granddad didn't frighten me one bit. We would face each other across the breakfast table and he would tell me the name of each soldier I dipped in my egg. For example, "That one's the brigadier," or the colonel or captain. I would picture the little fellow squirming in my grasp as I plunged him repeatedly into my drippy yellow yolk' I would fish him out and mercilessly bite his eggy head off. Brandishing the next victim at my Granddad

"And who's this one?" I'd demand.

Granddad's hair was grey and sparse, his eyes a merry twinkling blue beneath brown rimmed spectacles. His nose was strangely misshapen, due to the tumour, but I didn't know that, I just knew he had to blow it continuously.

"It keeps on running you know, but I'll catch it one day," he'd jest.

Poor Granddad was forever in bother with my Nana, fifty plus years together had given them plenty of time to find new ways of winding each other up.

On warm sunny afternoons Nana would try and banish him from the flat so that she could have a proper clean up in peace, or, which was more probable, watch some afternoon Western on the television undisturbed.

Granddad would accept his banishment with good grace, so long as I went along to share it with him.

Some of my most treasured memories of my Granddad include the days we would go out walking, or in my case riding, as my little legs couldn't carry me far back then.

I was about three. He'd help me into my pushchair, and Nana would tie a summer bonnet on me and ensure I'd got a cardigan in case it turned chilly. Granddad would wear a lightweight trilby or flat cap to protect his now shiny head, and off we'd go.

Slowly, we'd amble down to the park, Granddad pointing out anything of interest, which of course means everything when you're three years old. For an old man not known for his patience, he was endlessly so with me. I'd rattle on incessantly - "what's that?", "why does this?", "who is that?", "when will we?", "why can't we?" - and he'd smile and chuckle and find just the right answer to give a young enquiring mind.

When we got to the park we would select a bench in a bright sunny spot and Granddad would buy us both an ice-cream.

I'd sit on the bench and swing my legs, and Granddad would point out the different flowers in the park and tell me little stories about the bees, while at the same time fending off the wasps that came near me with a large white handkerchief.

Our little rest over, I'd hop back into the pushchair and he would wheel me further up the park to the swings. This was my favourite part, even better than ice-cream.

Granddad would push me while I shouted, "Higher Granddad, higher!" in a commanding voice. He would push me for ages and ages until his poor old arms were tired, but he could never push me as long as I would have wanted. I would have stayed there all day!

Eventually, Granddad would give me one last, huge high shove, and then he'd sit down on the swing next to me, mopping his brow.

"I'll have to catch my breath now," he'd remark, which I knew was the signal that meant playtime was over, Granddad was just too tired to push me any more. Once he had recovered we would set off for home.

Granddad knew a different route back, it involved a call into the newsagents, where he would get a quarter of his favourite black and green striped humbugs, and I'd be treated to some sweets, and occasionally a comic, or even a little plastic toy of some sort if he was feeling particularly flush that day.

We would meander along until we came to the school at the bottom of our road. This was another of Granddad's stop-off points, he'd sit at the top of the school field by the gates, and most afternoons we would see the children come out to play for their break time. Granddad would tell me more stories about school, and how I'd go there too some day.

I used to look at the children running around, they looked impossibly tall and old to me, almost adults. I believed that my school days must be far away still, I certainly hoped they were. How could I go to the park with Granddad if I was expected to be cooped up in a school all afternoon?

Once back home, Granddad was ready for a sit down and a "nice cup of tea". I would follow Nana round as she made it, regaling her with the tale of all the wondrous things we'd seen and done.

Also featuring largely in my life at that time was my Uncle Louis.

Uncle Louis lived with my Nana and Granddad, just as I shared a room with my Nana. I only saw Uncle Louis in the evening, at teatime, as he was out hard at work all day. As the one remaining unmarried child of my grandparents, he had decided that he would be the one to stay at home with them and see the bills were paid and they were well taken care of in their increasing age.

Uncle Louis was always smiling and laughing, you would hear him singing all round the flat. All my family had beautiful voices, and they could harmonise perfectly. My Uncles sounded like the crooners they admired, Dean Martin, Nat King Cole, Sammy Davis Jr, Matt Monroe, Johnny Mathis and Frank Sinatra. My Aunty Mary and my Mum had the melodic voices of Judy Garland, Doris day or Patsy Cline, every word ringing out true and clear.

As a little girl I would sit and listen for hours. There were no radios on in our flat, everyone made their own music. My Nana had a voice like the trill of a nightingale, she sang me to sleep every night.

When they weren't singing they would whistle. I could hear my uncles heading home for lunch on a Sunday from blocks away, their merry whistling floating in on the breeze.

Nan was an excellent whistler too. I would watch her, transfixed, purse up my lips and blow, but no sound ever came out, no matter how hard I tried. So I sang instead, if I didn't know the words I simply made them up. Sometimes the flat would be alive to several voices all singing different songs at the same time, with the odd whistle thrown in for good measure. Granddad didn't sing or whistle, but he'd sit good-naturedly listening to the cacophony all around.

Every Sunday lunchtime Granddad, Uncle Louis, Uncle Jack and Uncle Ace (Horace adopted this shortened version of his name in later years) would stumble in from the pub together, laughing, singing and whistling.

"Berrypie!" My Uncle Ace would shout in delight at seeing me, "Did I ever tell you you're my favourite niece?" (As I grew older I would point out that was all well and good, seeing as I was his only niece!)

His blue eyes would twinkle merrily as he'd catch me up for a smacking kiss on the cheek, then Granddad would give the other cheek a good drubbing of chin-pie (I'm not sure if this is a purely northern custom, but it involves rubbing a stubbly chin good-naturedly across a child's soft one) not quite so sand-paperish as usual, because at least he would have shaved before going out.

Uncle Jack would roll his hat down his arm and catch it in his hand, then fish a raspberry truffle from behind my ear -"Where did that come from?"

Finally I would run shrieking from Uncle Louis, who always had the iciest cold hands, bright red and raw-looking from never wearing gloves. He would chase any child within arms length and put his cold palms on their faces till they were as frozen as he was.

Aunty Mary and Uncle Jack lived next-door-but-one to my Nana and Granddad, at the far end of the veranda.

Young Lou, who was about sixteen now, also lived with them, but he saw his Dad, my Uncle Ace, every weekend, when he came to visit and have some time with his parents and siblings.

Sometimes, he brought his three daughters, Julie, Leslie and Alyson; my older, more worldly-wise cousins. Aunty Doreen didn't visit very often; she was the matron at their local hospital and worked long unsociable hours.

Aunty Mary came to Nana's flat every day. They would make endless lists of shopping and devise gargantuan meals on a budget to feed all the family.

I would usually go shopping with them, clinging tight to one hand or another, fighting to rid myself of gloves or hat or scarf. I hated to be fettered by these garments, but Nana would be insistent, "Put those gloves on, you'll catch your death of cold!" or "Don't take that hat off, your ears are going red!"

We would traipse up to the village every day come rain or shine.

This was before the days of giant supermarkets, and every meal was decided on the day and vegetables and fruit bought fresh.

Idle village, famed for its "Idle Working Men's club", (a long-standing joke amongst the residents of the village), was picturesque when I was small, cobbled streets and innumerable quaint little shops full of hidden delights and treasures.

There were three bakeries, four public houses, two chemists, two grocers, a butchers shop, a haberdashery, two newsagents, a post office, a launderette and a hairdresser.

My personal favourite was the toy shop, which was small and overcrowded with every conceivable toy. I would usually find some way to drag my Aunty Mary "just to look" in the window, and more often than not inveigle her inside, where she'd part with some hard earned pennies to amuse me. Little plastic dolls, lucky bags, rings that I was convinced had real diamonds in them.

Nana's favourite place was the betting office. Aunty Mary and I would wait outside whilst she just slipped in to put a bet on.

"Don't tell your Granddad," she'd admonish me, as if it was some grave secret, when everyone knew the pair of them would bet on two flies crawling up a wall!

The shop owners were familiar faces to me, almost every week I'd hear someone declare, "Ooh hasn't she grown? Isn't she well behaved?" and I'd puff up with pride at having both my height and seemingly impeccable behaviour recognised.

Mr. Moxon, who owned the green grocers, would always polish up a bright red apple, free, he said, just for me, as his favourite customer. I wasn't really over keen on apples, but I'd always eat it then and there, just to please him.

Back home once more, Nana and Aunty Mary would set to "reckoning up," as Nana called it. This was a complicated process involving receipts, and trying to decide who bought what and who was owed money and there would be minor tussles.

"No, no, Mother I'll pay for that!"

"No Mary, that's my treat."

I'd sit at the table, swinging my legs, playing with my latest reward for being so patient all morning, half listening to them, half watching in bewilderment. Even to my mind so young, it seemed apparent that as they shopped together every day, and cooked together, and shared everything anyway, it would make sense in the long run to just halve the bill and be done with it.

Then there was Uncle Jack. Uncle Jack lived in the mysterious land of the flat at the end of the veranda. Sometimes, usually when I'd worn everyone out with my incessant questions, Aunty Mary would take me by the hand and say ,"Come on, let's go see Uncle Jack."

Uncle Jack would be sat in his chair, which happened to be in the exact same spot as Granddad's in the other flat I noticed, just by the balcony door. (Probably to repel borders and fight off marauding invaders, I expect, or throw the odd cauldron of boiling oil over the balcony if the natives got too close).

His face would light up in an enormous smile when he saw me, and then we'd launch into a nonsense world of sweets that vanished and had to be tracked down, usually to be plucked, after an exhaustive search, from behind my ear.

He would put on a record with some music he called "Bagpipes" (that sent Aunty Mary running from the room in mock disgust) and we'd both don imaginary kilts and do some extraordinarily wild dancing.

I had a doll called "Sandy Macintyre" (named by Uncle Jack I suspect) who wore a kilt and a tam-o-shanter, so when we were both worn out from doing the "Highland fling" Uncle Jack would pick up Sandy and make her dance for us instead.

It was Uncle Jack that taught me to read.

Long before school decided to start me off, he crafted a set of "flash cards" and diligently sat with me every night until I'd mastered three new words. I had wanted to read from the moment I saw my Nana pick up her "cowboy" novels, I would copy her and stare angrily at the page. I always felt I had known how to read before, but now it seemed it was a skill I must re-learn. Uncle Jack gave me the key to a treasure trove of delight, and never was I happier than curled up with a book.

Young Lou would sometimes appear to say hello, although I was of course far too young to be of any major interest. Aunty Mary would tease him to "Get his hair cut, did he think he was one of the Beatles, or worse still a Rolling Stone!"

Young Lou would just laugh at her good naturedly. I didn't know his name was Louis though for many years, my infant tongue declared Uncle Lou and Young Lou to be "Boo" and "Booarr", and my family cheerfully adopted these names for them too.

At some point I realised that Uncle Lou was Louis, but it wasn't until I was ten that my cousin's wife, Lynda, took me to one side and said, "You know Jane, I really think it's time to tell you, he isn't really called Booarr, his name is Louis," that the penny dropped. No wonder all my friends assumed my cousin was some exotic person from a foreign land; not one of them had a relative called Booarr!

My early memories of my parents are of a glamorous, bubbly couple, who flitted in and out of my life, in much the same way as the rest of our large extended family. I knew Mummy and Daddy were somehow mine exclusively, but as far as I was concerned, I was where I was supposed to be and that was that.

Over the years there were several attempts to integrate me back into a home with them, but I stubbornly refused to leave Nana's flat. My powers of negotiation at that age were simple – scream the house down all night so that no-one gets any sleep, hold your breath until you're blue in the face, and repeatedly ask to "go home."

Poor Mum and Dad, no amount of cajoling, cuddling or affirming that my home was with them would move me. Resignedly they would take me back to Nana's, the general consensus being that I'd change my mind when I was older.

It wasn't that I didn't like being with my parents. Mum was a beautiful red-head, in gorgeous clothes, who sang wonderful songs to me and laughed nearly all the time. She wafted in and out of my days on the scent of "Blue Grass" like some glittering princess passing by.

Dad was the fellow with the shock of grey hair, deep voice (especially if he sang, which was rare, but kind of essential in our family, because everyone did), he had the same eye colour as me too, a grey/blue, or as I once pointed out to all the family, "Look, I have lovely red eyes like my Daddy."

71

Uncle Ace and Uncle Louis fell about laughing, as Dad was a little the worse for wear that evening.

"Yes, you can say that again!"

Frequent visitors to the flat were Uncle Jim, Aunty Margery and "the boys". Despite the label, "the boys" weren't in fact a collective. They were respectively; Martin, already seven when I was born, quietly confident in his position as eldest boy, academic, shy and polite. Nick, five years my senior, highly intelligent, full of mischief and fun, and Matthew, so close in age to me that we were virtually twins, and inseparable as such.

Uncle Jim was the stern but kindly uncle, quite different from Uncle Ace and Uncle Lou in his demeanour. You could always tell he was overjoyed to see you, but there was no way this uncle was about to chase you down the hall with freezing red hands, pull on your pigtails, or try to administer chin pie.

Aunty Margery was lovely and incapable of being still. Even in someone else's home she would be busy, trying to find ways to be helpful. Endlessly being chased from the kitchen and urged to sit and relax. Full of nervous energy, she was the sort of mother who is on the go from morning 'til night, running after her charges, nothing ever too much trouble for her to take on. If ever we visited her home she would go into overdrive, scurrying around in an endless flurry of tea-making, cake baking, sandwich-dispersing fever.

This was the world I arrived into, full of larger than life characters who sang and whistled their way through the working day. Good-humoured, a little tetchy at times, full of fun and laughter. I was blessed to join their ever growing ranks.

I can only think that when I selected which family to be born into this lifetime round, I chose wisely!

Settling in

When I was a child it was most often said of me "that girl's got a good imagination."

I'm sure in part this is true, I only have to see how creative my own three children are to know there is definitely a gene that I passed on somewhere. Sometimes, though, I can't help wondering how much was imagination and how much were things I just saw, heard and took for granted, and the adults assumed in their logical way I must be making it up.

I know through talking with friends that most people don't remember much further back than their third or fourth birthdays. Strangely, I have an extremely vivid memory of being swished back and forth in a bath, laughing, while my Aunty Mary held me saying, "Swim, swim, swim."

I recall that on one level I was enjoying this in a totally childlike way, and yet on a deeper level I was actually thinking in a very adult fashion, I knew who I was, where I was, who I was with and why (which I hasten to add is far more than I can comprehend most of the time nowadays).

Suddenly, Uncle Louis appeared in the doorway of the bathroom and said "smile!" to my aunty and I, and that instant is frozen in time on an old photograph.

I have that photograph still. I am less than one year old on it, yet I remember the moment vividly.

I have pondered over this many times and, as you may imagine, this declaration has been met with a fair amount of ridicule amongst my less open-minded friends and family. However, it fits in with several books I have had the pleasure of reading in recent years. They suggest we choose to be born and arrive here with a foreknowledge of what we hope to achieve in this lifetime.

Normally, it is suggested that at birth all our previous knowledge and memories are somehow wiped out, although in some people this process doesn't always work as well, and they take longer to fade. I can understand this. I imagine the struggle of learning to walk, talk, feed and toilet train oneself would be enough to take anyone's mind back to basics again.

Apparently, both my mother and I had the same strange trait as children of coming out with statements such as "when I lived before" or "when I was a lady" or "before I was born".

I remember having a vivid recollection at the age of three of my aunt and uncle's time in Singapore, where they had lived many years before I was born. They would be remembering old times and I would join in quite knowledgeably.

"But you weren't there, you hadn't been born then!" Aunty Mary once told me looking perplexed. I remember for the first time being puzzled. Not there, not born then, I knew I'd been around somewhere, but the more I looked for the answer the deeper the fog in my mind became.

More recent investigation has provided me with a possible explanation. It seems that prior to birth, while we are still making our choices for this next life, we frequently watch over people with whom we will have a "contract" in this incarnation (an agreement made prior to both our birth and theirs, such as you will be my aunty, mother, brother, etc).

That would explain why I was so familiar with their time in Singapore, and why I was so confused when I tried to work out where I was at that time; before I was born.

Old grey wolf

Simba, Uncle Louis's magnificent Alsatian, was my constant companion as a child.

From the day they brought me to live at Nana's flat he took up his place alongside my cot, keeping guard.

This caused problems occasionally, like the time I was ill and he guarded me so ferociously the doctor was in fear of his life. Uncle Louis had to persuade Simba to go on a nice long walk that day!

My first tottering steps were taken hanging on to his broad back. Simba would stand stock still as I dragged myself to my chubby feet, clinging to his silky hair, probably helping myself to a few handfuls in the process.

An extremely intelligent animal, he understood instinctively that his role was to be "gentle," and "look after the baby," he took it very seriously. For a large and powerful animal he radiated love and warmth around small children.

My cousin Matthew put this to the ultimate test one time. Still at the crawling stage, he dragged himself on all fours until he and the dog were eyeball to eyeball. Simba lying quiet and still on the ground remained so as the little boy decided to stick his two new teeth into the soft part of the Alsatians' snout.

Mum looked round in horror to see Matthew clamped securely

to Simba's nose, using it as a teething ring. The faithful pet remained still and silent, whilst tears of pain watered from his eyes. Hurriedly, Mum unclamped the little boy's jaw, and passed him to a horrified Uncle Jim.

Had it been any other dog the outcome could have been tragic, but as always Simba's love and devotion to the family outweighed his own personal discomfort.

As a small girl tucked up in bed at night I often used to dream of a life spent under the stars. I imagined I was sleeping in a tepee, and then would awaken in surprise to find myself in Nana's bedroom.

In my Indian dreams I had a wolf that slept beside me for protection. In my waking hours I had an Alsatian with the size, build and power of a wolf. I slept securely knowing Simba was there. Across incarnations, centuries and creeds my faithful old grey wolf remained at my side.

My brother doesn't look like that!

When I was about two years old there was a great deal of excitement in the family. I was going to have a new little brother or sister. Of course I knew that already, it was going to be a little brother and I could picture exactly how he was going to look. What I didn't realise was that the image that came into my head was from two years in the future.

So, there I was at the hospital with Nana and Aunty Mary, I had to be quiet I was told, we could go and see Mummy and the new baby for just two minutes.

Grasping tight to Nana's hand we entered the room. There was Mummy in a big bed smiling at me, but where was my brother? I peered under the bed. Was he hiding from me? He must know I wanted to play with him.

"Here's your new baby brother, Lee," Mum said.

There in a cot, wrapped so tightly only his screwed up eyes and the tip of his nose showed was a tiny, mewling, scrap of humanity. What was this, this wasn't what I was expecting to get, and I knew already what he looked like. I most certainly wasn't impressed.

Mum and Dad had finally got a nice new house. Now that the

new baby had arrived it was decided it was time I moved in too. Unfortunately, they totally forgot to consult me about it.

I was two and a half: I had strong opinions, a stubborn disposition and a very loud scream. One night's attempt to integrate me into the nursery convinced everybody that this might not be a good idea. So, I stayed with Nana, "just for the time being," and the weeks ran into months and years.

Mum decided Dad needed another career; one that she could be involved in too. What was the point, she told him, of being married to someone and only seeing them at the end of the day. They decided that it would be fun to work together, so they put in to manage a club.

Waiting for a suitable club to become available, they sold the house and got a flat again, temporarily. It was in the block opposite Nana's and I went to visit them there now and again.

One day something wonderful happened, I went into one of the bedrooms and my little brother (the one I was supposed to get) had finally arrived. He was standing in his cot, a prisoner.

"Get out," I suggested.

He couldn't, so I got in.

Lee wanted to see how I did that, so I demonstrated. The problem was I had longer legs than him so I tried pulling his legs a bit but they wouldn't stretch.

Then we tried again. Lee discovered that if he could hook his ankle bone over the lip of the cot, it gave him enough leverage to hoist the rest of him up and over, and he was out.

So that was it, now Lee had discovered his freedom there was no holding him, cots, playpens, even front doors if you stood on a dog, were no barrier anymore.

Young Lou had got married to his childhood sweetheart, Lynda, and they lived in a flat in the same block as Mum, Dad and Lee, one floor above. Naturally they were ideal candidates for babysitting. (Mum and Dad needed to go out lots and see what pubs and clubs were like, if they were going to run one!).

One night when Lynda was babysitting, she felt a cold draught coming down the hallway and went to investigate.

It was midnight and, alarmingly, Lee was not tucked up in his cot where she'd left him. Further investigation revealed Sheba the Alsatian was also missing, and horror of horrors the front door was open!

Lynda ran outside in a panic. Lee was not to be found on the veranda, or in the stairwell. Beside herself with worry she ran downstairs to the bottom of the flat. There, sitting on the grass making beautiful mud pies, was two year old Lee, with faithful Sheba, like a sentinel, on guard beside him!

Bewitched

I continued to live with Nana while Mum and Dad tried to get to grips with their son, the escapologist. I decided I quite liked him after all.

I would occasionally spend my afternoons at Mum and Dad's flat. Lee was confined to a dilapidated playpen that he was systematically taking apart bar by bar. Dad had fastened it together as best he could with rope and string and copious amounts of masking tape. I would sit drawing, swinging my legs and singing to myself, Lee would stand, face pressed against the bars, looking at me, envious of my freedom.

"Hey!" he'd shout, I'd look up and smile, he'd wave, and then go back to planning his latest great escape.

Someone had bought Lee a wooden block with assorted shapes cut out of it: there were corresponding shapes to go in the holes, and a small wooden mallet to hammer them in with. Lee had indeed hammered them in: brute strength had made him the expert at putting the proverbial square peg in a round hole, or a rectangular peg in a triangular hole for that matter.

No amount of Dad's prizing with pliers would free those shapes ever again. Lee wasn't bothered; he had discovered a far better use for his little wooden mallet. I watched amazed and amused as he smashed it repeatedly against the wooden bars of the playpen until they splintered. In a feat reminiscent of "The Incredible Hulk" he would prize the broken bars apart and clamber out. With a triumphant grin, he would set off giggling down the hall.

"Mummy, Lee's escaped again," I felt duty bound to report, but only after giving him a head start; it seemed only fair.

Mum would appear from the kitchen, chase the little miscreant down the hallway, scoop him up, and bring him back, where she would attempt to make the playpen secure again.

"What we need for you my lad is a strait jacket," she'd exclaim, exasperated.

Lee would let out an infectiously mischievous gurgle, stand and watch till she was out of sight, then give me a delighted grin and brandish the wooden mallet again.

Fortunately for Mum, Lee was still of an age where it was possible to get him down for a nap (probably by administering an elephant tranquilizer!). When this had been achieved we had some time together at last.

Mum would often sit and draw with me. She'd sing songs, and tell stories, sometimes she would put the television on. She liked something called "I love Lucy" which did nothing for me at all, the show I liked was called "Bewitched", about a young pretty witch (called Samantha, I think) and her long-suffering husband Darren. Samantha made magic just by twitching her nose.

"I'm a witch," Mum told me.

I looked at her suspiciously, "Are you?"

Mum would twitch her nose, "See?"

I wasn't totally convinced, but then I knew my parents never told lies. I could wrinkle my nose too, I wondered if that meant I was a witch.

"Not yet," Mum told me. "But you will be one day, all the women in our family are very powerful witches."

That was interesting; I really loved my brother Lee but I couldn't help wondering if he'd enjoy being a frog!

Matthew

For as long as I can remember, and trust me, I can remember a long way back, there has always been Matthew.

We arrived so close together that we almost came as a package, Matthew making his appearance in the material world just over a month after me.

From being babes in arms we were inseparable, happiest always when we were in each other's company. It was contrived that we should be put together as frequently as possible, as this had the added value of us keeping each other amused.

Matthew had dark brown hair and eyes, I was fair and blue/grey eyed. He was a boy and I was a girl. Beyond that we were almost indistinguishable. Together we were creative, smart and bright as buttons. We could play quietly for hours with barely a word spoken as if reading one another's minds. We could also be noisy.

Matthew created a game called "fighting with the bears". This was not, shall we say, one of his most imaginative creations. The whole premise of the game being that a bear (of which I had many) would leap out at you from the top of a wardrobe or cupboard, and you would be obliged to fight it, pummelling the creature mercilessly, whilst making growling sound effects and blood-curdling screams, for several minutes, upon which, invariably you would pronounce the creature was dead, and then another one would be launched at you and the whole scenario would have to be re-enacted again.

There was also "the golden trapdoor", a far more exciting proposition, where our intrepid explorers, having divested the world of bears successfully, stumble across a golden cushion - sorry, trapdoor - the entry through which takes them to another land and fresh adventure every time.

Sometimes we played "cowboys and indians". Matthew was always the cowboy, because he owned a hat and a realistic gun, I was the Indian, because I had the long warrior's hair and because I was convinced I'd been one in a former life (much to my Nana's disgust, as she had most definitely been a cowboy!).

We inherited a love of drawing and writing, and would create little magazines together, inspired to entertain one another.

There was good-natured rivalry, but we were always part of the mutual admiration society. We canvassed one another's opinions on the world at large, formulated views and plans for the future, queried anything and everything.

Unfortunately, as we grew older I started to realise our main discrepancy, Matthew was increasingly sceptical about the magic in the world around us, whereas I remained steadfastly entranced by it. Matthew was beginning to buy into the "having a good imagination" theory that the adults around us always espoused. I, meanwhile, knew the difference between the games we played and the other phenomena I encountered. The games were definitely pretend, Matthew and I agreed on that. On the other hand I was aware of a grey area, things that seemed to bring a quizzical look to the grown-ups faces when I mentioned them, things that I still believed were real, but Matthew was starting to dismiss also as imagination.

This was terrible; Matthew was starting to forget who he was and where we had come from. Little did I realise then, but this is usually the way it is for everyone. We had just hung on to the memories a little longer than the average child does!

Time after time

When I was very young I had extremely vivid dreams, within these dreams I was often a lot older than in reality. I came to think and speak of these dreams as memories of my "other lives".

At three, I dreamt I was inside a magnificent pyramid, the walls were lined with gold and sculptures and sparkling treasures. I was standing next to a sarcophagus; the embalmed figure laid to rest inside it was my husband.

There were other people all around; I could tell they were as frightened as I was. The impression I had was that we were all to be entombed with my dead husband, I as his wife, and they as his servants, we were deemed his possessions, and we had to be with him for eternity. We were waiting for the tomb to be sealed.

I woke up in a cold sweat calling for my Nana who reassured me it was just a dream and nothing to be afraid of. However, I suffered from claustrophobia for most of my early childhood, I would never use the lift in the flats and insisted on running up and down the stairs on every trip out.

Another dream that woke me screaming was one I had when I was five.

In my dream I was a fairly young teenager and I was trying to fight my way through an angry crowd of villagers. My clothes, and those of the rest of the crowd were dull and grey, tatty and old; I knew we were really poor. The mob was on its way to my grandmother's cottage. They had decided she was a witch. I was desperately trying to get ahead and warn her, but I couldn't push through as I was too small and weak, instead I was just swept along with the tide of bodies.

I watched helplessly as they brayed on the door. When she opened it, small and defiant, they snatched her up and carried her along with them to the village green where a stake had been erected.

Hysterically screaming and crying I watched as they tied this poor old woman to the stake and set it alight.

I screamed myself awake from that dream and it took my Nana a long time to calm me down and convince me it wasn't real and she was safe with me, unharmed.

I was also obsessively drawn to the Tudor times. While most girls were watching their idols on "Top of the Pops" I was reading everything I could lay my hands on about the court of Henry the Eighth.

"Strange," Aunty Mary observed.

My Mum had equally been obsessed with this period from infancy, once accurately describing the dress of a Tudor Lady down to the finest detail when she was only three.

When my Nana asked how she knew all this, my mother haughtily told her that this was how she herself had dressed "when she was a lady."

Both my mother and I were obsessed with Anne Boleyn, the second wife of Henry the Eighth who was beheaded.

"Do you think one of us was her?" Mum would laugh. "Maybe one was the head and one was the body," she'd joke.

Joking apart we were both fascinated from a very early age. I know what you're thinking; everyone believes they were Cleopatra or Napoleon, don't they?

Still, it gave me food for thought when many years later my mother passed away, on the 19th May 1986, exactly four hundred and fifty years to the day of Anne's execution!

Do I believe in reincarnation? Absolutely, and have done since before I could talk.

If the bewildering dreams in themselves were not enough, there was the strange thoughts I can still recall: looking up at my Dad as a giant towering over me and thinking how frustrating it was to find myself small again, and wondering how long it would take for me to catch up height wise; picking up one of my Nana's books and being infuriated when I couldn't make sense of the words on the page, thinking I was going to have to learn to read all over again; looking out at the windows of the bus and thinking how ugly the architecture of the buildings was; announcing to Aunty Mary and Nana that I didn't like living in the 1970s, as if I'd ever had chance of anything else in my short life!

I was a strange child to be sure, my head full of half remembered things, the feeling that I already knew some things and now I was expected to learn them all over again.

Sometimes, even more bizarrely, the feeling that not only did I remember the past; I had a foreknowledge of the future too. When my family gathered excitedly round the television to watch the Moon Landings I said precociously, "We've only just landed on the moon?" in disgust, as if I expected to be in a far more advanced time than that!

I'm sure at times my family weren't sure what to make of me at all, but they'd resort to the old failsafe of "a good imagination."

Halos

From the age of three onwards I had a fascination with storytelling. From the first time I wrapped my chubby mitts around a crayon and started to scrawl on a piece of paper stories were forming in my head.

"What are you doing Jane?" Nana and Aunty Mary would ask, relieved to see me quietly occupied for so long.

"I'm making a book," I would respond.

My first stories were in picture forms, short stubby people with rudimentary bodies, heads with eyes and a mouth but no nose, legs but no arms, occasionally with hair so long it went off the page, but always, always, with another circle round their heads. Aunty Mary thought everyone was wearing space helmets. I didn't have words to express what I saw when I looked at people.

One day someone left a children's bible behind at our flat accidentally, naturally I found it and spent hours pouring over the pictures, whilst sitting under the dining table; a favourite spot of mine. To my delight most of the people in the book had the same circle depicted round their heads, unlike all the princesses in my other story books.

I showed Aunty Mary that the pictures in the book were like my drawings (ok, they were slightly better, they had arms and noses too) and she understood at last.

"How very odd," she told anyone who cared to listen. "Jane draws people with halos round their heads all the time".

Dad was not amused, he didn't want his daughter getting her head full of a load of religious nonsense. He was a lapsed Catholic himself, and no longer had any time for the church.

The book mysteriously vanished. I didn't have a clue what the fuss was all about, all that I drew was what I could see with my own two eyes.

I realise now that for the first few years of my life I could see the aura around each person, shining like a beacon of light, particularly around their heads, where it was brightest. I drew the things that stood out as most important to me at that age. Interestingly, by the age of five my pictures no longer had that extra circle around the head. But on the plus side, they had gained arms and noses.

A new cousin

Young Lou had got married to his childhood sweetheart, Lynda, and they had a flat in the same block as my Mum, Dad and Lee, as I've said previously. This meant that there was a room to spare in Aunty Mary and Uncle Jack's flat, so it was decided I should live there. I didn't mind as it was still very close to Nana, and I spent a lot of time with Aunty Mary and Uncle Jack anyway. It was strange having a whole room to myself, but I soon adapted to it and it was surprising how quickly I filled it full of clutter.

One day, Aunty Mary had an announcement to make; I had a new baby cousin. Young Lou and Lynda had a little son, and they had named him Heath. My first impressions of baby Heath was that he must be an angel. He had huge blue eyes like saucers, and the palest, softest blonde hair. He seemed to have a permanent smile on his toothless face. I sensed immediately that despite the disparity in our ages we would be good friends, in time.

The Doll

When I was small I loved dolls. My room would have been filled with nothing else had someone not seen the necessity of putting a bed in it for me. I would play happily for hours lost in the realms of imagination, dressing them, undressing them, curling their hair, washing their faces, but mostly just mothering them, loving them, cuddling and talking to them, kissing them and putting them to bed. In this respect, if none other, I was a very girly, girl.

Our milkman was a very nice chap who had a daughter three or four years older than me. One day when collecting the milk money from my Aunty Mary he announced he had a present for me. I was about five at the time and I knew exactly what a "present" was, so I danced about with excitement, peeking out from behind Aunty Mary's legs, waiting to see what "the present," was.

Would I like a doll?

What a remarkable thing to ask, when would I not like a doll, if every meal could have been replaced by a new doll instead I would have starved to death and been ecstatically happy in the process. So Aunty Mary thanked the milkman profusely and accepted the gift on my behalf. She said goodbye and closed the door, then bent to put it in my outstretched eager hands.

"Wasn't that kind?" She said. "Look, he says this doll has real hair, just feel it."

Then the doll was in my waiting hands and Aunty Mary went back into the kitchen leaving me with my treasure.

Looking at the doll for the first time, I remember a strange feeling settling over me, instead of my usual delight at this new acquisition I felt a shudder of revulsion. The doll did indeed have real hair, which in itself was unusual, it must have been around a very long time. The hair was thick and slightly matted, course to the touch, and grey. The face and limbs were made of rubber and pliable in a way unfamiliar to me, as all my other dolls were made of hard plastic. But it was the eyes that drew me. Instead of the bright blue, unseeing eyes of my other dolls, these were grey and misty, almost filmy, staring back at me with the rheumy gaze of an ancient being. I was in no doubt that they could see me, right into me. With a sharp intake of breath, I did something unforgivable, I threw the present to the floor and let out a yell, "I don't want it, I don't want it!"

Aunty Mary roused once more from her washing up came back into the hall in amazement, "Jane!"

I ran into the bedroom and slammed the door shut tight behind me. This was of course no use, as Aunty Mary just pursued me, carrying the doll with her.

"Whatever's the matter, look it's lovely, feel the hair. This is your new baby, don't leave her out in the hallway," and she deposited the wretched thing on the end of my bed and left me alone with it again. Tentatively, I picked the doll up by one arm, tossed it in the air and slung it on top of the bedroom chair and down the back, where it came to rest, tilted at an odd angle, the eyes peering out at me malevolently from behind the chair leg.

The doll remained there for the rest of the day until, once I was tucked up in bed asleep, Aunty Mary dutifully tidying up my room, decided to retrieve it, and sat it with my other dolls inside my doll's cradle.

This became the pattern for the next few days. Every morning I would wake up, find the doll once more back in the cradle and remove it, throwing it behind the chair, once again out of view. Each evening Aunty Mary would tidy my room and the doll would be back in the cradle the next morning.

My efforts to remove the doll seemed futile, so I opted to ignore it completely and played around with my other prettier dolls.

Now, I know it probably sounds bizarre to say that I believe the doll was jealous, but that is the only way I can describe the vibes I was picking up from it.

I would be cradling and nursing my other dolls, dressing them up and singing to them, and all the while I felt as though I was being watched. I remember once feeling a pang of guilt that I had left the poor thing alone and all unloved in the cradle and going across to lift it out and try and make amends. However, no sooner had its gaze met mine than I had thrust it aside again shuddering with revulsion.

My behaviour, so I'm told, became increasingly erratic, on two occasions I came out of what, I can only describe as a trance to find I had taken nail scissors to the beautiful long blonde locks of my favourite doll and quite cheerfully scalped her. On another occasion I discovered I had drawn squiggles and swirls all over the face of another treasured possession, the marks indelibly etched, forever.

Things came to a climax on the day my aunt found me repeatedly slamming the head of the hated doll in my bedroom door, screaming "I hate you, I hate you, I will kill you!" with an expression of desperate madness and loathing written all over my face. I think this finally convinced Aunty Mary that the doll had to go, so she gently but firmly removed the offending article and hid it away in a cupboard out of view. I hasten to add, this sort of behaviour was totally alien to my nature, and Aunty Mary confessed it quite rattled her to see me so strangely enraged.

Of course, true to all good tales of the supernatural, the story doesn't end there. The doll seemed to return time and again to my room, only to be followed by another episode of my beating it savagely, and my poor beleaguered aunt removing it, utterly bewildered as to how it had left the cupboard.

She told me later that by this time it was evoking feelings of distaste in her also. Aunty Mary decided the only way to be truly rid of it was to give it away, and much in the same way the milkman had presented me with a "gift" she decided to pass it on to my older cousins, young Lou and Lynda, for Heath, their little boy now aged about eighteen months, in case he would like it.

So that was that, the doll was gone and much to everyone's relief I reverted back to my normal happy self, pouring love and affection onto my dolls instead of trying to beat some unexplained life-force out of them.

About thirty years later I was having a coffee at my cousin's house and the conversation turned to unexplained incidences and past remembrances.

Lynda asked me if I remembered "the doll" that had been passed on to her little boy, and as soon as she recounted how obsessed by it I'd become of course I knew which one she meant. Lynda told me that the doll had never been passed to Heath, because Lou, her husband, my cousin, being a real "man's man" said. "no son of his, even if he wasn't yet two, was going to start playing with dolls".

Lynda knew better than to argue with him and admitted she felt a bit distasteful towards this particular doll herself, but not wishing to appear ungrateful for the gift decided she had better keep it. The doll was put into a suitcase alongside a rather tatty, but much-loved childhood doll of Lynda's.

That night Lynda was awakened by a strange sound from the bedroom next to hers, banging and clattering, and the sound of knocking against a door. Terrified, she shook Lou awake, and he too sat frozen with fear wondering what the noises could be. Eventually, as it dawned on them that the noise was emanating from the room their baby was sleeping in, they plucked up the courage to investigate.

"You go see," said Lou, all six foot three of him huddling beneath the blankets, "I'll be right here if you need me."

Lynda shaking, but now convinced it was up to her to see off the intruder in her son's bedroom, tiptoed to his door. Abruptly, the noises ceased. Holding her breath she thrust the door open, turned on the light and marched intrepidly into the room…

Nothing.

Little Heath was fast asleep in his cot, with no apparent signs of noticing anything at all. Lynda looked around the room; there was nothing of note at all except that the wardrobe door seemed to have worked its way open slightly. She pushed it shut, tucked Heath in snugly, turned off the light and returned to her own bed feeling perplexed. As they lived in a block of flats Lou and Lynda decided the noise must have come from another flat after all.

Next morning Lynda was changing the bedding on Heath's cot when she noticed the wardrobe door was ajar once more.

She went to close it but it was wedged open by something. Surprised she discovered the suitcase now partially open pushing on the door. She pulled it out and the contents spilled out onto the floor, causing her to let out a started cry of horror, "Lou, Lou!"

Lou rushed in and they both stood aghast. There lying on the floor was the doll with its ancient all-seeing gaze. Next to it was Lynda's treasured childhood possession, headless, limbless, and the face smashed beyond all recognition. Searching for a logical explanation Lynda rounded on Lou, "Did you do this? Do you think it's funny?"

"No, he bloody well didn't," came back the retort to both questions. They looked to the baby playing merrily in his cot, oblivious; clearly, it wasn't his doing either. They both looked at the doll.

Lou told me later that the expression on its face hadn't changed, not really, but they both got the distinct impression it was smiling at them. Lou isn't what you'd call a superstitious individual in any shape or form, however, he said, in that moment he knew exactly what needed doing. He took the doll into the kitchen and laid it on a chopping board. To Lynda's amazement, he then proceeded to carve its rubbery limbs and head into slices with the aid of a very sharp butcher's knife, until only the eyes were left, still glaring at him. This done he tied everything up in a bag and took it downstairs to the bottom of the flats where he deposited it at the bottom of the biggest , deepest, communal dustbin he could find, safe in the added knowledge that the contents of the bin were to be incinerated.

Thirty years later I leaned toward him intently. "Why did you do that?" I asked.

"Just to be sure…" Lou grimaced, "…that whatever it was, it could never, ever, come back!"

A sad tail

I first heard of death when I was five years old. Aunty Mary mentioned someone but said they had died many years before.

"Died, what's that?" I wondered.

Aunty Mary explained that when you died you went to Jesus in Heaven, which was a wonderful place and nothing to be worried about. I recall being overtaken by rage, stamping my feet and declaring, "I'm not going back there again, I only just got here!"

Aunty Mary asked me what I meant, but I found I really didn't know, I knew I'd come from somewhere to be with her, but I could no longer remember where it was.

Uncle Jack and I were taking a walk up into the village one evening, just going to the corner shop for ice creams. We had crossed the main road, me holding tight to his hand as always, when somewhere behind us we heard a familiar bark. I looked back where we'd been, a little black and tan Yorkshire terrier was gambolling along after us.

"Uncle Jack, Skippy's here!" I said. A troubled look crossed Uncle Jack's face. "Oh no, how did he get out?"

We both looked just in time to see Skip run into the road. Uncle Jack let out a yell "NO Skip!!!" just as I heard a car screech to a halt. Fortunately for me, I was too small to see what happened. Uncle Jack's face was white, he turned to me and said, "Jane you stay there, do not move – do you understand?"

I nodded yes, clearly something was very wrong, but I couldn't grasp what it was, and I wanted to know where Skippy had disappeared to.

I saw Uncle Jack go into the middle of the road and bend down. Gently, he wrapped something I couldn't see in his jacket and tucked it beneath one arm. With his free hand, he came back and took mine, we crossed the road again.

There was a builders' yard nearby and Uncle Jack went there and had a word with one of the men, asking if they had a box. The man was wearing blue overalls and had very dirty hands, but he had a nice face and gave me a kind of sad smile.

Uncle Jack and I started walking home, him still carrying the box. I was perplexed, why hadn't we bought ice cream like we were supposed to, and where had Skippy vanished to, suddenly?

I asked Uncle Jack who, to my surprise, seemed to be crying a bit, but that couldn't be right; he must have runny eyes, I guessed.

"Skippy has gone to Jesus now," Uncle Jack told me in a funny choked voice. I looked at him, puzzled. That was quick; one minute he'd been running up the road and now he'd gone to Jesus.

Suddenly the penny dropped, "Did Jesus put Skippy in that box?" I asked. Uncle Jack nodded, he clearly couldn't speak.

All the way home I mused how strange it was that Jesus actually lived in that work yard and not in Heaven at all. What on Earth was he doing wearing overalls, and why didn't he have a beard? I guessed he must have been in disguise.

From that day onwards, every time I went up to the village, I would crane my neck to see into the builders yard, hoping for a further glimpse of Jesus, so I could ask him just what he thought he was doing, putting a perfectly good dog in a cardboard box like that, but I never did see him, or Skippy, again.

Waiting in the wings.

When I was young I was too small to be allowed to play outside our block of flats; we were five floors up. However, it was permissible for me to play on the veranda.

On our side was Aunty Mary and Uncle Jack's flat, Mr and Mrs Yeadon in the middle and Nana, Granddad and Uncle Louis at the end. There were also three flats opposite ours; they were all inhabited by sweet old ladies. Every morning the old ladies, my Nana and Aunty Mary would go out and mop the outside balcony with bleach so that it was clean and fresh. Therefore, it was deemed safe for me to play, as long as I didn't go in the lift or stairwell.

One of the old ladies was called Mrs Charlesworth. She was tiny with grey curly hair and she used to like talking to me when I was out playing. Occasionally, with Nana's permission, I was allowed to go into her flat for a biscuit and a look around on the strict understanding I wasn't to "make a nuisance of myself."

Mrs Charlesworth had a beautiful china cabinet full of pretty porcelain figurines; I would sit for ages admiring them. Frequently, I would see reflections of other people in the glass behind me, but when I looked over my shoulder there would just be old Mrs Charlesworth and me. The older she and I got the more I sensed the presences in the flat, yet Mrs Charlesworth had lived alone for a long time. She passed away when I was six years old; I think her family had been waiting for her long enough.

Chapter Six
The age of innocence

Jenny in the looking glass

Before I reached school age I was often left to my own devices as Aunty Mary and Nana would be very busy with all the shopping, cooking and housework.

I used to play in the bedroom I had shared with Nana when I was younger. When I was lonely I would sit and look in the dressing table mirror. Gradually a girl's reflection would appear next to mine. She told me her name was Jenny, she was quite a bit older than me, maybe twelve, and she was very sensible; unlike me.

She used to advise me, especially as I got a bit older and was struggling to come to terms with school life. I always took note of her guidance; I just wished I could reach out and touch her. She appeared to be sitting at the side of me, but she was only visible to me in the mirror.

My Nana was forever asking me who I was talking to.

"Just Jenny," I'd say. She'd look round the door, smile at me, then trot back to the kitchen.

Jenny eventually disappeared from the mirror when I reached about eight. I'd look for her from time to time but she never appeared to me again.

Many years later, when I was at college and old enough to discuss these things Aunty Mary told me she was unable to have children, she had miscarried once many years before I was born, and had been unable to have any others. It would have been a girl if she had lived, she told me. Aunty Mary had already picked out a name; her daughter would have been called Jenny. I sometimes wonder if Jenny was in fact my spirit guide and not the figment of my imagination everyone supposed she was back then.

Heavenly voices

One of my favourite pastimes, even as a child, was like a form of meditation. I would spend hours on Nana's bedroom windowsill. In the daytime there was a spectacular view over hills and trees and fields, vast expanses of blue sky and ever changing swirling clouds. I would sit, transfixed, just watching them go by.

At night, the landscape was dark, but I would stare endlessly at the stars, or watch the clouds crossing the moon. There was something so tranquil in contemplating the elements that at times it seemed to quiet the restless soul within me. I would listen and gradually I could make out distant voices singing from far away, it was like tuning in to somewhere I half remembered but couldn't quite place anymore. Wherever it was, that was really my home I used to think. I would often feel lonely for a place I couldn't adequately describe, and people I no longer could visualise.

My family would look in on me from time to time, "What's she doing?"

"Oh, just staring at the moon again."

"She's just like her mother, Jan used to do that all the time too, remember?"

I recall one Christmas Eve, when I was about six, going along the veranda from Aunty Mary's flat to visit Nana, Granddad and Uncle Louis. Just before I knocked on their door something caught my attention and I stopped, mesmerised, staring across the estate behind the flats and above to the night sky.

It built up slowly, a feeling and a sound all in one, as if every Angel in Heaven was pouring out its song. I felt as if my heart would burst at the beauty and enormity of the sensation I was being allowed to feel and hear.

The night sky seemed to swell and suddenly the clouds were a swirling mass of gold and silver, churning overhead. It was the most breathtaking experience of my young life, and yet I had the understanding that below me people were going about their business totally unaware. I felt as if I'd been given a glimpse into another dimension, and it was miraculous.

I don't know how long I stood there, enraptured, gazing at the sky, probably quite long enough that if anyone had cared to look up and see me they'd have said, "that girl's not right in the head you know." Given as I was to these sudden trances, it's amazing my sanity was never questioned!

Slowly, the vision cleared and the sounds and feelings dissipated, leaving me just standing in the darkness, hand still poised to knock on the door. I was let in by Nana.

"Did you hear it too?" I asked, telling her what I'd seen. I don't expect for a moment she had, but Nana never missed a beat, of course the Angels would be singing she agreed, it was Christmas Eve after all. Then she sat me down and poured me a snowball to celebrate.

Sadly, I don't hear the songs from the Heavens anymore, but I can remember how beautiful it sounded to a little girl sitting on a windowsill many years ago.

A Sunday stroll

For some reason, known only to him I'm sure, Dad decided to volunteer his services as dog walker to Simba, Uncle Lou's magnificent Alsatian, one Sunday afternoon. I think the scenario may have gone like this; after a pint or seven before the Sunday roast, possibly whilst weaving their way back to Nan's flat, Uncle Lou may have bemoaned the fact that Simba would be expecting his usual nice long Sunday walk after lunch, and perhaps Uncle Lou didn't feel quite up to it this once. My Dad, ever the obliging and generous soul, at this juncture will have proffered his services. After all, he liked Simba; Simba liked him, how hard could this be?

Dinner over, and ever true to his word, Dad slipped on Simba's nice strong collar and chain.

"Come on lad, like to go for a walk with your Uncle Sidney?" He enticed the dog, who of course didn't reply, but acquiesced by getting up and walking out of the door with him anyway.

It was a glorious day, blue skies, warm and sunny. Man and dog headed down towards the canal in perfect harmony. Bees buzzed, butterflies fluttered by, this was the life, Sid reflected, he should volunteer to do this more often.

Children ran past giggling, ice cream vans tinkled "Greensleeves", elderly residents pottered in their gardens. Men passing by doffed their hats, "My, that's a fine big dog you have there sir."

Sid bantered with them jovially, Simba walked to heel, stopped when Sid stopped looked neither left nor right, this dog-walking lark was a doddle Dad decided.

From out of nowhere a pack of four mangy mutts appeared, barking at Simba, sidling as near as they dared, always just out of reach, growling slightly, baring their teeth, issuing a challenge.

Proud Simba stared ahead regally, it was as if he neither saw nor heard the annoying animals, he just kept on walking at his steady pace by Sid's side. The dog's wouldn't let it lie; they circled Dad and Simba, still growling, one trying to get a little closer, trying to get in a sly nip at Simba's heels. That ticked Sid off; he let out a yell,

"Now then, be off with you!" and stamped his foot angrily at the four mutts.

Simba's ears pricked up, the master had issued an order, and he wanted the other dogs disposed of.

A deep voiced snarl leapt from Simba's throat, startling both Sid and the four antagonists. All pretence of bravado fled, the dogs let out a collective yelp and took to their heels.

Sid watched in satisfaction at their flight, until his arm was practically wrenched out of its socket as Simba gave chase. Sid was left holding the Alsatian's chain, snapped clean in half!

"Simba, come back!" he spluttered.

Too late! The dog had the enemy in his sights and it would have taken several tanks and a nuclear warhead or two to put him off target. Sid had no option but to run after them waving the now useless chain.

Down street after street Simba pursued the dogs, Sid pursuing Simba, the Alsatian ever gaining on his prey. The lead dog saw an opportunity to shake the angry pursuant off, he hot-footed it up a garden path and in through an open back door. Three equally quaking, shaking, mongrels followed. One large, powerful Alsatian bounded in behind them. One harassed, sweaty, totally out of breath human paused momentarily on the doorstep, then took a breath and plunged into the breech.

A cheerful family of six were just in the process of sitting down to their roast beef and Yorkshire pudding as four dogs came yelping into the kitchen. Seeking a place to hide they dove under the table cowering and barking.

"What the hell..?" The father of the house watched in amazement as a fifth dog, three times the size of the others, charged in behind them, and likewise made a dive beneath the kitchen table.

Four dogs shot out of the other end of the table and started to dart about the kitchen as the human occupants leapt up onto chairs, holding their plates aloft in astonishment. Sid, red-faced with embarrassment, heat and anger, stumbled in behind the menagerie. Polite as ever he entreated the household, "So sorry, please don't get up on our account."

The four dogs sped out of the door again, Simba shook the table off his back, sending the contents of the gravy boat flying across the room along with a half carved side of roast beef, and charged after them.

Sid apologetically put the joint back on the table, nodded good day to the speechless family and fled.

Down to the canal the entourage gambolled, at which point the dogs had the good sense to scatter, three in all directions, and the ring leader of the pack straight into the oily, slime filled, rubbish choked water.

Without pausing for a beat, the Alsatian leapt in still in pursuit. Sid stopped at the water's edge, flailing his arms for balance, gasping for breath.

"Simba!!!" He roared.

Perhaps the shock of the cold water had calmed the enraged dog's brain at last, or maybe it was the sheer joy of being free, and being wet on such a hot day. Whatever it was Simba finally gave up the chase, letting the other dog doggy paddle his way to freedom.

There was just one problem, the sides of the canal were deep, and the Alsatian, who was showing absolutely no intention of getting out of the water, paddling around with a huge doggy grin on his chops, was extremely heavy.

Sid had to jump in the water beside Simba and bodily hoist the dog out before him. Sitting dripping at the side of the canal, covered in slime and frog spawn, Sid shook his head. "Bloody dogs," he muttered whilst wringing out his shirt and shaking tadpoles out of his sandals.

Turning, he saw Simba rolling in the grass in the field behind.

"That's right, dry yourself off before I take you home!" He admonished the dog.

Clearly, the animal was having a whale of a time, all pretence of his usual composed demeanour gone he rolled and snorted and waggled his legs in the air; he looked like a rhinoceros sporting itself in mud. In fact, speaking of mud, what was that brown stuff that kept flying in the air as Simba rolled?

With a sinking feeling Sid realised that just to cap the episode off nicely Simba had found himself a huge, stinky cow pat to roll around in. His beautiful brown and black fur was generously coated in thick stringy globules of the stuff, while the essence of oil and pollution from the canal made him look like some prehistoric swamp beast.

Sid took off his belt and fashioned a temporary lead for the Alsatian.

"Come on Simba, heel," he said hopefully.

Back on form the Alsatian took up his position at "the master's" side. Obediently he walked home, head up, back straight.

Uncle Louis opened the door to the flat. Dad stood there bedraggled, Simba even worse. "What have you done to my dog?" Louis gasped.

"Never mind what I have done to your dog," Sid said. "Ask him what he's done to me!"

My Dad didn't take Simba on any more relaxing Sunday strolls, and maybe not surprisingly, Uncle Louis never suggested it again!

Hauntings

When I was about four or five years old, my parents managed a club for a few years. I didn't live with my parents at this time, but I used to visit most weekends in order to spend time with them and my brother Lee.

The Trades Hall club was large and sprawling and the living quarters were on four levels. The ground floor had a large kitchen and a living room, the first floor, my parent's bedroom and the bathroom, the second floor, the spare room – and Lee and I (when I was there) occupied the attic bedroom.

Because my parents invariably had to work in the club long and unsociable hours Lee and I had a variety of babysitters.

My Granddad (on my mother's side of the family) would often sit happily downstairs in the lounge in return for a couple of smuggled pints and a packet of cheese and onion crisps. Yes, very happy to sit downstairs, but he would never venture up them beyond the first floor landing. Usually on a "toilet break" he would bellow up the stairs. "Lee, Jane, are you alright?"

We would call back that we were, and that would be that. He would quickly scurry back down to the living room again.

My Granddad, you may recall, was a brave chap who had fought voluntarily in both world wars. He was an atheist with no belief in the afterlife whatsoever. "When you're dead, you're dead," was his motto and he stuck to it. Strange then, his reluctance to climb the stairs at the Trades Hall.

"There's something up there," he confided to other adult family members, and no amount of persuading would convince him otherwise.

Granddad, unbeliever though he was, was right. The Trades Hall was riddled with strange phenomena – but nothing quite as frightening as the spare room on the second floor landing.

The very day we moved into the club I went along to explore Mum, Dad and Lee's new home (and my occasional weekend residence).

Lee and I had been told our room would be the attic at the top, so excitedly we negotiated the winding stairwell. As we passed the door on the second floor the temperature dropped rapidly, there was a persistent icy chill that came from the room, even in the summer you could see your breath clouding the air in that spot.

On this occasion the door was open, there was nothing to see except bare floorboards, a window, and a couple of empty boxes and suitcases my parents had hurriedly dumped in there.

I walked towards the door and to my surprise it just swung shut. Lee and I pushed against it, but it wouldn't budge. Mum shouted out to leave that door alone and go on up to our room, so we did.

My mother was extremely psychic and my father was extremely sceptical, but even so, when my mother told my father what she thought of that room he didn't need much persuading to ensure it was securely locked up and all the gaps around it sealed from the day we moved in until the day we moved out. Apart from the empty boxes and luggage it remained bare and unused.

Visitors to the house had to share a room with Lee when I was not there and slept downstairs on the settee when I was. It was as if the spare room didn't exist – although everyone was chillingly aware of its presence, closed up or not.

So there Lee and I would be, tucked up in bed, Lee sticking pink fluff from his blankets up his nose (a strange comfort habit that took years for him to grow out of), me reading and drawing, and Granddad ensconced far below in the living room with the TV turned up full blast and the door to the stairwell firmly closed.

Sometimes I would hear noises coming from the room below. It used to sound as if someone was moving the boxes around and throwing the suitcases about – I could hear them sliding across the floor and colliding with the walls. I'd shout down the stairs expecting Granddad to appear but he never did, although this would usually make the noises stop for a while.

Lee would generally be hard and fast asleep by this time, so I would pull the covers up to my chin and tell myself fairy stories till I fell asleep. After all, Granddad was downstairs, so everything was alright, wasn't it?

Coming forward thirty seven years, whilst doing research for this book, I happened to mention to my brother that I was writing about paranormal experiences I could recall within our family. Without further prompting Lee exclaimed, "The Trades Hall!" and then went on to recount his own experiences of which I had been previously unaware (remember, I only lived there on some weekends, and as Lee was only two and a half to three when we moved in I'd never thought to consult with him, as I didn't expect he'd remember anything much).

Lee reminded me that we used to have a small black and white television in our bedroom. I think it was a bribe to make us stay quietly in bed while our parents were working, not that there was anything much exciting to watch for a three year old and a six year old in those days – the highlight of the night was "The Wheel Tappers and Shunters Club," if we could stay awake long enough to watch it. (Now there's a blast from the past for anyone old enough to recall it).

Anyway, Lee was a bit of a night owl back then, and would generally still be awake when viewing came to an end and all that was left was the static screen. (No, I'm not about to recount the scene from "Poltergeist", to the best of his recollection not even once did my brother get sucked inside the television).

Lee would tiptoe across the room to the TV, stand on his toes to turn it off, then run as fast as he could back into bed and pull the blankets up over his head. This was probably at the point he discovered sticking fluff up his nose as an aid to comfort!

Lee recalled that this was when the noises would start, a cross between low moans and chanting. Night after night, he would burrow down into his bed and try to sleep. Given his age, eventually sleep did overtake him, and when he woke the next morning all would be quiet and normal again.

Apparently, Lee had told Mum about this several times and years later she reminded him he also used to talk about "the little brown men" that sometimes appeared in his room.

To a certain degree this had been dismissed as childish fantasy, or night terrors by the adults, until one of them witnessed "the little brown men" for himself.

My Uncle Ace, one of my Mum's older brothers, also very perceptive and sensitive to other worldly things, had fallen asleep on Lee's bed after an afternoon's drinking session in the club and a large Sunday dinner.

He awoke in the early evening, with a slight buzz in his head, and opened his eyes to the most amazing sight... several monks, visible only from the waist up, came rising through the floor (as if ascending stairs) and disappeared straight through the wall opposite out into mid-air.

He sat, momentarily stunned, rubbing his eyes to ascertain if he was really awake. As the last apparition vanished through the wall he leapt off the bed and descended the stairs three steps at a time as if the hounds of Hell were chasing him.

Uncle Ace arrived in the living room to the astonishment of the rest of the family, who had never seen him move so fast, and breathlessly recounted his vision. Not surprisingly this was greeted with great hilarity and remonstrations not to drink so much.

It made a good story to tell around the tap room of an evening so word soon got out among the locals in the village.

However, Uncle Ace had the last laugh when it was revealed that the club was thought to have actually been built on the site of an old monastery, partly borne out by the fact that there was a very old church just opposite that had once stood within its grounds. It certainly gave the sceptics food for thought.

Another strange encounter was a gentleman who was seen in the club one evening after it had been locked up for the night. Aunty Mary saw him in the billiard room. Thinking he had been accidentally locked in she followed him, an old gent in a flat cap with a great coat and scarf on. However, before she had managed to catch up to him, he passed through a doorway and promptly vanished.

In the lounge bar at the other side of the door the gentleman had passed through were my Dad, cousins Lynda and Lou, and one of the barmaids, Janet (who became Uncle Lou's fiancée shortly after), all in the process of cleaning up. (Practically all the family had second jobs running the club with my parents.)

"Where did he go?" Aunty Mary asked,

"Who?" came back the puzzled reply.

Thinking one of the regular customers must be drifting round the club trying to find an exit a thorough search ensued, but despite all the doors still being securely locked he was never found.

Again, further discussions with the regular customers revealed that the club had a reputation for being haunted, and several previous managers had recalled odd goings on of a night after lock up. After that no-one was keen to enter a room alone after close of business, and all the females insisted in working in pairs.

In recent years the club has been demolished and there is now a petrol station on that site. A shame really, I would have liked to have visited it sometime to see how it felt nowadays. I sometimes wonder if there have been any ghostly goings on there since. Maybe one day I'll call in and ask the staff.

Childhood Companions

Cousin Heath grew older and Lee and I spent more and more time with him. Heath had the face of an angel and the disposition of a little imp. He and Lee were forever into some mischief or other, for which Lee invariably got the blame.

Unlike Heath, with his wide blue-eyed innocent smile, Lee had a crazy mop of unruly hair, twinkling hazel eyes which betrayed the devilment within, a spattering of freckles across an upturned nose, and a smile that permanently said, "you'll never guess what I've just been up to."

"He's a good-looking boy," my Nana would say. "In a roguish type of way."

As the eldest I was expected to somehow keep charge of these two ne'er-do-wells. This was achieved by sporadic shows of affection interspersed with extreme bossiness and occasional scuffles, usually between Lee and me, on the odd occasion he tried to usurp my power.

What Lee still lacked in stature he made up for in cunning. He figured that by getting Heath on his side against the bossy older female they could launch a two pronged attack, which they literally did on numerous occasions!

Into the fray would usually enter our cousin Matthew. He had the advantage, as a boy, of speaking their language, and could usually restore peace successfully. If all else failed however, he generally came down on my side, and we would use our superior strength to truss the demonic duo up like chickens with the aid of a skipping rope or two. Bizarrely they seemed to enjoy this rough handling; I can only assume it's a boy thing!

My early childhood revolved around these three individuals. Suffice it to say, despite my love of dolls and usually quiet nature, I really didn't stand much chance of becoming a real girl. I refused to wear trousers for many years, as I insisted that only boys wore such garments, which meant I was permanently blessed with scabby knees and bruised up legs.

I insisted on growing my hair long, as that was how a lady's hair should be, but by the same token could not bear to have it adorned with clips or ribbons or headbands. I would sit dutifully enjoying the gentle administrations of Nana or Aunty Mary whilst they brushed and tied up my hair, then, as soon as I was out of sight, tear out the gaily coloured ribbons and scatter the clips to the elements. I liked my hair to flow freely behind me like a Red Indian brave's, with the result that by the end of the day it was generally a tangled mess of leaves, grass and debris, a veritable crow's nest rather than my crowning glory.

Matthew, Lee, Heath and I frolicked through our early childhood. Through the long hot summers we would be out from dawn until dusk, creating elaborate dens out of newly cut grass or up in the trees, making dams in the stream or fighting in lumps with each other or rival gangs of marauding enemies, both real and imagined.

We would plan strategies for world domination, enact plays (usually devised by Matthew and myself), write songs, and make up ridiculous rhymes, and torment one another, other children, or unsuspecting adults.

Having run ourselves ragged, we would go home filthy and exhausted, then get up and do it all over again the next day.

Most weekends we were taken out for a drive in the country, or to some nearby place of historical interest. Aunty Margery, Uncle Jim, Uncle Louis and the older boys in Uncle Jim's car, Aunty Mary, Uncle Jack, Matthew, Lee, Heath and I, inseparable as always, squashed together on the back seat of "Betsy" - Uncle Jack's faithful old jalopy.

This was before the days when child seats or even seatbelts were the law, (songs like "In the Summertime" by Mungo Jerry advised we should all "have a drink, have a drive," and no-one thought this was an odd suggestion!). We crammed as many people as would fit into each vehicle, sometimes with a dog or two thrown in for good measure, rolling about on the back seat, usually singing "Chitty Chitty Bang Bang" or similar.

We would laugh and scream and hug each other in delight as Uncle Jack would find the twistiest winding roads he could and fly down and up them as quickly as possible so that we felt we had "left our stomachs behind" and laugh as we were thrown about mercilessly.

"Again, again!" we'd demand. We called this going on the "switchbacks", it was our equivalent of a roller coaster ride and we loved it.

Up ahead, or more likely far behind, Uncle Jim and co. would be tootling along sedately, listening to Matt Monroe on the cassette recorder.

When we had reached our destination the adults would disembark, gingerly stretching, and flexing aching legs. We would run around dementedly until someone, usually Aunty Mary, would sensibly round us up and take us all in search of the nearest toilets. There would follow a tour of that day's main attraction. This was my favourite part, as I would instantly find myself transported to another place and time, wandering around curiously aware I had one foot in this world and one foot in another.

Matthew, Lee and Heath would sometimes agree they saw things too, but it was hard to tell if they were just playing along and humouring me or genuinely tuning in, as I was. With our ancestral links, they were as likely to see the other world as I could, if they had wanted to.

Tour over, it would be time for a picnic; this was where Aunty Margery came into her own. Four or five bag loads of assorted sandwiches would emerge from the car boot, with giant containers of lemon and lime juice and orange squash, plastic cups, disposable napkins, packets of buns or tins of home made cakes, enormous picnic blankets, and folding chairs for the adults. She would set them all up whilst Uncle Jim would organise everyone with military precision. Not only did I read Enid Blyton, I lived the lifestyle!

Eventually everyone would be replete, and the adults would want to rest and relax for a while to "let their lunch settle".

We children felt no such desire and this would be our cue to take off like wild things, gambolling through the ornamental gardens, and dashing precariously along the edges of duck ponds and lakes. Poor Nick and Martin would be left behind with the adults, deemed far too old to want to scurry around with us. Actually, I expect they were relieved.

On one trip we were out on some craggy moor land with huge rocks, warm from the sun, where we could sit, or leap courageously across, fancying ourselves as fearless mountaineers. Far below us the adult contingent warmed themselves in the sun.

I found myself on the most enormous rock. Crawling to the edge I realised it overhung a steep drop; I was peering over a precipice at jutting rocks and stones below. The view was spectacular and, not thinking, I edged closer to get a better look.

Suddenly I was aware of Aunty Mary shouting my name, and Matthew several rocks away let out a warning gasp. I had overreached myself and was on the verge of toppling over the edge and down to the waiting crags below.

Bizarrely, I felt no panic. As I started to lurch forward it was as if someone invisible put their hands on my shoulders and gently pushed me up. I felt a little hand grasp the back of my underskirt and tug me back, righting me again. It was only at this point that self-preservation kicked in and I scrambled backwards in surprise.

Heath had pulled me to safety, quick thinking for a three year old, and an amazing show of strength, when in reality my superior weight and the force of gravity should have seen us both plummeting over the edge.

Lee and Matthew scurried up to join us. They were far more shaken than Heath and I, as were the watching adults, who had seen the danger, but had been too far away to help.

From then on we were limited in our freedom on day trips, until every conceivable danger had been assessed and identified. Little Heath was the unchallenged hero of the day, his superhuman strength a topic of discussion for quite some time.

Someone to watch over Lee

If cats have nine lives, then so does my little brother Lee.

Around the time we were living in the haunted club Lee seemed to excel in putting his guardian angel to the test. When the angel was busy, it was usually Dad that got roped in instead!

There was the time, one Saturday morning, when a cooked breakfast got a bit out of hand and the kitchen went up in flames. After hustling Mum out of the door so she couldn't further complicate matters, Dad had to race back through the flames, up several flights of stairs, and pluck Lee from his bed in the attic. Dad then had to run back downstairs with Lee tucked under one arm, through the flaming kitchen again, and deposit him in the yard with Mum (the kitchen door being the only exit).

This little adventure would be enough for most men but Dad then decided to run back into the kitchen and tackle the blaze himself, although the fire brigade were on their way.

Somehow he managed to get the fire under control but burnt his hands a little in the process. (A little matter of running about with a blazing frying pan in his hands, I believe).

The rest of the family didn't know whether to applaud his bravery or upbraid him for the risk he took putting the fire out. When asked about his hands, however, Dad replied with his usual composure, "Oh it's nothing, a couple of blisters".

My Dad; a lifelong master of the under-statement!

My other grandparents lived a long way away, in the far off seaside kingdom of Blackpool (that's how it appeared to me, anyway). So Lee and I didn't get to see them often, though once or twice a year Mum, Dad, Lee and I would go and stay at their boarding house (never in high season you understand).

I remember my Grandma and Granddad as warm loving people who were always laughing and smiling, but very busy; Granddad bustling about doing whatever "people that run boarding houses" do, Grandma in the kitchen, her face florid in the heat, dishing up meal after meal for the other boarders, with Mum and Dad trying to be helpful and Lee and I invariably getting under everybody's feet.

We spent happy days on the sands, wrapped up against the elements, as it was probably March or October. Mum in a headscarf, still trying to be glamorous, Dad wrestling with deckchairs and wind breaks, Lee and I making sandcastles or digging holes full of gloopy mud that we could throw at each other. We would have picnic lunches on the beach, real sand in the sandwiches, naturally, finished off with pink candyfloss that I refused to eat just in case it was really cotton wool until Lee demolished his so quickly he convinced me not only was it not poisonous, it was actually rather nice "and he would eat mine too if I didn't eat up quick and stop being such a wuss."

We loved the penny arcades, rode on endless carousels (but never enough), ate bags of vinegary chips while walking on the front, and had to be piggy-backed to the boarding house by Dad.

The highlight of the autumn stay would be a drive through the glittering tableaux of the Blackpool Illuminations, lighting up the streets from pier to pier, on the final night there.

We would travel home enriched by plastic toys, toffee apples, and buckets and spades that once back home Lee would use to make mud pie castles!

It was on the return home from one of these holidays that Mum decided she wanted time to herself to unpack.

"Sid, why don't you take the kids out for a nice long walk?" she suggested. "It will keep them out of mischief."

It was a nice, bright, sunny afternoon, so Dad agreed. He decided it would be fun for us to take a walk around Yeadon Tarn, a small lake that lay in the middle of the village. There might even be some ducks to feed, he suggested, so Lee and I were eager to get going.

We had not long been at the Tarn before Dad bumped into a teenager he knew; his Mum was one of Dad's cleaners at the club.

As we paused at the edge of the water to chat, Teddy, the boy, was forced to get Lee in a headlock to keep him still. Lee was yelling and thrashing about, the way four year old boys are likely to do when restrained by an older male they are trying to impress. Dad just stood laughing; my behaviour was impeccable (naturally).

"Listen mate," Teddy addressed Lee. "This is serious, don't you go near the edge of the Tarn…it's really slippery!"

He explained to Dad how if you put your foot in a certain place you would definitely go straight in the water, Dad agreed.

Teddy had let Lee loose again and I watched him as Dad continued to discuss how treacherous the Tarn could be with our friend. Lee edged closer and closer to the water, I tugged at Dad's sleeve, "Daaa…deee!"

Dad looked down at me, "What is it Jane?"

SPLASH!

Lee disappeared into the water. Instinctively, I started forward but Dad pulled me back and thrust me into Teddy's hands. "Not you too…stay there!"

Dad ran to the edge and jumped in. Now they were both under the water, where had they gone?

Somewhere near the middle of the Tarn Lee resurfaced. He didn't know how to swim but some kind of animal instinct seemed to have kicked in and now he was doing a frantic doggy paddle out into the deep water. Teddy and I leapt about on the bank, trying to encourage him to turn round and head back.

Fortunately, at this point Dad reappeared, just behind Lee. In a swift movement he had the little miscreant under the chin and was swimming strongly back to us. Teddy helped them out and we went straight home.

Mum glanced up from unpacking, "You're back early… "

She looked from Lee to Dad and back again; two slimy swamp beasts dripping bilge water all over her new orange and purple swirl carpet (hey, this was the seventies; they were the height of fashion).

"Sidney Berry…!" She began.

Lee and I beat a hasty retreat up to the bathroom so that he could smear mud all over the bath and I could berate him in a big-sisterly fashion. Downstairs Mum was explaining the finer points of child care to Dad. Poor Dad!

Mum and Dad had invested in a brand new suite to go with the trendy carpet. It was a three seater and two chairs in real "mock" leather (so that would be plastic, I expect) in a startling shade of orange that matched the curtains too. They loved it, Lee and I loved it too. It had castors on the chairs, and you could give one another "funfair" rides up and down the lounge in them if you pushed really hard. Long evenings flew by as we trundled up and down the room, shrieking, "Faster, faster!"

One fun-filled evening Mum and Dad hadn't managed to secure a baby-sitter. As they were only in the club, which adjoined the living quarters, it was assumed we couldn't come to much harm. They also intended to bob in and out a few times throughout the night to check on us. We were even being trusted to put ourselves to bed, as I had a watch and at seven could tell the time quite well.

So Lee and I passed the usual sort of "Home Alone" evening. We put a plastic Woody Woodpecker figure and a little doll in a yellow bathing suit upside down in glasses of orange juice and popped them in the fridge to freeze (home made lollipops for the morning). We ate crisps and drank pop, had burping competitions (Lee won hands down, I couldn't get the hang of it), watched something on TV, pummelled each other with cushions a bit, pummelled each other without cushions for a while too, had a name calling session, got upset, gave one another a hug, made friends again and decided to ride the armchairs round the room for a while before bed. Good as gold at eight o'clock by my watch we trundled sleepily up to bed.

Around eleven o'clock Dad got us back up again. Sleepily, we followed him downstairs – was it morning already? The staircase smelt a bit funny. When we got to the living room it was filled with inky black, noxious smelling fumes. Dad quickly ushered us through there and out of the kitchen into the club itself where we sat in a corner with some lemonade, hiding quietly by the coat rack. An hour or so later Mum led us back into the living room and up to bed.

"What happened Mummy?" I wondered. Mum said they'd tell us in the morning.

So, the next morning we were back in the strange smelling living room, lined up in front of Dad, who looked a little stern.

"Who left one of the chairs pushed right up against the gas fire?" He asked.

Lee and I looked at each other, nonplussed. What did he mean?

By way of explanation Dad turned the back of one of the new chairs to face us. A large hole had melted through the plastic and foam back of the chair, the orange had turned black and crispy at the edges. It was a bit scary to look at now. So that was what the smell was!

Apparently, the fire brigade had been called (again), they had just stuck the melted chair out in the garden for a while and opened all the windows till the smoke cleared.

Dad was not impressed. Mum was mortified by the state of her chair but they couldn't afford to replace it, so they kept it as a testament to the foolishness of wayward children. I think Dad removed the castors after that!

Sam

Aunty Mary and Uncle Jack had a golden retriever for a few years. A sweet dog with a lovely, gentle temperament, in many ways unremarkable after the rogues' gallery of pets they had had in the past, with one exception - Sam took his title of retriever very seriously indeed. He loved to retrieve things; old burst footballs, discarded shoes, broken toys. He once came home with a baby's dummy clasped between his lips, looking for the all world as if it was rightfully his!

Aunty Mary and Uncle Jack would laugh and accept his tokens of affection graciously then deposit them down the rubbish chute while he was sleeping, so that he wouldn't be offended.

One exceptionally crisp, winter's night Uncle Jack was taking Sam for the last walk of the day. Tonight he seemed determined to have a good forage down by the stream and Uncle Jack waited patiently, shivering a little, until he was ready to return. He came back, tail wagging, something in his mouth as usual.

"Good Dog," Uncle Jack said. "What have you got this time boy? A ball is it?"

He couldn't see as the night was so dark, but it looked like a small circular object.

Back home, Sam trotted straight into the kitchen. Uncle Jack and Aunty Mary followed him, amused to see what offering he had for them tonight. Gently, Sam dropped something to the floor and nuzzled it with his nose towards his food and water bowls. Aunty Mary let out a little squeal of surprise.

Uncle Jack peered closer. "Well, blow me down, it's not a ball, it's a hedgehog!"

Sam had very gently carried the little creature between the soft parts of his mouth so as not to hurt it with his teeth. He looked at Uncle Jack expectantly, then at the hedgehog, slowly uncurling by the food bowl.

"Have you brought the hedgehog home so we can feed it?" Uncle Jack asked, amazed.

Sam let out an agreeable woof in response.

Aunty Mary smiled. "Poor little thing, it must have been half frozen out there tonight, and I expect the stream was frozen over too so it wouldn't be able to drink."

She put some milk on a saucer and deposited it in front of the little creature. Sam let out a snort of approval and lay down, tail wagging all the while, to watch as it lapped up the milk.

Once the hedgehog had had its fill and warmed up, Uncle Jack wrapped it carefully in a tea towel and took it back out to the stream, as close to where Sam had found it as possible.

Every night for a fortnight Sam found the hedgehog and brought it gently home for its supper. When the cold snap ended the hedgehog moved on too and Sam was happy enough to go back to foraging for rubbish again. Uncle Jack was amazed, never had he seen a dog with such compassion for another creature.

The New Inn

When I was eight and Lee almost six Mum and Dad moved again. This time they had bought their own pub, having cut their teeth managing "The Trades Hall" complete with its resident ghosts.

The new pub was extremely old, and considerably smaller than their previous residence, something Mum and Dad remedied in later years by extending into what was once a shop next door, but had long been boarded up and derelict.

Despite its extreme age, at least a couple of hundred years or more, to my disappointment, there were no other worldly presences within its walls, and the building itself held scant interest for me. What I did find delightful, however, was the fact that it stood right next door to a church, complete with overflowing graveyard.

St Oswald's, my mother informed me, was one of the oldest churches for miles around, and is even reputedly recorded in the Doomsday book.

It did not take long, that first evening after moving in, for Lee and me to escape into the grounds of the church for some serious exploration. We paid little attention to the building itself, interesting though the architecture was, but hastened down the path and straight into the middle of the graveyard.

I was immediately struck by the atmosphere; it was like walking into another world. Although we weren't far from a main road, and the day was actually still quite bright and sunny, within the walls of the graveyard the sounds of the outside seemed hushed and distant. A low mist rolled around the grass, lapping at the gravesides. Lee scooted off ahead in delight until I cautioned him to be careful and respectful of where he was standing.

I expect I was hoping to catch a glimpse of at least one ghost that afternoon. Strangely, it had never occurred to me that the shady figures, visions and occasional dead relatives I encountered from time to time were anything other than my imagination. Too many children's programmes had led me to believe that real apparitions looked like sheets with eyeholes, and I'd certainly never encountered anything like that!

As I walked from gravestone to gravestone I was transfixed by the images presented to me. I would read the names of entire households entombed there from centuries ago and be impressed by fleeting images of their lives before me. I do not think that I was encountering spirits but the residue left by their physical energy; psychic snapshots recorded in the ether rather than communication from a still living entity. I felt over awed, treading amongst those who had lived, loved and died many years before I was born.

The place was so ancient that there were very few recent graves to be found. I half imagined the vicar would soon have to put up a sign "No Vacancies" like they did in boarding houses at the seaside. Strangely, the more recent gravesites seemed emptiest of all; they lacked a lot of the resonance of the older tombs.

I now realise this should not be surprising. Contrary to popular belief, spirits do not hover around their graves in the hope a family member will stop by and visit. Neither are they endlessly grieving for their physical remains, as they are well aware that it is of no use whatsoever and now have a perfectly good etheric body, thank you very much. Once they have crossed over, they have lives that continue very merrily on the other side. They visit us whenever they wish, so if we happen to visit their graveside or memorial garden they will sometimes come along out of curiosity, or compassion for us if we are grieving, and then, when we have pulled ourselves together, they will travel back home with us again. No wonder the more recent graves felt empty, there was definitely no one in residence, as they all had far more interesting places to be!

Over the years, Lee and I often explored the graveyard. I never considered it to be a frightening place, it was just tranquil and atmospheric. It heightened my senses, but also gave me a wonderful feeling of peace. This never felt to me like a place where things had ended, more a wonderful starting point where something had actually begun.

Mum liked to go there too, sometimes. She and I would wander hand in hand and try to find the oldest gravestone. Some of them were dated centuries ago and a few lying on the ground had worn down so much the writing was no longer visible. Many a time we thought we were on a path but when looking down we would realise we were actually standing on the slabs themselves.

I love the sound of church bells and on a weekend, especially in summer, it would be a joy to hear them ringing out gaily to announce a wedding. What was not so joyous was the one lonely bell that intoned for hours every Sunday morning. I do not know if this was to call people to Sunday service or bell ringing practise for one lone enthusiast. I used to picture him, swinging around on the same blessed rope like some modern day Quasimodo. Except the bells weren't driving him mad, it was me they were incensing. I used to put the pillow over my head and try in vain to go back to sleep, all to no avail.

Chapter Seven
Growing Pains

Flash

When good old Simba passed away Uncle Louis was heart-broken. He swore he would never have another dog as long as he lived, because being parted from them was almost unbearable.

The family seemed incomplete without an Alsatian so Mum and Dad decided they would get one as it was many years since their own dog Sheba had gone to the "happy hunting ground" too. Lee and I were overjoyed when they brought home a large bundle of fluff, all nose and ears. We named him Flash because of the speed he could travel round a room.

Flash was a magnificent animal. He lacked the nobility of Simba, being far and away too puppyish and playful even into old age, but he was just as loyal and family orientated. He was a long-haired golden Alsatian, whereas Simba's hair had been shorter, darker, and sleeker. Flash was a bundle of fluff that moulted continuously. Wherever he'd been he left a trail that Mum christened "Flash hairs". He shed enough every day to stuff a small cushion with.

Flash loved to play. He would stand still patiently whilst Lee and I dressed him up in old curtains (meant to be royal robes) and plonked a paper crown on his head, then chased him round the pub crying, "All Hail, good king Flash!"

Wherever we went he wanted to go too and would obediently walk out with us, matching his stride to ours, never dragging or pulling on the reigns. He obeyed our every command immediately, so gentle that we could pass a crisp between our lips to his without him even touching us.

This same gentle giant was a fearless guard dog with a well-respected reputation around the local community. Our bar staff were always treated to a few drinks after closing, Mum and Dad being the original twenty-four hour party people. One night, yobs brayed on the pub windows after seeing the dim lights in the bar and realising there were people inside. Imagine their surprise when out of the darkness something approximately the size of a small donkey let out one almighty bark and leapt straight through a plate glass window at them, clearing two sets of tables in one bound! Amazingly, the same thing happened a few weeks later making Dad very popular with the local glazier. Fortunately, Flash never cut himself during these escapades and the drunken fools found themselves becoming Greek athletes in their fleet-footed flight home to change their sodden trousers!

Flash was the sort of dog that read your mind. Often before we uttered the words "do you want to go for a walk?" he would be standing ready at the door, or bringing his lead to you.

He would gaze into our faces with an intensity and devotion that said he understood everything we thought and felt. The type of dog who would know instinctively if you were sad and come to lie his teddy bear head in your lap, sorrowful eyes saying, "I know what you're thinking."

Flash always sensed when family were due to visit and would prick up his ears and dart about excitedly for twenty minutes before they arrived at the pub.

He loved nothing better than to go for a ride. Fortunately Dad had always loved large cars and the back seat of his Jaguar just about allowed Lee, Flash and I to sit comfortably together.

Flash always had to have the window seat so he could do that dog thing; head sticking out, ears whipping back in the wind, tongue lolling, eyes laughing, with me and Lee trying to hold him steady as Dad threw the car around bends and up and down hills and valleys.

We would arrive at our destination; Flash excited and refreshed, Lee and I covered in so much dog hair we looked like miniature abominable snowmen.

Mum and Dad purchased a chalet at the seaside town of Withernsea for weekends away. Flash liked nothing better than to race up and down the beach with me and Lee.

He knew when he was in holiday mode and never troubled passers-by. He didn't even give them a second glance, but you could tell they were a little wary to see such a large dog unrestrained, and hurried by hastily. Lee and I were used to having a large part of the beach to ourselves as people seemed to keep a respectful distance away!

Flash loved winter. Even as an old dog he wanted to be out by Lee's side.

One particularly cold season Lee took himself off to the park, faithful dog by his side as always. He had purchased a rather good sledge and spent hours of fun whizzing up and down the hill on it, as Flash raced alongside.

Eventually, Lee paused to think. Poor old Flash's eyes were laughing as always but he was looking tired and his coat was not as thick these days. The dog appeared to be shivering, whereas all the running about had made Lee rather warm. A sudden brain-wave hit home. Lee took off his sleeveless body warmer and put it on his old pal back to front, zipping it securely across Flash's back, so that his tummy was covered in the quilted jacket. Flash followed Lee back to the top of the hill where Lee coaxed him onto the sledge. With an almighty push the sled shot off down the hill with the large Alsatian in the luminous blue body-warmer sitting on it, barking delightedly all the way to the bottom. Several onlookers did a double take, then dived out of the way as he hurtled past, followed by Lee, screaming and whooping with laughter.

The dog enjoyed the experience so much they stayed the entire afternoon. Lee and Flash returned home, tired and happy, the dog still resplendent in Lee's electric blue jacket – quite a sight to behold!

Family Holiday.

My Mum had one sister, Mary, and three brothers, Jim, Horace and Louis, my Aunt and Uncles. Uncle Jim, as the eldest, had a no-nonsense logical view on life. Like my Granddad before him he was an atheist, and had no time for the "delusional" concepts of the rest of the family. Mum's other brothers Ace and Louis, although of no religious denomination, both had a strong sense of the supernatural and a keen interest in it. Mum, Uncle Ace and Uncle Louis. as the three youngest of the family. were as thick as thieves, both in childhood and adulthood. My Dad, being of a similar nature to them, was also part of the clan, and they would holiday together in much the same way Aunty Mary and Uncle Jim (the two eldest) and their families would spend a lot of time together.

Uncle Ace had a wicked sense of humour, he was always laughing and joking. The only one of the five siblings to inherit his father's blue eyes, they twinkled and reflected the permanent devilment bubbling inside. He had the tanned, swarthy skin inherited from the French and gypsy lineage, long curling black hair and a drooping moustache reminiscent of a cavalier.

He was the sort of character that made an instant impression on everyone he met, the kind of person it felt good to be around whatever the circumstances.

When I was eight my Mum and Dad hired a Villa in Ibiza. This was extremely adventurous at the time, I was the only child in my school to go abroad that year. It was at a time when Ibiza was largely unspoilt; the era of the package holiday was only just getting underway.

My Mum, Dad, Lee, Aunty Mary, Uncle Jack, Uncle Ace, Uncle Louis, Nana and I jetted off to the sun. Uncle Jim and Aunty Margery were keeping an eye on Granddad for us as he refused to come, being terrified of aeroplanes. My Mum pointed out that if it was his destiny to die by plane one would probably fall on him, but he wasn't convinced.

The island of Ibiza seemed very exotic. The dirt roads, the constantly chirping crickets, the scented trees, the heat, the little lizards they call geckos, the unfamiliar language all made it seem like being on another planet, especially when we discovered you couldn't drink the water directly from the tap; you had to boil it first, fancy that!

Lee and I ran around the villa exclaiming at everything, while the adults tried to recover from the flight and unpack.

True to form Nana and Aunty Mary started preparing food and drinks (aided by a foraging expedition to the local shop spearheaded by Mum in search of alcohol).

We were all well prepared for this foreign land, everyone was totally trained to say "gracias" and "porfavour" and of course as long as you could say please and thank you in someone's language (we reasoned) they would be happy for you to mime the rest.

Uncle Ace was standing admiring the swimming pool when Lee came tearing out of the villa in some psychedelic swimming shorts. Before he could say, "Where are your arm bands?" - SPLASH! - Lee was in and under, having leapt straight in at the deep end (naturally!).

What could Uncle Ace do? He was fully clothed so he leant down and made a grab for his nephew's flailing limbs, managing to yank him bodily from the water. Lee coughed and spluttered for a moment, then figured out where the shallow end was and ran and jumped into that instead.

Uncle Ace straightened up to a painful twinge, he had put his back out within the first ten minutes of the holiday, that nephew of his should come with a warning sticker attached! Not that a bad back was enough to dampen Uncle Ace's enthusiasm, he was as full of mischief as ever.

Mum, Dad and Uncle Lou discovered a nice bar within walking, or in Uncle Ace's case, hobbling distance, and that was where the majority of the adults would end each day. Nana was a willing babysitter, providing she had some Guinness, a good western novel, and a fire lit for those cool evenings once the sun went down.

Lee amused himself in various ways, mostly either getting into mischief or winding me up, but that's what being six is for, surely. I had a drawing pad and I spent my evenings creating books; picture stories with a little writing that I could try out on Lee as I finished each one. It kept him out of trouble briefly, and now and again he'd beg some paper and start one of his own.

Meanwhile, down in the bar, the locals took an instant shine to Uncle Ace, with his flashing smile and twinkling eyes. He soon had them engaged in friendly banter about who he was or where he was from.

For some strange reason he decided to tell them he was a travelling magician who could foretell the future. (Goodness knows how many San Miguel's he'd sampled by that point!). Yeah, right!

The locals thought he was hysterical, Mum said everyone was laughing, Uncle Ace most of all.

"Prove it!" His new friends urged.

Uncle Ace pondered for a while. He had noticed the island was very dry. Did they get much rain?

"No," there had been no rain for weeks they assured him; it was not the rainy season.

"Aha!" said Uncle Ace, twiddling his moustache in his best wizard impersonation.

"I will make the rains come, tomorrow, torrential rains for several hours, all over the island."

The locals laughed good naturedly and placed bets on his prediction. Everyone headed home highly amused.

The next morning Lee and I woke to the sound of rain lashing the villa. We looked outside; a thunderstorm of biblical proportions had hit the island.

Trees bent under the force of the onslaught, lightning crackled across the sky and rain bounced to waist height on contact with the ground, the dirt roads had turned to mud tracks.

Mum got up and started making coffee for everyone. The rest of the family surfaced one by one, shaking their heads in disbelief.

"I thought this was meant to be a hot and sunny place?" Lee queried.

"It's your Uncle Ace's fault," Mum said cryptically, we didn't have a clue what she meant. "Ace, looks like you won your bet."

"Told them I could do it," Uncle Ace grinned, gingerly sitting himself down with his coffee.

"Great, but where are we supposed to go now, we're trapped for the day," Mum pointed out. Uncle Ace put a mystical expression on his face (this involved screwing up his nose and eyes and wiggling the fingers of both hands at Lee and me).

"I predict this will all die down by two o'clock and then…beautiful sunshine!" Everyone got out their books and found a place to curl up for a while.

At two o'clock the rain passed over and the sun came out. Uncle Ace just raised an eyebrow at Mum.

"Lucky guess," she said.

Back at the bar that night the locals were impressed but still a bit sceptical.

"What else do you see?" they pressed him.

Uncle Ace closed his eyes and put on the best "fake psychic" impersonation he could muster, wrapping a bar towel around his head. They were all laughing again, no-one more so than the assorted relatives seated with him.

"The mists are clearing…" he said in a wavering voice. "I see…tomorrow…the big fish is coming!"

My Dad and Uncle Lou nearly choked on their pints. "Big fish!"

"Aha," said Uncle Ace. "Tomorrow you will see."

The third evening found them all in the bar again. This time the locals gathered round Uncle Ace in awed silence.

"What's the matter?" he laughed.

"Today," they told him, "A whale was washed up on the beach."

Mum, Dad and Uncle Louis exchanged looks of incredulity.

"Now," they pressed. "Tell us what you see for tomorrow." Uncle Ace started wrinkling his nose again.

"Horatio...No!" Mum said firmly (this was like calling Dad, Sidney, and meant "if you continue there'll be trouble!").

Enough was enough, she told everybody back at the Villa, she dreaded to think what his fertile imagination would conjure up next… volcanoes, hurricanes, the lost island of Atlantis rising from the ocean…

So could Uncle Ace predict the future? Stranger still, could he create the future? I guess that will remain one of life's mysteries, as Uncle Ace couldn't explain how he did it himself. He just told us he was "magic," and anyone fortunate enough to have known my Uncle Ace would definitely have agreed with that.

A helping hand

When I was ten years old Aunty Mary was diagnosed with cancer. To be honest, I really was too young to grasp the gravity of the matter. Aunty Mary went into hospital for a week for what she assured me was a "minor operation." Uncle Jack and I managed with a little help from Nana and before I knew it Aunty Mary was home safe and sound again.

It didn't take me long to realise that my Aunty was actually much more poorly than she let on. No amount of stiff upper lips could hide the fact she was weak and shaky, losing her hair and being sick many times each day. In actual fact it was the combination of a radical mastectomy, and a punishing course of chemotherapy that was taking its toll on her, but, true to form, Aunty Mary made light of it all, and soldiered on.

We had acquired a young dog named Mischief, shortly before Aunty Mary became ill. He was another intelligent animal, a black and white mongrel with constantly pricked up ears as if on the alert for something. He was afforded all the love and affection my Aunt and Uncle lavished on every pet they had, and returned the devotion many times over.

One day I overheard Aunty Mary talking quietly to Uncle Jack and Nana about how clever Mischief was. Aunty Mary had been in the house alone when she had suddenly come over very faint. We had no telephone and Aunty Mary panicked a bit as the door was not only locked but bolted on the inside. If she passed out no-one would know, or be able to get in without breaking the door down. She sat head forward in her hands, feeling a blackness descend, and as she started to slip from consciousness whispered, "Oh God, help me."

The next thing she was aware of was something cold and wet washing her face and hands repeatedly, drawing her back from the brink of passing out. Relieved, she opened her eyes to see Mischief licking her hands and cheeks over and over, a concerned look on his little canine features. He didn't stop until she was able to sit herself up properly and reassure him with a "good dog, good boy."

"That dog knew I was in danger and, bless him, he knew exactly how to bring me round," she told Uncle Jack and Nana in admiration and gratitude.

It was unusual, as Mischief never licked anyone. My Aunt and Uncle didn't approve of dogs' licking, especially faces, as they considered it unhygienic, so Mischief had taken it upon himself to go against everything he had been trained not to do in order to save the day.

A month or so later I was in bed reading. It was quite late at night, about ten thirty, and only Aunty Mary and I were in as Uncle Jack was working nights. I heard her call my name weakly from the living room, jumped out of bed, and rushed through to her. Poor Aunty Mary looked dreadful. She had gone drip white, tinged with blue around the lips, and a cold, clammy sweat had broken out on her brow. I ran and clutched her hands. They were icy cold and I felt really frightened.

"What's the matter?" I gasped. Aunty Mary was trying to be brave but her eyes were as scared as mine.

"I feel very sick," she whispered.

I ran to the bathroom and got a bowl for her to be sick in. Racing back I thrust it into her lap. She leaned forward and dry heaved a couple of times.

To my despair her head suddenly slumped forward, her eyes rolling, her arms falling limp at her sides, and there came a horrible gurgling sound from her throat. I was only eleven and I was terrified. I knew the sound I could hear was bile rising in her throat and that if I couldn't bring her round she was probably about to choke on her own vomit.

I was in the house alone, there was no phone; I didn't dare to leave her for the time it would take to run and get Nana from the other flat. I clasped my hands together.

"What can I do, what can I do?" I implored the silent room.

A very calm voice in my head said, "Remember, what did Mischief do?"

Quick as a flash I ran and got a wet flannel and flew back to her side. I washed her face and hands whilst imploring her, "Come on Aunty Mary wake up."

Suddenly she let out a cough and jerked back. I instinctively pulled her jaw open, pressed her tongue down and supported her forehead with my hand as she lent forward and retched green bile into the bowl.

My hands trembling I washed her face again. She smiled at me weakly. "Thank you, did I faint for a moment there?"

I confirmed that she had, but it was ok, I had known what to do. Well certainly someone had known what was to be done and they had managed to communicate it to both myself and Mischief the dog.

Close encounters of the soggy kind

We were on holiday again; I was ten, Lee almost eight. This time Mum and Dad, Nana, Uncle Ace, Uncle Lou, Janet (Uncle Lou's girlfriend), Lee and I were staying in a hotel in Ibiza. (Aunty Mary and Uncle Jack had declined to come, as they had decided they really didn't like flying).

The days were filled with me and my little brother endlessly exploring the surrounding area (it was that or sit by the bar with the adults all day – the hotel was nice, but it wasn't big on entertaining children). Actually, Lee did all the exploring, I just tried to keep up, keep track of where we were, and keep him out of trouble.

Lee was a force of nature; he could not be argued or reasoned with once he had an idea in his head. To compensate for his utter recklessness I was cautious, very cautious; I had to be cautious for two. We were in a strange land, we barely spoke the language beyond being polite and knowing how to order food and drink. I had a better grip on the exchange rate for currency; Lee would pay with any old bill and run off without waiting for the change. This wasn't a holiday come to think of it, it was bloomin' hard work!

Midway into the second week salvation arrived in the form of a girl called Christina and her younger brother Paul.

Christina was twelve but looked older. We got on ok but hadn't much in common. She was far more interested in making eyes at the young Spanish waiters and their friends who hung about the place. I was still on a quest to ensure Lee survived the holiday. Her brother Paul, a year younger than me at nine, was a better proposition for friendship; I was always easier in the company of boys back then. Paul had a cockney accent, which amused Lee and me, as much as our northern one must have amused him. We hung around together mimicking each other's turn of phrase, good-naturedly.

Paul had been to this part of Ibiza before and knew it pretty well so he became the self-appointed tour guide for us, which kept Lee as occupied as I could wish. Paul was an excellent swimmer whereas Lee and I still hadn't mastered the skill at all. He offered to teach us over the holiday, so we arranged to meet by the pool the next afternoon.

As Paul walked away I got a sudden vision of Lee leaping into the pool and going under.

"What will you do?" A voice in my head asked.

Paul would save him of course, I told myself, why worry?

"Lee will be too strong for Paul," the voice insisted.

"What will you do?" It asked again.

I thought back to all the public information films I'd ever seen. I knew, as a non-swimmer myself, the worst thing I could do was jump in as well. I'd have to lie down and stretch out my arms to Paul of course. This seemed to silence the voice of the "good imagination" everyone said I was blessed with. Anyway, I told myself, the pool is always full of people, so there is no chance of anything like that happening.

The next day, just after lunch, I made my way to the poolside as arranged. Lee was dawdling behind, trying to blow up some armbands in our room, I'd left him to it so that we wouldn't both be late for Paul.

As it happened he was already waiting by the pool for us, an empty, curiously deserted pool. Everyone must have gone in for second sitting at lunch that day except us.

Paul and I were standing chatting by the side of the pool discussing the best way to start our lesson. I was telling him the little I knew about keeping afloat. Lee, true to form, came shooting past us out of nowhere, wearing bright orange arm bands. Paul spun to see him and shouted out a warning, "Not that end Lee, it's the deep end!"

SPLASH!

Paul and I ran to the edge of the pool. Thank goodness he had his armbands on, I told myself, feeling a curious sense of déjà vu coming over me.

Lee, it turned out, hadn't inflated the armbands properly in his eagerness to get to the pool. The force of connecting with the water had driven any last puff of air out of them, and now he was floundering wildly, going under for the third and final time, as they say.

My new friend muttered something that sounded a little like "oh s**t!" but he was such a nice polite boy, I expect I hadn't heard him properly.

Paul dived into the pool. I stood on the edge, feeling remarkably calm, watching as the scenario that had played through my mind the day before became reality. He had got to Lee and was attempting to get him on his back, cupping his hand under his chin to keep his head above water.

Lee was thrashing about in blind panic and, as they were both of a similar age and size, he was succeeding in dragging Paul under with him. They were quite a distance from the edge of the pool, in very deep water.

I looked around, Paul's predicament slowly dawning on me. There was a very real possibility they were both about to drown before my very eyes. Typically there was no-one around, and I certainly didn't have time to go looking for anyone.

"You know what to do," the inner voice calmly reminded me. I had a flashback to the solution from the day before. Throwing myself to the ground I hooked one of my feet around the poolside table, fortunately made of cast iron, not plastic.

I stretched myself out as far as I could without overbalancing and reached across the pool. My fingers connected with the tips of Paul's for a second, but then Lee thrashed them apart again. I stretched out further, catching a handful of Lee's hair this time, and gave him a good hard yank towards me. This brought Paul closer too. Now I was able to clasp his arm fast at the wrist and, between pulling him with one hand and dragging Lee's head clear of the water with the other, which calmed him slightly, I was able to manhandle them both to the side.

Coughing and spluttering Paul hoisted Lee up to my waiting arms and I dragged him out of the pool. I gave Paul a helping hand too, and they both collapsed in a heap at the side coughing and spluttering.

I pounded Lee (none too gently) on the back, until I was sure he had coughed and puked all the water out of his lungs. Paul sat, head in hands, coughing and wheezing too.

"Whew, that was a close shave," he gasped when he could finally speak. "If you hadn't reacted so fast I don't think Lee or I would have been coming out of the pool alive."

Lee looked a bit embarrassed. "Sorry," he coughed.

When they were at last able to stand we hobbled back to the hotel. Paul went up to his room and Lee and I found the family gathered in the bar.

"Guess what, I nearly drowned!" Lee described the whole scenario.

"What, again?" Uncle Ace raised an eyebrow. "You better get this boy taught to swim before he drowns himself or somebody else for that matter."

The adults laughed and returned to their drinks. Lee nearly drowning was becoming a regular feature of the summer, therefore, apparently, no big deal.

Poor Paul couldn't swim for the rest of the holiday as he developed an inner ear infection from getting water in his ears from the pool. His Dad told him off for swimming underwater too much but Lee and I suspected there was something else that caused it.

Lee was unnaturally cautious around water for the rest of the holiday. He took to climbing walls and cliff faces instead.

I found myself often musing just what would have happened if I hadn't foreseen and practised my reaction the day before. Was it my good imagination? Or was someone out there watching over Lee, as usual. It was a blooming shame he couldn't hear the warnings for himself. Then again, when did Lee ever heed a warning? I decided Lee was a cat in a former life, he clearly kept his nine lives for this incarnation, but he was going through them fast!

Part Three

The moving finger writes, and having writ,
Moves on, nor all thy piety nor wit
Shall lure it back to cancel half a line
Nor all thy tears wash out a word of it.

The Rubaiyat of Omar Khayyam

Chapter Eight
Turbulent Teenager

Soulmates

A lot of people spend years searching for their soul mate. They agonise over whether this person is "the one" or whether they should wait. I was fortunate in that I knew the instant I met my husband that this was the person I was destined to marry in this lifetime.

From being about three I had a fixation with the name Mark, but I didn't know why exactly.

I was sitting in my English class. We were doing creative writing, always a favourite of mine even then, and as usual my friend Diane and I were comparing notes on our essays. I read her mine and then she recounted hers; it began with the main characters in her story being herself, her friend Helen and someone called Mark. As soon as she said this mystery boy's name I felt a tingle down my spine, like recognition.

"Who's that?" I broke her off mid-sentence. She explained it was a friend who lived on her street. We continued reading her essay; I couldn't understand why someone's name would thrill me so much.

Several weeks passed. Suddenly, in the middle of an art class at school, I was overcome by a strange feeling of euphoria. I had no reason to feel so excited, yet I couldn't shake the feeling. It was as if something really exciting was about to happen although as far as I knew nothing was. I went home in a good mood but slightly puzzled.

I had just finished tea when our intercom buzzed (this was the way in which people gained entry to our flat). It was my friend Graham calling to see if I wanted to go out.

Graham and I were sitting on the garage roof outside my block of flats. We were talking about inconsequential things as teenagers do (we were both thirteen), when suddenly a dark-haired boy hailed Graham from across the stream and started running towards us.

"It's my friend Mark, I've been telling him about you and he wants to be introduced," Graham announced.

I practically fell off the roof in surprise. Why any boy in his right mind would actively seek to be introduced to a bespectacled girl with prominent teeth and no fashion sense whatsoever I couldn't comprehend. What on earth had Graham told him to arouse this interest? (It turns out he'd said I was a secret agent – but that's another story entirely!).

The stranger sat down by Graham, introduced himself. We looked into each other's eyes and that was that.

"I'm going to marry him!" A voice said in my head.

Now don't get me wrong, I just wasn't the type to go weak at the knees over boys, I certainly didn't want a boyfriend and I had no illusion whatsoever about how alluring I was. It was just as if someone had given me a nudge and said, "Remember, this is part of your life plan..."

And as the story develops, you will see that voice in my head was right!

Premonitions

Throughout my life I have become accustomed to having strange premonitions. Sometimes these come in the form of dreams, and other times flashes of inspiration out of the blue.

I was born and raised in Bradford and throughout my early teenage years the main point of discussion was the notorious Yorkshire Ripper, who terrorised the North of England for several years, murdering thirteen women and attacking several others. Teenagers, girls in particular, needed to go around in pairs or larger groups and speculation was rife about who it could be and where he might come from.

People were thrown off the scent for a while with everyone on the lookout for a chap with a Sunderland accent after a hoax tape was sent to the police. My friends and I were less wary of the local men than we would otherwise have been.

One night, when I was around thirteen years old, I had a vivid dream – so clear I can still recall it thirty years later.

In the dream I was walking down by the stream opposite the flats I grew up in. It was dark and there was mist all around, so I headed towards the only source of light, which was the telephone box at the bottom of the road. As I drew nearer I realised that there was a man loitering inside the telephone box. In the dream, although I felt apprehensive at this point, I also felt there was nowhere else to run.

The man stepped outside the phone box and I stopped – we were face to face. He was taller than me with a thick mop of hair and a beard and moustache, so dark it was almost black. I knew this was the Yorkshire Ripper.

Then he spoke.

"I've seen you around a few times recently but it's ok, I've decided to pass you over," and with that he stepped aside and let me pass. In the dream I started to run as fast as I could… and awoke in bed, my heart pounding, relieved to find it had just been a dream.

I thought about the dream several times over the next couple of years. The man in the dream hadn't spoken with the Sunderland accent we had heard played repeatedly; it was undoubtedly a Bradford one.

When Peter Sutcliffe was finally arrested and I looked at the photograph in the paper there was the man from my dream, the bearded stranger of my nightmare.

At school in my history lesson that day my friend Helen, who usually sat behind me, wasn't in class. The next day I discovered why.

Helen lived next door but one to Peter Sutcliffe and no-one had been allowed beyond the police blockade or to leave the street on the day he was arrested.

Finally, what he said in the dream made sense. His home was close to our school (I was now at upper school in Heaton, Bradford) and it would have been perfectly possible for him to have seen me and my friends pass nearby on several occasions, particularly if we had been calling at Helen's house after school. Strange to think how close to evil we had come, and how fortunate for us that it had chosen to pass us by.

This is the first dream premonition I can recall having, but it was far from the last.

Eye of the Tiger

Mum and Dad had friends that lived in Canada and they were fortunate enough to get an invite to go out for a visit.

Excitedly they packed their cases, Mum taking everything bar the kitchen sink, deposited Lee to stay with me at Aunty Mary's, left Uncle Lou and Janet in charge of the pub, and they were on their way without a backward glance.

Their friends, Sheila and Tom, were overjoyed to see them and they had a wonderful time relaxing round the pool, having barbeques, drinking and sightseeing. They took fantastic photos of a magnificent killer whale on show at a nearby sea life centre and had a trip out to Niagara Falls, an experience never to forget.

After a fortnight of their friends' hospitality they ended the wonderful holiday with a week in America. Whilst they were there Pope John Paul the second visited, his cavalcade passing right beneath their hotel balcony.

They ended their once in a lifetime experience with a meal in a revolving restaurant at the top of a skyscraper. It was truly magical.

The only downside to the holiday was that Mum lost her beautiful Tiger's-Eye ring. She had worn it every day of the holiday, as it was one of her favourite jewellery items, but then one day, having taken it off to wash her hands in the hotel toilets, she discovered it was missing. Frantically, she searched everywhere. Helpful staff scoured the rest rooms too, but it was nowhere to be found.

Mum returned home. She'd had a wonderful time but there was sadly no hope she'd ever see her favourite ring again.

Everyone was thrilled to have Mum and Dad home. Presents were lavishly dished out for all the family and Lee was happy to return home to the pub, having managed to survive three weeks of my constant, big-sisterly attention. Uncle Lou and Janet had kept the pub running smoothly whilst my parents were away, but were nonetheless happy to hand it back to them again.

Mum and Dad proudly showed their photos and regaled them with tales to make them envious for years to come. Finally Mum confessed to the only fly in the ointment, the loss of her Tiger's-Eye ring. Janet looked at her, puzzled, and then vanished off to the bedroom. She returned clutching an item tightly in her hand.

"Do you mean this, Jan?" she asked.

There in her palm was Mum's missing ring. Mum disbelievingly took it from her.

"Where on Earth did you find this?" She demanded.

Janet explained that she'd been dusting the dressing table two days before, just as she'd done several times over the past three weeks.

"It caught my eye and I remarked to Louis how strange it was that you'd left it behind, as you always wear it. Plus, it was the first time I'd noticed it there," she said.

Strange but true, Mum's Tiger's-Eye ring had somehow been transported several thousand miles home by itself. Whether Mum had somehow willed it back, or it had been apported by some helpful spirit, we will never know. All I can say is that sometimes things defy any logical explanation, and the mysterious world of the paranormal is all we can look to for an answer!

Dolly

I first met Dorothea Cranmer, known to all and sundry as Dolly, Mark's mother, when I was thirteen. She was an imposing woman, not in stature but by nature. Her hair, which was blue black, was worn piled high on her head in a fifties style beehive. She had a strong square-set jaw and determined mouth but her hard appearance was softened by expressive blue eyes that crinkled at the corners and a warm endearing smile.

When my friend Diane and I would call round to Mark's house she would always greet us like long lost friends, ushering us in, making us welcome and chiding Mark to hurry up.

"I don't know why these two girls are waiting for you, they're far too pretty for you."

Mark would grin and roll his eyes in a way that said, "mothers, who'd have them?" Clearly, he'd heard this many times before, but we were flattered nonetheless.

One evening we were at Diane and her younger brother Peter's house, Mark and I completing the foursome that could squeeze around the kitchen table. Diane's parents were talking about the supernatural when Mark piped up that his mother was psychic and could sometimes see the future. Without further ado, Mark was ushered out of the door, under orders to bring her across straight away. I really didn't expect her to come but within ten minutes Mark was back, his bewildered mother following behind.

We were all gathered in the living room and the best crystal glasses were brought out.

Before she had even sat down Mrs Cranmer was being offered cherry brandy and rich tea biscuits, looking utterly perplexed at both options. After a brief introduction between the parents who, although being neighbours, had not actually had call to speak to each other before now.

Mark gave his mum a dig in the ribs, and said, "Go on Mum, tell them about your psychic experiences."

Mark was clearly oblivious to the fact that his mother looked as if she would rather do anything else in the world at that moment but, backed into a corner as she was, or at least until she'd downed a generous helping of cherry brandy and nibbled a biscuit or two, she admitted she had, in fact, had one or two dreams that came true.

We all listened with bated breath as Mrs Cranmer regaled us with a tale about dreaming of people walking out of her husband's relatives' home, carrying furniture. The very next morning she discovered that there had been a burglary at her brother-in-law's house and the television had been stolen!

Warming to her theme, and the cherry brandy, she then went on to recount several further stories while we all looked on, our eyes wide like saucers, perching on the edge of our seats as if we expected her to pull a rabbit out of her handbag at any moment.

Mark was beaming like the Cheshire Cat, having been the one to provide the evening's entertainment. Poor Mrs Cranmer didn't get to escape for a good couple of hours and only then when she realised her husband's tea was most likely to be burnt to a crisp.

If I had had a premonition in that moment that this was to be my future mother-in-law I may have run a mile. I thought her a little scary to begin with, but it seemed I hadn't known the half of it. I tactfully didn't mention that my mother was a witch; allegedly. I really didn't think Diane's parents had enough cherry brandy in at that point in time!

The Prince of Darkness

Mark Cranmer, aged thirteen, black hair, blue eyes, impeccable dresser, was fast becoming one of my closest friends. Odd as that may seem, given the fact I had no dress sense, goofy teeth, bottle-bottom glasses and all the street cred I possessed came from the fact half the neighbourhood was under the delusion that I was actually a secret agent!

Mark had besotted teenage girls swooning at his feet whereas I was more likely to have any male daft enough to make a pass at me laid out at mine.

My Nana had brought me up not to "take any nonsense," from boys.

"If they try anything," she'd advised, "slap them round the kisser."

The few that did chance their arm would invariably end up with a thick lip or bust nose for their trouble.

I had also been taught at the family school of boxing; standing in line with Lee and Heath and entreated to spar with assorted uncles. I wasn't aggressive, just programmed to react. I was also known to assault lads who got too close with my handbag. It was meant to be a slightly good humoured "Dick Emery" style ("Ooh, you are awful!") fending off but, as I carried everything but the kitchen sink within its compartments, anyone encountering a swift clonk to the head was a candidate for mild concussion. I had only to kick Mark in the shins once and now we understood each other perfectly.

Strongly in Mark's favour as a male friend was the fact that from their first meeting my Aunty Mary adored him. He ranked high on the politeness scale as opposed to a lot of the local Neanderthals - not, I hasten to add, that I was ever likely to bring them round to the flat for a cup of tea. (They were probably lying in the road somewhere, having been mercilessly bludgeoned by my handbag – a kind of cave woman role reversal).

Amongst the slight hitches in our burgeoning relationship was the fact that Mark really did think I was a secret agent. He also thought that my cousin Matthew was a secret agent too, by the real name of Pete, who was masquerading as my cousin under the very noses of my family. Remember, he had met my family and this obviously seemed plausible to him.

I could go much deeper into this scenario, but for the sake of your sanity, dear reader, it's probably best that I don't!

Mark, it has to be said, had his own brand of peculiarities. For one he was a soul boy, he told me. I hadn't a clue what he was talking about, so he played me some strange music (I had only just graduated from Johnny Mathis to Abba, most music was foreign to me!), showed me a few bizarre dance moves, and told me he wanted some "pegs" for his next birthday. I thought he was easily pleased until he pointed out they were actually an item of clothing!

I was far more interested in his other obsession. Mark was an avid fan of all the old "Hammer Horror" movies. He knew all kinds of weird and wonderful facts about the actors and sets, when they were all made, etc. This was all very fascinating in itself but best of all he loved to use stage make-up and blood and dress up like them too! (Perhaps now you begin to see where our meeting of minds began, in our own little ways we were actually both as nutty as fruitcakes!).

Mark bought some fangs, some theatrical blood, and made himself a large black cape. Dressed as Count Dracula, he would leap from his mother's outhouse roof to the impressed "oohs and awws" of an assembled audience below. This was generally myself, and our mutual friends, Diane, Peter, Bev, Russell, his little nephew Lee (who followed him everywhere) and my cousin Matthew AKA Pete (who was far too cool to be impressed by this prancing around in vampire costumes, and would watch the performance from behind mirrored sun glasses, arms folded, and a sardonic smile playing about his mouth).

When we weren't being secret agents (we did eventually come clean to selected friends, though we left the neighbourhood at large to draw their own conclusions) and when Mark wasn't being a vampire or fiendish hunch-backed mutant, we found other ways to amuse ourselves.

At one point we decided to make our own photo novels; these were a collection of photographs depicting a series of adventures in "The Land of the Tubeless Tyres". This included several scenes which were shot down in the school fields and required Mark and Matthew to strut around with tea towels on their heads while Diane, Peter, Bev, Russell, assorted other friends and I (all way too unimportant to wear tea towels) plucked newspapers out of trees. The final act entailed a bloodthirsty battle between us and some tyres that had been cemented onto the school playground (not by us, I hasten to add, in case you were wondering).

As an extra I died early on and then was photographed dead in several different poses, as I kept forgetting to lay still. I have to say the tyres were excellent at playing dead, not one of them moved an inch! Sadly, the one flaw in the plan to make our mark on the world with these tales of derring-do and heroism was making me the "keeper of the photographic film". Before we even had chance to get the majority of the photos developed yours truly had managed to lose them! Don't ask me where they went, perhaps they were just spirited away.

I can safely say there can't be many women who can lay claim to have met their future husband while sitting on a garage roof, and courted when he was wearing a tea towel on his head or dripping fake blood and adorned in a cape. Then again, men who fell for their future spouse while under the impression she was a cold-hearted secret agent with a licence to kill are probably few and far between as well. I didn't actually have a licence to kill but I was pretty lethal with my left hook and a fully-loaded handbag in tow!

Jellyfish

Mum, Dad, Lee and I went on holiday to Malta for a week when I was fourteen and Lee eleven.

The holiday did not get off to a particularly good start as no sooner had we settled into the hotel than Dad announced his intention to go for a walk to explore. Mum had other ideas; it was early evening, and she fancied a relaxing time spent in the bar, just the four of us, having a few drinks after dinner.

Uncharacteristically, Dad was adamant on going for a walk and enlisted Lee's help, saying the two of them would enjoy a bit of father and son time, exploring the surroundings. Mum was not amused. Lee and I were at odds as to what to do or say as we had never known our parents not to be in perfect good humour and accord with one another.

Dad saw Mum and I seated in a cosy corner of the bar, lined us up a couple of drinks each and some nibbles, dropped a kiss on Mum's forehead and said he and Lee wouldn't be long. Mum raised a perfectly arched eyebrow at Dad.

"You should know better than to cross me Sidney, I'm warning you, you'll be sorry!"

Dad let out a little nonchalant laugh, waved her comment off good-naturedly, and headed out of the bar. Lee shrugged at me, then scooted after Dad, leaving me with the unenviable task of soothing a rather irate mother.

I don't recall ever seeing her so cross with Dad. Her eyes flashed angrily as she muttered, more to herself than to me, that he had no right leaving us on our own the first night in a foreign land, and she had a good mind to put a hex on him.

"What exactly is a hex?" I enquired.

She looked at me exasperatedly; it was a bad luck spell, a curse, she explained, had I forgotten she was a witch?

"It must have slipped my mind," I joked. Besides, wasn't she a good witch?

"More a grey witch," she decided, generally good, but quite capable of a bit of mischief here and there if crossed and boy was she cross now.

She launched into a series of tales of people who had made her angry in the past and how misfortune had befallen them after she had hexed them. I listened, politely, with a smile on my face. Had I been as knowledgeable as I am now (and not listening patronisingly half thinking my mother was a nutcase) I would have realised that, in effect, the hex she sent out would actually be a stream of negative energy, which clearly hit its mark on the unguarded victim – my mother had pretty good aim when focusing energy, good or bad!

As we talked I noticed something peculiar, when she was angry, my Mum's warm brown eyes turned black. I supposed this was a trick of the light; we were in a dark, dimly lit corner of the room. The atmosphere felt crackly, like a storm brewing. Must be the humidity on the island, I surmised.

A couple of drinks later, after venting her spleen to me for forty minutes or so, Mum started to relax at last. Before long we were chattering away light-heartedly, making plans for the week ahead. Mum's eyes were brown again, and everything felt calm and tranquil once more.

Lee and Dad came back from their walk. Dad was deathly pale, and Lee was supporting him. Mum and I jumped to our feet.

"Dad, what's the matter?" I gasped. It was a fact that Dad was never, ever ill, beyond occasionally pulling a muscle in his back dropping barrels in the pub.

"I need to go straight to our room now!" he declared. We all scurried to the lift.

We just made it into Mum and Dad's room and Dad dashed into the bathroom where he remained retching and vomiting repeatedly for a good twenty minutes. Lee explained that they hadn't got very far from the hotel before Dad started to feel unwell. Resilient as ever, he had ignored the sensations in his head and gut and persisted with the walk.

After about half an hour he doubled up with stomach cramps and was starting to look decidedly green around the gills. At this point he conceded he had really better head back. Lee assisted him from there on.

Dad staggered from the bathroom, wiping a damp cloth around his face. Sitting on the bed he fixed Mum with a knowing glare.

"Jan, you did this!" he declared.

Mum laughed. "Don't be so silly, it will be something you ate at dinner, Spanish tummy."

He shook his head. "You said if I crossed you I'd be sorry, and now look."

Mum took the wet cloth out of his hand and wiped his face again.

"You know you don't believe in such things," she reminded him.

"No, I don't usually, but I believe anything where you're concerned," he half laughed.

"Don't worry, you'll be fine now," Mum predicted and she ushered me and Lee out of the door towards our own room.

I looked across at Dad. The colour was slowly coming back to his face; he was falling asleep. Mum smiled. As she closed the door she gave a conspiratorial wink and wrinkled her nose.

The next day Dad was fine, as good as new, in fact.

Mum and he were the best of friends again and we were able to proceed with the holiday at last. This consisted of Mum and Dad sitting around the pool drinking and reading, me in my room reading, as I couldn't bear the heat and hated to be disturbed (I had started to read "The Stand" by Stephen King and couldn't be prised from it), and Lee, left to his own devices as usual, running around like a lunatic, exploring every nook and cranny of the surrounding area.

He'd be in the pool by daybreak and would have gone down again at midnight if the hotel had permitted it. Since he'd finally learned to swim he couldn't be kept out of the water. I declined to join him; my book would get wet.

One morning, at breakfast, Lee declared that he had found a quiet little sandy cove nearby and could he please, please, please, go swimming there. Mum said no, probably remembering his past propensity for getting into trouble. I said it was probably not a good idea and Dad, forever the optimist, said, "Why not? Lee's a good strong swimmer now, as long as he stays in the shallow water he should be fine."

Before Mum had further chance to respond Lee had hit the floor running. By the time I reached our room, he was flying back out with his swimming trunks wrapped in a towel and a snorkel on his head.

An hour later I was lying on the bed, my nose still stuck in the book, when Lee came back. With an uncustomary moan, he flung himself face down on the bed.

"What's the matter?" I wondered, without looking up.

"My back hurts," he grimaced. I flashed a glance in his direction, and then put my book down. Actually, he didn't look well.

"Let me look," I demanded my right as big sister and general person-in-charge-in-the-absence-of-an-adult. He obligingly pulled up his shirt.

Large angry red welts, like whip lashes, stood out across his back. I prodded one and he let out a yell.

"What on earth are these?" I demanded, in a "what have you gone and done now?" type of voice.

"What are what?" he asked, puzzled. He couldn't see his own back and there were no mirrors handy. I decided I better get Mum and Dad. Lee didn't argue, so he must have felt bad!

"He's been stung by jellyfish," the hotel doctor declared. "I'll give you a prescription for some soothing lotion, in the meantime the best thing is to put ice on the stings. He's very lucky, some of the jellyfish have a sting so poisonous they can kill, but they tend to be the larger one's further out at sea."

Dad dashed off with the prescription. Lee lay moaning on Dad's bed while Mum rang reception and requested some ice be brought up.

A nice young Maltese waiter, about eighteen, came in carrying the ice. I smiled at him, Mum directed him to put it down on the work surface where she proceeded to wrap several pieces in a tea towel.

The waiter stood looking perplexed, awaiting further instructions.

The room was an L shape. From the bed I was sitting on I could see the waiter standing by the door. From her central position Mum could see Lee lying on the bed and me sitting, book in hand, on the other bed.

The waiter could not see Lee round the corner, just me, and Mum still faffing about with the ice.

Without looking up Mum called over her shoulder to Lee. "Now, lie down on your tummy whilst I put this ice on your back."

From my vantage point on the bed I saw the young waiter's eyes grow very large.

"Pardon, Senora…?" He stuttered,

Mum picked up the ice parcel, there was a crash as the young waiter nearly broke the door in a scramble to get out and I simultaneously fell off the bed laughing at the look on his face.

Mum looked at me, amazed.

"Get up! What on earth are you doing on the floor, and where has that young lad scurried off to in such a hurry? I was going to ask him to bring us more ice."

Her face was a picture as I explained he was obviously making a quick getaway from this kinky mother and daughter who had lured him to their room in order to cover him in ice cubes!

Lee couldn't stop laughing, even though it hurt.

"Well, they say laughter's the best medicine," Mum declared, and, whether it was the ice or the laughter, Lee was soon much recovered.

At dinner that evening the waiter was nowhere to be seen.

"I'm not bloody surprised!" Dad laughed, incredulous, when we told him. "I can guarantee we won't see him again for the rest of the holiday."

And what a surprise – we didn't.

A dog's tale

I was now fifteen, still living in the flats with Aunty Mary, Uncle Jack and Mischief, our little black mongrel.

Every morning Uncle Jack would take Mischief for a nice long walk before breakfast, while I would be getting ready for school. The walk usually ended with Uncle Jack letting Mischief off the lead so he could have a run up and down the field and give his legs a proper stretch. (Uncle Jack was in his sixties and not quite up to romping up and down the field with a dog).

Usually Mischief would come straight back to Uncle Jack following his run, but occasionally he'd decide to take off on his own for a couple of days (usually if there was a lady dog around, if you get my gist!). He invariably came back tired and hungry within forty-eight hours.

One time he ran off again and, as usual, we expected his return within a day or two. But this time he didn't return.

A week passed and Uncle Jack scoured the area everyday, trying to track him down. We rang the dog warden and contacted local kennels, all to no avail. Then Uncle Jack heard that several other dogs in the neighbourhood had also gone missing, mysteriously. Naturally, by this time we feared the worst.

Mischief never did come back, nor did any of the other missing neighbourhood dogs.

A year passed. One night Uncle Jack and Aunty Mary had gone out and I was in my bedroom writing up some papers for school. When I had finished it occurred to me that, as I had the flat to myself for once, I may as well sit and read in the living room, just for a change of scenery. I took my book and curled up on the settee, before long I was immersed in its pages. The only sound was the ticking of the clock on the mantelpiece.

Somewhere subconsciously I became aware of another sound. A soft pad, padding along the hall and into the living room. This ended in the unmistakeable sound of a dog circling and letting out a contented sigh as it flopped down into its favourite resting place behind the settee. I had heard this many times over the years,

"It's only Mischief," I said to myself as I turned another page. Then I sat bolt upright – Mischief! The dog had been gone, presumed dead, for at least a year now and the front door was locked securely so nothing and no-one could come in.

I leapt to my feet and raced out of the room, not daring to look behind me. I shot straight into my bedroom, closed the door tight and collapsed, shaking, on the bed, my heart racing.

I stayed there for about half an hour, hardly daring to move or breathe, until a knock on the door made me jump out of my skin – Uncle Jack and Aunty Mary were back. I ran to the door, still not looking down the hall, and shakily let them in.

As soon as they were through the doorway I babbled out what had happened. We all walked down the hall to the living room together and, of course, there was nothing there to see.

Funnily enough Aunty Mary and Uncle Jack never tried to persuade me that what I'd heard wasn't Mischief. In fact, they, like me, seemed convinced that our poor lost dog had finally found his way home at last.

Once I had got over the shock and amazement of what had happened I was extremely pleased and happy. We never did hear his footfall, or his contented sigh as he flopped down, again. But that doesn't mean he didn't come back every so often to visit, I just think he didn't want to startle us again, so he was very, very, quiet.

So should anyone wonder – yes, animals do live on after physical death, and they remain close to those they love most.

Chapter Nine
College daze

Patch – the second

We were dog-less, an almost unheard of situation in our household. Uncle Jack said he was getting too old for chasing after dogs and, sadly, Aunty Mary agreed.

Poor Aunty Mary was not well, I knew she suspected a resurgence of the cancer and, although she was as strong and resilient as always, it was apparent she was putting on a brave face. This was affecting Uncle Jack too.

Something had to be done to cheer them up, but what?

Occasionally we got the local paper. I found myself idly browsing through the adverts and wanted ads one evening when I saw it.

"Labrador pups for sale to good home".

The address to contact was only just up the road from us. As it turned out, once I showed him the advert, Uncle Jack was actually a pushover. He had his hat on and was out of the door in a flash, obviously anxious to get there before they'd all been snapped up.

I didn't say anything to Aunty Mary when she wondered where he'd dashed off to in such a hurry, I didn't want to get her hopes up in case all the pups were gone, or spoil the surprise if Uncle Jack brought one back.

Uncle Jack returned home smiling with a suspicious bundle tucked into his jacket.

"Mary, close your eyes," he commanded.

She complied with a quizzical smile on her face. I watched as Uncle Jack gently put a little black fuzzy ball in her lap.Instantly, a small pink tongue shot out and licked her hands.Aunty Mary started in fright.

"Oh!" Her eyes opened in surprise, then widened in delight. "What is it?" she gasped.

Uncle Jack was laughing at her response. "It's a dog, a Labrador pup, I got it for you." Though it was apparent he was as besotted as she was.

"I thought we weren't getting any more dogs?" She scolded, still smiling.

Uncle Jack nodded. "You're right, give him here, I better take him back quick."

Aunty Mary clutched the little bundle to her. "No, now he's here, he's staying!"

And stay he did. We named him Patch, despite the fact he was totally black from head to foot, in the hope that naming him after the intelligent dog that Uncle Jack and bought for Aunty Mary years earlier may cause him to inherit some of his predecessor's characteristics. This Patch, however, was not overly intelligent, though what he lacked in that respect, he made up for in cunning. He also obligingly, developed a small white patch on his chest, as if in tribute to the name we gave him.

As a pup he was a delight. Wild and nimble, he was into anything and everything, whizzing about like a furry tornado.

Aunty Mary and Uncle Jack never tired of his antics. Through my closed bedroom door I could hear them laughing and playing with him from morning till night, until eventually I'd have to tear myself away from my books or records to join them all.

Patch decided his rightful place was on Uncle Jack's chair even when, in fact, especially when, Uncle Jack was sitting in it. As a pup this was not a problem but even as a fully grown dog he would love to scramble up onto Uncle Jack's lap, flattening down the newspaper his master was reading as if to say, "I'm here now, look how wonderful I am," and Uncle Jack would laughingly oblige.

"Come on then old chap," he'd say, ruffling the dog about the ears and head. It wouldn't be long before the newspaper was rolled up and used in a tug of war between them.

That Christmas we had snow, when Patch was only a few weeks old. From my bedroom window, a good vantage point for Aunty Mary and me, we watched Uncle Jack carry the little dog down to the pavement in front of the flats. Even here the snow had drifted deeply and Uncle Jack was wearing large, padded snow boots.

Carefully, he put Patch down on the snow. We watched as the pup looked around in surprise, then it collapsed beneath his feet and he disappeared into a drift. Quick as a flash he jumped up again, only to vanish once more into another pile of snow. We could hear excited barking and Uncle Jack laughing hysterically far below.

They traversed the whole front of the flats in this manner, interspersed with the dog snapping at mini snowballs Uncle Jack threw up in the air for his amusement. They returned home, Uncle Jack's eyes twinkling merrily, and Patch's fur stuck out in spiky icicles of snow. It was obvious they'd both enjoyed the escapade immensely.

I started college the following September. By this time I was sixteen and heavily into politics, strongly opposed to Margaret Thatcher's regime at a time when she was at the height of her popularity following the Falklands war in 1982.

A working class girl in a group of middle class friends, I argued my political beliefs hotly, wore a red coat and beret, and was affectionately nicknamed "Trotsky" by my classmates.

Patch had taken to giving Uncle Jack the slip on his early morning walks. Once off the lead he resolutely defied calls to come back and would return whenever it suited him. By now he was a large dog in need of exercise, so reluctantly Uncle Jack let him go, knowing that once he'd prowled round to his hearts content he'd make his own way back.

Patch had made himself well-known to everyone in the block of flats. He would come back home and let out one resounding bark outside the doors to the block. The caretaker or his wife would scurry out, pet him, then put him in the lift and send him up to our floor. Even then he didn't always come straight home. He sometimes went to Uncle Lou's flat first, where Uncle Lou, Janet, Nana and Granddad would spoil him with biscuits and tit-bits and lots of stroking and tickling. Then he would stop off at the neighbour, who lived in-between our two flats. Mrs Yeadon would take him in and make a fuss of him next, he had his own jar at her flat, she confided, and he was partial to Garibaldi biscuits.

It was little wonder Patch was slowly turning from a young svelte dog into a little round barrel.

We discovered he had an army of admiring fans in the form of several old ladies up and down the estate. Somehow he had wormed his way into the affections of four or five households, all of whom took him in for treats when he leapt up and rattled the letterboxes on their doors - a trick he'd devised all by himself. He was having three or four full dinners a day, and he was never one to turn down a meal!

One day Uncle Jack was in the village doing a bit of shopping, when he spotted Patch hanging about outside the butcher's shop.

"What's that dog doing in the village?" Uncle Jack muttered to himself, and started to make his way across to get the errant mutt.

As he approached two sweet little old dears came out of the shop and one tickled the dog under the chin, turning to her friend she said loudly, "He's ever so good, you know, escorts me safely up to the shops every day, there and back, so I treat him to a nice bit of stewing steak when we get home. It's the least I can do."

Uncle Jack paused hearing this; Patch looked over his shoulder at him, a look that said, "pretend you don't know me." Then he turned back with a snort, gave the old lady's hand an affectionate nuzzle, and they set off together companionably.

"Come on, Butch," she said. Uncle Jack stood there in front of the butchers shop, laughing to himself.

"Butch?" He wondered how many other names Patch went by during the course of the day.

Some mornings Patch would follow me to the bus stop on my way to college.

"Go home, Patch!" I'd admonish him, on more than one occasion chasing him back up the field waving my umbrella like someone demented.

I was always worried he would decide to cross the road just as the bus was coming. Good naturedly he'd gambol back up the field, letting me think I'd driven him away, but then as I stood by the bus stop again I'd spot him, hiding behind a tree by the stream, watching me till I was safely on board the bus and on my way to college.

I suppose on the dark, misty mornings he felt it was his duty to protect me. The thing was, he was still hiding behind trees and bushes at the height of summer. I should be thankful that at least he wasn't quite as bright as the original Patch or I expect I'd have found him sitting three seats behind me on the bus wearing a trilby and shades!

Ticket to ride

I was seventeen, at college, training to be a nursery nurse, and as part of that course we had gone away on a trip to London.

Naturally, we were all really excited and had spent the first day exploring. My friends and I had been round the Natural History and Science museums, had a pot of tea in Harrods, wandered round Oxford Street and Piccadilly Circus, and negotiated London buses. We had also eaten in a very seedy café chosen by the college tutors, for some unknown reason, and spent the first night in an extremely run down hotel; four of us crammed in one room, complaining and giggling nonetheless at our accommodation.

The second day, also the day of our return home, we were taken on a sightseeing tour, after which the plan was that we'd be free to explore again for a few hours.

My friends and I were looking through our travel guides, and arguing good-naturedly about where we should visit today. My friend Yvonne fancied another trip to the Natural History Museum, as there was so much to see we hadn't got round it all the first time.

"These plans will all change anyway after the crash," said a voice in my head.

"What nonsense are you talking about?" I asked myself, "What crash?"

The day before as we had first entered London we had gone through an underpass. As we'd been coming out of the other side I'd had a sudden vision of a coach like ours, crashed and broken at the roadside. I had looked out of the window and seen a hotel just past the exit from the tunnel. People could go in there to recover, I'd thought. But there wasn't a coach there, so what on earth was I daydreaming about?

Now, here we were, on our sightseeing tour, and here I was talking nonsense in my head again. It was a bright clear day, the

149

roads were fine, and I'd never been a nervous traveller (incompetent at going anywhere alone – yes, nervous –no).

I looked up and realised we were heading into the underpass again, the same route as yesterday. As we approached the exit I looked towards the front of the coach. I could see the traffic had slowed, unfortunately I could also see the coach driver seemed oblivious to this and was hurtling towards the back of a blue truck. I was too far down the coach to alert him and we were approaching too fast to stop.

Strangely, I felt incredibly calm. I just had time to reach my arm round my friend Yvonne and pull her forwards.

"Put your head down we're going to crash," I informed her. She didn't argue.

The coach smashed into the back of the truck with an almighty bang. There were terrified screams. The windscreen crystallised and shattered, glass fragments scattering down the full length of the coach.

I heard Yvonne muttering to herself. "Please don't catch on fire," over and over, like a mantra. I gave her hand a squeeze.

"It's ok," I said.

Sticking my head up over the back of the seat I observed the damage. As far as I could see everyone looked ok, just somewhat shaken. I checked on my friends in the seats front and back. They hadn't sustained any injuries thankfully.

The tutor in charge of the trip came down the aisle checking if everyone was ok. I enquired after the coach driver, as he would have borne the main brunt of the impact. By a miracle he was totally unharmed; the flying glass had passed him without as much as a scratch. The only casualty was a student who had nodded off at the back of the coach; she'd banged her head against the window and incurred a mild concussion.

I followed my tutor to the front of the coach and asked if I could get off for a moment.

Just as in my vision the day before, I walked into the lobby of the hotel outside. Finding someone in charge I explained what had happened and enquired if anyone needing to recover from the shock could sit inside. They agreed.

Back on the coach I relayed this information to the tutors who were very pleased that it had occurred to me.

It was only much later that day, on a different coach heading home, that it struck me how odd the whole incident had been.

Arrivals

I spent my eighteenth birthday working on a maternity ward at St. Luke's hospital in Bradford. This was part of my training as a nursery nurse, a three week stint to introduce us to working in a hospital and handling newborns.

I had been to the hospital on numerous occasions before, having a collection of ill and elderly relatives meant I visited there frequently over the years. I was accustomed to the pale green walls, antiseptic smell, and quiet air of desperation that seemed to permeate the corridors.

I was surprised to find the sensation of a maternity ward very different. On a logical level you may assume, and rightly so, that this was partly because out of all the wards in a hospital the maternity ward is the one associated with joyous occasions. Obviously, that in itself contributes to a change in the atmosphere. But it was somehow more than this. If a hospital could be likened to an Arrivals and Departures lounge for the soul, then I was in Grand Central Station. From morning to night we bustled with the newly arrived bundles of joy, I imagined overworked storks crying, "Incoming!" as they deposited the new deliveries.

Here, I discovered, was a buzz in the air, not unlike the tingle I had felt many years before, hearing Angelic voices raised in song standing on the veranda outside my Nana's flat. The atmosphere in this maternity unit was the closest I had ever come to touching the divine secrets of the Universe, without actually being in the process of being born or dying myself. In a way I was too young to realise just what I was experiencing. There was just a kind of magic in the air, like one might experience at midnight on Christmas Eve, or when coming face to face with a soul mate for the very first time.

Not that working with newborn babies is in any way glamorous. My first job on arrival each day was to "top and tail" seventeen of them, and have them freshly presented as fragrant bundles to the new mothers (who were far more pampered by the hospitals in those days than the current trend of hatching and dispatching mother and baby in a six hour turnaround).

Seventeen faces and pairs of hands to wash and wipe, seventeen smelly nappies to remove, seventeen little bottoms to wash, trying to fight impossibly small people into terry towelling nappies the size of a small tablecloth, remembering how to do the "kite" fold whilst not impaling them on safety pins the same size as their pink shiny arms, little puckered faces searching for milk, then erupting into shrieks of anguish when it wasn't forthcoming and every other baby taking up the chorus in sympathy like tuning forks in a row. Exasperated midwives looking at me as if to say "now look what you've done." Wheeling screeching tots along the ward to try and match them with the correct mother. The mother looking askance, as if to say, "What have you done to my baby, you fiend?" By morning break I was almost a quivering wreck!

A quick coffee and back out into the breech, assisting the mothers with feeding their offspring. If I had expected the mothers to be serene and smiling Madonnas then I was wrong. Raging hormones and aches and pains in unfortunate places, turned these women into screeching, tearful, venomous harridans.

At eighteen years old (just), and very wet behind the ears, it is hard to appear confident and in control when faced with a pack of demanding she-wolves. I was beginning to see why the most successful midwives on the ward had faces like granite and an iron will, "Now then, don't be a silly girl!" being the most commonly heard phrase coming from their lips, as they bullied the inmates into getting bathed, dressed, or taking part in feeding, washing and clothing their new baby.

My soft and gentle approach had mixed results. Be too kind to a new mother and she is likely to dissolve into tears of self pity, while you sit patting her hand and trying to get her baby to feed from its bottle.

The other type of new mother wants to chew you up and spit you out. "Here, you feed this baby, I can't," they snarl, thrusting a squirming bundle of arms and legs at you.

Of course I'd try to oblige, telling myself they were probably very nice women in the real world, when not in the grip of "post-natal possession by the Devil".

Why is it, women like that, are always the ones with the babies that have projectile vomit with an aim so accurate it can hit the ward sister squarely in the chest at forty paces?

At lunch time, I'd meet up with my friend Yvonne, who had been assigned to the ward below. We would compare notes over a hastily eaten sandwich. Somehow she seemed to have landed herself in a ward run by easy going, laid back, motherly staff, whereas I was surrounded by iron willed harpies on all sides.

The afternoon session was much easier by comparison. Some-one had decreed the new mothers needed to sleep for at least two hours, so the ward would be peaceful at last.

In the babies' dormitory two of the younger midwives and I settled to the task of bathing the seventeen tots. No-one had warned me that, before bathing a baby for the first time, it is deemed advisable to sprout an extra pair of arms. For someone so small and seemingly helpless they presented themselves like wriggly eels, forever trying to squirm out of my soapy grasp. I managed reasonably well for a novice, well, none of them drowned in the process, which was an achievement in itself. I also managed to successfully dry them in my lap without even one succeeding in throwing itself to the floor – something they all seemed to be trying to do.

By the time they were safely powdered, nappied and wrestled into a baby-gro I felt deserving of a medal.

I might have gone off newborns altogether if it weren't for one extraordinary child.

I'd had the shift from hell (again) and it was nearly the end of the day on my eighteenth birthday. I was sitting, soaked through, despite the supposed water proof apron, from tussles in the bath, bespattered once more with speckles of vomit and mucus, smelling vaguely of baby sick and even less pleasant infantile deposits. I was just about to attempt cleaning myself up before traipsing home when one of the midwives came stomping in with another baby.

"Don't go yet," she commanded. "We seem to have missed one, it needs bathing and there's only you available."

"Oh joy!" I thought. Where had they managed to misplace it until now, under a bed, behind a screen, in the janitor's closet?

I changed my wet apron for a fresh one, which no doubt would be equally soaked within minutes, washed my hands, prepared a fresh bath, girded my loins, gritted my teeth, and prepared for the final challenge of the day. The midwife unceremoniously dumped the child in my lap, turned on her heel, and marched off through the swinging plastic doors, no doubt to upbraid some poor woman for crying too loudly.

I looked at the baby, and it gazed back at me. This was no pink faced wretch, angry at its sudden entrance to the world. This little girl had eyes like bottomless pools, ageless with unspoken knowledge and power.

I had the dizzying realisation that this child knew far more in this moment, of why she was here, than I, having reached my eighteen year majority, had even begun to comprehend. (Ok, I had known things once, but life had knocked all the knowledge out of me by this time!).

I recalled Nana's assertion that she had recognised me for an "old soul" the first time she held me, and suddenly I knew exactly what she meant. I had become accustomed to wriggly, sickly, squirmy babies, waving fists and screwed up angry faces at the world. This child lay still, she gazed deeply into my eyes. I could have sworn she was reading my thoughts, and was no doubt amused by them.

I proceeded with the bath, fully expecting the shock of the rapidly cooling water to break the spell and her and my composure. It didn't. Through all my inexpert, gauche, administrations she lay contentedly. For the first time in my three week "trial" in the maternity unit I felt a degree of serenity, a sudden realisation that actually, I could do this.

Washed and wrapped securely, I took the time out to feed the child a bottle before laying her back in her cot to sleep. Throughout all of this she made no murmur of discomfort or discontent, it was as if she had been the one in control of the situation.

My work done for the day, I travelled home tired but extremely happy for once. Aunty Mary threw a surprise party for my eighteenth and it was lovely to be surrounded by close friends and family.

Of all the gifts I received that day perhaps the greatest was on a spiritual level. I had seen with my own eyes the tranquillity and self-possession of one who has lived before and returned. I had often suspected that reincarnation was a reality but now I felt I had seen the evidence for myself.

It was like another piece in an age old puzzle falling into place, and it was fascinating.

Chapter Ten
Dark night of the soul

Time to say goodbye

When people are dying, sometimes they have a foreknowledge of the event, and sometimes we do too.

My Nana passed away when I was nineteen years of age. For my entire life she had lived next-door-but-one to where I resided with Aunty Mary and Uncle Jack.

On the day it happened I got up late, recovering from a night out clubbing with friends, and still in my pyjamas at two-thirty in the afternoon.

Aunty Mary had nipped out to see if my Nana and Granddad, now in their mid eighties, fancied anything to eat, as they both had poor appetites of late, and they didn't tend to bother with large Sunday dinners anymore.

Suddenly she was back, bursting into my room. "Jane, come quick I think your Nana's dying!"

I threw some clothes on and raced back along the veranda linking the two flats. Nana lay in bed, her eyes shut her breathing laboured. She didn't respond when we called her. Aunty Mary rang the doctor while I sat with Nan.

Moments before, Aunty Mary told me, she'd been fine and declared she would have a bit of porridge. Aunty Mary had been in the process of cooking this when she'd heard the strange loud breathing coming from Nana's bedroom. Aunty Mary and I traded places, she sat by Nan and I quickly rang round all the family close enough to come.

The doctor arrived, took one look at Nana and said sympathetically there was nothing he could do and to call back when it was over, then he left.

My uncles returned from the pub where they had been as always for a Sunday lunch session of dominos and a pint or two. Gradually, the family gathered round the bed. The last person to

156

arrive was my mother, she rushed in and grasped my Nana's hand and declared, "I'm here Mum!"

At this point my Nana let out one long last rattling breath and was still, as if she had been waiting until everyone able to be there was assembled.

Everyone dispersed to the living room to try and come to terms with the suddenness of Nana's departure. Except me. I just sat for a while still holding her hand and wondering aloud, "Where have you gone, Nan?"

It seemed surreal; one moment she had been there, her body still warm and breathing, then suddenly no longer within it. Yet somehow her presence still felt as if it lingered in the room around me.

Eventually I left the bedroom and my brother Lee and I made cups of tea and copious amounts of sandwiches for everyone congregating in the lounge. We joined them and I slipped into a chair next to my cousin, Young Lou.

"She knew, you know," he said, conversationally.

As usual that morning he had called in to have a chat with her before going to the pub with the uncles. Nan had been propped up in bed looking out of the window; she'd smiled as he came in,

"Would you open the window, Lou?" she'd asked. It was a bright and sunny day in early June and the room was a little bit stuffy. As he turned to open the window she enquired what time it was.

"Twelve o'clock, Nan," Lou told her.

Then she said something he found rather strange.

"Only three hours to go then."

"What Nan?" he'd asked her, puzzled, turning round to look at her.

"It's a lovely day isn't it?" She said, smiling at him again, as if her previous comment hadn't been uttered. Lou didn't pursue it.

My Nana died on the stroke of three o'clock. As she had seemingly been aware, there had indeed only been three hours left of a life spanning over eighty-six years. As we sat taking this in I looked up and saw in wonderment that the ceiling light above our heads was twirling. In a room with not a breath of air stirring in it, the light fitting spun slowly and rhythmically first one way as far as it could turn, and then deliberately back the other way. Lou saw the direction of my gaze and also looked up, slowly one by one all the family fell silent and joined in contemplation of the strange phenomena. "It's Nan!" Lou declared.

It was as if her energy, still present, was trying to attract our attention. The life-force, no longer able to animate her body, was concentrating all her efforts on the light fitting instead, as if to say, "I'm still here!" It was only after the undertaker had been and gone that the twirling finally ceased, forty minutes later.

That night I slept fitfully. Each time I half awoke I had the impression of Nan just sitting at the side of my bed, smiling her gentle smile as always. The strange thing was, my Nana was a little old lady of eighty-six when she died, with silver hair and diminutive stature, the Nan I saw by my bed through the night looked well and strong and had a head full of glossy dark brown hair, such as she had in her early life, long before I was born.

I puzzled over my "dream" when I awoke the next morning; it wasn't until many years later that I discovered that in spirit we return to the form where we felt most vibrant and strong. Now I know it wasn't a dream after all, just Nan showing up to reassure me she was fine!

Dolly again, and Dennis

As if on cue, just when I needed him, Mark came back into my life two days after my Nana's passing, before we had even had the funeral.

We had seen very little of each other over the past three years. I had been wrapped up in college and nursery nursing and he had become a punk rocker and moved out of his parents' house, aged sixteen, to live with a variety of friends in numerous dodgy residences.

Our lives could not have been further apart. Nonetheless, I was delighted to run into him on a bus one day, and we were soon chatting as if the three years had melted away in an instant.

Somehow the likelihood of my earlier premonition, that this was the man I would marry, had never seemed more remote. The prim little college girl, newly working for the civil service, and the dishevelled musician with the stud in his nose and flaming orange pony tail (his head was shaved apart from this) must have seemed an incongruous pairing!

Over the next few months we slipped back into the old easy friendship we had always had. Mark may have looked strange but he declared I was the strangest girl he had ever met. He meant this as a compliment, which was exactly how I took it! We were both passionate about politics, reading good books, and music. Admittedly, not the same type of music, but we both attempted to compromise; I glazed over listening to his Jimi Hendrix, the Doors and the Sex Pistols albums and he actually winced at my Barry Manilow and Abba. Eventually we both agreed to disagree on that front.

During this time I was re-acquainted with Mark's mum, Dolly. I was startled to find the black beehive now gone, replaced by a salt and pepper coloured perm. Two things had happened; one, she had stopped dyeing her hair at last, and two, Mark's older brother was a hairdresser who needed willing victims (I mean clients) to try out various styles. I strongly suspected Mark had shaved his head to get out of that one.

Dolly and I struck up a friendship. She was, admittedly, not always the easiest of women to get along with, being both endearing and prickly by turns as the mood took her, but, by and large, there was a great rapport between us. An enduring affection which lasted through some very troubled times, mercifully still ahead at this point.

Mark's Dad, Dennis, was a quiet man. He had worked all his life in the mills, part of Bradford's once booming textile industry. He was now an overlooker at one of the few remaining mills, highly respected by his colleagues for his easy-going but completely fair manner. Where Dolly could be loud, outrageous and blustery, with Dennis it was more a case of still waters running deep, (either that or he hadn't managed to get a word in edgewise for years). He was short by comparison to Mark, but sturdy, like his character.

Dennis had the same twinkly look in his eye that I recognised from my Uncle Ace, the sure sign of a quietly mischievous nature bubbling away beneath the surface. He loved to laugh, and with his mischievious family, often the joke was on him, but he never seemed to mind. He would double up, convulsed, while tears of laughter streamed down his cheeks, to the extent where he would have to pause and wipe his glasses.

I didn't realise it at this time, but these two loveable and sometimes vexatious characters were about to step into leading roles in the next chapter of my life.

Mama's dream

Not long after my Nana had passed over I visited my Mum. Mum and Dad were no longer running a pub, the recession had hit hard, and they were now living in a rented house on the outskirts of Guiseley. Mum had been badly affected by the loss of the pub and it had taken a toll on her health. Dad, as ever, was optimistic and resilient. He was sure something else would turn up and cheerfully refused to let life get him down.

Mum used to stay up into the small hours every night. Dad and Lee usually went off to bed around midnight but Mum would sit up and watch old musicals, singing along with a drink in her hand. She liked it when I stayed over, which was infrequent now that I was working and socialising a lot, as young women in their late teens tend to do. So, when I was there we made the most of it. We would watch old films and chat into the small hours about anything and everything, catching up with our news, well, my news mainly, sadly I knew exactly the pattern of Mum's days of late.

Mum confessed she had been finding it really hard since Nana had died, with more time on her hands than most of us she had spent a lot of it dwelling on her loss. Needless to say, the more we talked the more tearful she became. After much eye mopping and blowing her nose, Mum eventually recovered her composure. She fixed me with a brilliant smile. She needed my opinion on something, she said.

A few nights before, she had had a lucid dream. In it she bumped into my Nana and two other ladies who, on closer inspection, she recognised as her Aunty Olive and Aunty Leah, Nana's sisters that had died many years before. They were all dressed up for an outing, immaculately attired. Nana looked radiantly healthy, younger somehow. She was in the centre of the trio. They approached her smiling, Mum said, then to her surprise Nana spoke to her rapidly in French.

"Allez, allez, c'est tres bonne, vite ,vite" Beckoning her with a curled finger and a nod.

Mum's translation was that she was to come quickly because it was very good there. Having imparted this message, Nana and her sisters vanished and Mum found herself awake, trying to work out the English translation, wondering why they had spoken French in the first place. The best guess we could make was that because Nana's family had once been French, maybe they sometimes spoke in that language over on the other side.

Mum said that she had felt very comforted by the dream, for the first time in months. Then she grasped my hands. She had a feeling it was Nana's way of telling her she'd be coming to collect her soon, but I needed to remember she was prepared for that eventuality and it didn't scare or dismay her at all. Of course, I said not to be so silly, it was lovely she'd seen Nana, but she was going to be around for years yet. My Mother was only forty-eight.

Within a fortnight of that visit Mum had slipped into a coma induced by liver cirrhosis.

The day my Mum died I was at work. She had been in a coma for six weeks prior to this. I had seen her the day before, when I instinctively said my goodbyes.

As usual, when I arrived in work that morning, my friend and colleague Maureen asked if I'd been to the hospital that weekend.

"When will you be going next?" She wondered.

"Oh, I won't be seeing her again," I replied, without thinking.

Maureen looked horrified.

"What do you mean? Don't say that!" She remonstrated.

I looked at her, confused. Somehow I knew with certainty that my mother would not live out the day. I'd felt it the day before when I was leaving. It was as if some unspoken understanding had passed between us.

I was right.

A phone call came for me in the middle of the afternoon while I was still at work saying that my mother, Jan, had passed away quietly.

I have absolutely no doubt my Nana was there to collect her as she had promised.

Rollercoaster

In the space of a year I had lost both my Nana and my mother and I had begun a somewhat tempestuous relationship with Mark. Ideally suited as friends, we found a different partnership took some getting used to.

I had also started a new job and now, as the year progressed, I was finding it very hard to concentrate.

"Jane, what do you have on your shoulders?" My friend Thirza asked. She was an older lady in her late fifties, with a warm and loving disposition.

I looked at both of my shoulders, puzzled.

"Nothing," I replied.

There was a chuckle round my team

"Yes, that's what we thought." Thirza confirmed. I had to laugh with them.

I had thought I was coping, but I certainly wasn't on form. Hours would pass by and I would realise I had been staring idly into space, getting no work done, or worse, the work would come back making absolutely no sense at all. Everybody was very understanding but I was increasingly frustrated. I didn't understand what was happening to me.

Slowly, it was as if the lights were going out on my life. At the doctors suggestion I took some time off from work and the weeks began to turn into months as a black depression wrapped me in its cloak. Outwardly, I was trying to appear cheerful.

Aunty Mary was very ill now, the cancer spreading rapidly, and if she could be strong I was resolved I must be too. Granddad had taken to going for a walk each day, something unheard of for years, but I suppose it was his way of dealing with life without Nana.

The flat had rung to the sound of their bickering for decades, but of late I suppose the silence was louder. I would call in on him whenever I got the chance, chatting to Uncle Lou and Janet, all of us trying our hardest to proceed as normal, as if nothing had unexpectedly turned our world upside down.

My friend Yvonne suggested we took a holiday together to Austria. It seemed like a good way to try and shake off the black dog, so I agreed, and in no time we had it booked and organised.

Poor Yvonne, I was so convinced as I waved goodbye to Aunty Mary that I would never see her again that I cried all the way through France, Germany and up to the gates of our hotel in Austria.

"I'm ok," I kept saying, then I'd set off again snivelling into my handherchief.

"There, there," she'd say, ineffectually patting me on the shoulder. Poor lass, she'd never seen me in this state before, I was known for my cheerful optimism and now here she was, hundreds of miles from home, with this sobbing wreck.

I won't pretend to you things got better, but they did change. I stopped crying, and started being sick!

Yvonne took to going on excursions with a couple of friendly old ladies we had met on the coach (by old I mean in their forties or fifties - ancient by our standards back then!).I'd stay in our hotel room with my head over the toilet. Clearly the foreign food wasn't agreeing with me, must be the apple strudel I thought.

We came home, me still retching into a carrier bag, Yvonne sitting behind me squeamishly, patting my head occasionally and passing me wet wipes. The rest of the coach were all being very sympathetic, but secretly wondering what was wrong with the weepy sickly girl with her head in a bag.

"You're pregnant"

"No… I can't be… really? Give it here!"

Diane, my good friend, who was now a trainee nurse, had guessed as soon as she saw me and brought a home testing kit. Now we both sat looking at it mesmerised, it had been a clear liquid, now it had turned bright red.

"Congratulations," Diane said, for lack of a suitable expression.

To be honest everyone was very nice and supportive about it, being an unmarried mother wasn't quite as stigmatised as it used to be, but it wasn't the most desirable of circumstances either. Still, at least now I knew why I was being sick relentlessly day and night!

Mark, once he'd got over the surprise, was unusually cheerful, "Well, at least we'll have beautiful children," he grinned.

I looked at myself in the mirror. "Child, just the one, and what it looks like depends on the gene pool; lets hope it takes after you," I grimaced, grabbing a washing up bowl and throwing up again.

Aunty Mary called me to her one day. She told me she had consented to go in a hospice, she thought it would give Uncle Jack some respite from caring for her. I naively thought it was just so she could get a bit of rest too.

"I don't think I'll be able to stay till the baby arrives," she smiled wearily, then seeing my downcast face she said, "Perhaps it will be me, come back again."

"I don't think people reincarnate that fast," I told her, and then, seeing it was her turn to look crestfallen, I added, "But you never know."

And so, in our own way, we skirted around the subject. Aunty Mary went into St Gemma's Hospice, I continued to be sick, and Uncle Jack remained cheerful for us both, whistling excessively and taking Patch for long walks.

Then one day Uncle Lou came home from work, made a cup of tea for himself and Granddad and, whilst in the middle of his bacon butty, realised an odd thing; Granddad was letting his tea go cold. In fact, on closer inspection, Granddad had passed away an hour or so before, but not until he'd seen his last race of the day. Nan wouldn't have been so inconsiderate as to collect him before he'd seen the result of his final bet.

A final farewell

On the day my Aunty Mary passed over she had been rushed into hospital in the early hours of that morning.

She had been fighting cancer for the past ten years, but in the last six months it had become very aggressive and she had been in almost constant pain. She had been staying at St Gemma's Hospice for the last couple of weeks but after Granddad had passed away she had requested to come home at weekends. It was only nine days since his demise.

That morning the pain had exacerbated to the point that nothing we had at our disposal would alleviate it. The doctor had been summoned and rushed her into hospital to see if they were better able to manage the pain for her there.

I had been unable to go as, at that time, I was suffering from hyperemesis (an extreme form of morning sickness that persists all day and night). Uncle Jack had gone with her, of course, and I spent the day in bed being sick intermittently and waiting for news of how she was.

By nightfall Mark had called round, his best friend Tony accompanied him to try and cheer me up. I was gazing out of the window, only half listening to their chatter, it was dark but cloudless and the sky was lit with stars.

Suddenly I heard a distinct, "Goodbye, Jane." Aunty Mary's voice inside my head. I sat, stunned for a second, and then I grabbed Mark and started shaking his arm.

"Quick, go to Uncle Lou's, the hospital will have rung, I think something has happened to Aunty Mary!"

"What?" Mark looked at me, dazed and confused. I kept on shaking him whilst repeating my instruction again. We had never had a phone in our flat, we shared the one in my grandparents' flat (now Uncle Louis's, since their demise).

When it became necessary to repeat my request a third time I practically shouted it at Mark. He got up and stumbled to the door, clearly thinking I'd taken leave of my senses. As he opened the door, there on the doorstep, just about to knock, was my Uncle Louis and his partner Janet.

"I'm sorry," Uncle Louis said, struggling a little with his composure.

The hospital had just rung five minutes before to say Aunty Mary had died. But I already knew that, Aunty Mary had stopped by herself to wish me farewell.

A ray of hope

The days were dark, literally and figuratively speaking. It was the end of October and took all morning to get light, then plunged into blackness by teatime.

I sat in my bed, repeatedly being sick, trying to be cheerful around Uncle Jack who, in turn, tried to be cheerful around me, bustling about, making the plans for Aunty Mary's funeral, sorting out their financial affairs and taking Patch for long walks.

Mark called round each evening and both he and Uncle Jack tried to get me to eat, with me trying in vain to keep even water down. I didn't allow myself to think too deeply, I was focused on the battle with my body, the constant round of drink, retch, drink, retch again.

On the morning of Aunty Mary's funeral the doctor declared I was so ill I needed to be hospitalised. My weight had plummeted to just over seven stone and I hadn't kept above a mouthful of water down in a week. There was no way I could have attended the funeral, I couldn't even stand unaided by this point. Janet travelled up to the hospital with me, saw me safely deposited on the ward, and then scurried home to attend the funeral of my Aunty Mary with Uncle Louis and Uncle Jack.

I had never been in hospital as a patient before. I asked to keep the curtains drawn for a while and then, feeling truly alone for the first time in months, I allowed myself the luxury of a proper cry.

I wasn't even sure what I was crying for - the loss of my aunty, my mum, my grandparents, being unmarried and pregnant, not being able to attend the funeral, for the sadness of the rest of my family and being unable to console them, because I couldn't stop being sick, or because it was my first stay in a hospital and I was afraid of needles!

The curtain was drawn back a little and a bright, bubbly young woman with a sunny smile popped her head round.

"Oh dear," she said, seeing me snivelling away quietly, and disappeared. She reappeared a moment later with a box of tissues.

Sitting herself down next to me on the bed she passed me the tissues and patted me reassuringly on the shoulder, introducing herself as the junior doctor whose care I was in.

She asked what the matter was and I was momentarily thrown. I had not told anyone of my personal troubles, being a private sort of person I preferred to keep things to myself, so at the risk of sounding a complete wuss I told her I was afraid of having my blood taken.

Her laughing brown eyes were full of compassion; lots of people were, she assured me, but she had a trick so that I wouldn't feel a thing. I held out my arm and looked away, eyes closed and gritted teeth, I braced myself, I felt her give a swift tap on my arm.

"Please hurry up," I begged.

I wasn't sure how much longer I could be brave for. She laughingly told me the needle was already in, I hadn't felt a thing. Blood taken successfully, she told me her trick was simple. If you tap the arm and then quickly insert the needle apparently the brain is still processing the sensation of the initial tap and doesn't register the needle. She had learnt that at med school.

I was relieved and impressed; my phobia of needles had been cured in that instant (which was a good job, because there were a lot of them to come in future!).

I was starting to feel much better, if ever I was to think of someone as an Earth Angel (i.e., someone sent to give just the right amount of support at a crucial time) she would definitely fit the description. Warm and friendly, but not overbearingly so, I soon felt better in her company, to the extent that when she left I consented to have the curtains drawn back, at last.

Later that afternoon, visitors arrived, my cousins Matthew, Martin, Nick, and Nick's fiancée Amanda. All dressed in black straight from the funeral, I was pleased and surprised to see them. They told me how it had gone, and then set to cheering me up with lots of silly unrelated stories. It was a welcome distraction.

Just as they were about to leave Mark turned up, also in black, and bearing the most enormous bouquet of flowers. Knowing his financial circumstances, I remonstrated with him that he really shouldn't have bought them. He told me on his way to the hospital he had just called into a flower shop intending to get a small posy, however, fortuitously as it turned out, our friend Liam's wife happened to work there. When she heard who it was for and why she had taken it upon herself to make up the magnificent bouquet for next to nothing. I was really touched as I hardly knew her.

I was in hospital for five days, during which time I was started on a very limited liquid diet, then gradually re-introduced to simple solids, in an attempt to rehydrate me and to stop my body from virtually eating itself.

Little by little I got to know the other women on the ward, a friendly, lively bunch, who had seemed a little standoffish at first. They revealed to me that when I had seemed so withdrawn on the first day, and then been visited by all these sombre folk wearing black, they thought I was part of some strange religious cult and were wary of approaching me. Inappropriate though it may seem, when I explained everyone had just come straight from a funeral, we all dissolved into laughter at their misapprehension of the situation.

On my last night in the hospital I was sitting around one of the beds with a group of the other women (we were all in with different maternity problems), just joking and making small talk. I looked out of the window to the bright starlit sky and suddenly I felt surrounded by the loved ones I'd lost, as if they were all around me in that moment.

There was a sensation that I can only describe like this; imagine you were looking at a cartoon where the Fairy Godmother taps Cinderella with her magic wand and a shower of magical stars rain down on her. That would be the way it felt.

Suddenly, I had the realisation that this little bundle of cells, growing inside me and making me throw up all the time, was a real person. It was as if I was being formerly introduced, not just to the baby I would have, but to the eternal soul belonging to that baby. As if my relatives that had passed were introducing me to child that was yet to come.

I sat there awestruck. At a time when I should have been in the deepest, darkest of places it was as if somebody had turned a little light on somewhere, and it was the most beautiful, wonderful feeling in the world.

I returned home, no longer being sick, and the depression I had struggled with for months was gone at last. I was able to begin planning for the arrival of my baby, with a lot of help from my wonderful family and friends.

Uncle Jack decided to sign over the flat to me. He and Patch moved in with Uncle Louis and Janet.

Mark moved in with me. There was a brief breathing space while we grew accustomed to being under each others feet, before our duo became a trio!

Anthony Jack Cranmer arrived on the planet at nine-twenty at night on the twenty first of May. He had a shock of black hair (which later rubbed off and grew back a dark blonde) and eyes so enormous they eclipsed all the other features on his face. He was tiny and demanding and stubborn from the word go, but we were absolutely enchanted with him, and I had the strangest feeling we had met somewhere before!

Unconditional love

One of the things I find people struggling with on this side of life is the concept of other partners. For instance, if someone has had a long and happy marriage and then their partner dies, often the remaining partner struggles with a feeling of guilt when and if someone else comes into their life. If they do believe in an afterlife they feel there is a betrayal of the deceased spouse.

My understanding of love on the other side is that although it doesn't in anyway diminish, it doesn't include the human elements of possessiveness and jealousy that often complicate our relationships in the material world.

Our loved ones know that we will be together again, they also know that a love that will last an eternity is multiplied when shared with other kindred spirits. It is not unusual for them to work on the other side towards sending a new partner or companion to their bereaved partner.

Now, I know what you are thinking, how can I possibly know this?

When my Aunty Mary died my Uncle Jack lost his wife of forty-three years. He certainly would not have entertained the idea of replacing her, it would never have occurred to me that this would ever be a possibility. Uncle Jack had been eleven years older than Aunty Mary; he was seventy two with nothing on his mind but retaining his dignity and retiring to a quiet life in the Chelsea Pensioners home in London. Briefly, he moved in with Uncle Louis and Janet, until he had seen Anthony safely arrived and Mark and I settled as a family. Then he departed south (leaving Patch in Uncle Lou's capable hands) on what he and we assumed would be his last adventure.

I missed Uncle Jack terribly but I understood that to be here with Aunty Mary gone must have been incredibly painful for him. He needed the space and change of scenery in order to heal. Still, we wrote to each other every week, bright cheerful letters about Anthony's progress and Mark's college studies. (He had decided to further his education at last, as getting a job, with or without qualifications, was a near impossibility in the climate of mass unemployment that was a part of Thatcher's Britain in the 1980s).

Uncle Jack described forays into London and the sights and sounds of the big city. My brother Lee had also travelled south to study, so occasionally Uncle Jack would have some news of him too, though we can safely assume they didn't frequent the same haunts at that time.

One day, as I was walking along the veranda with Anthony (about six months old now) on my hip, my next door neighbour, Mrs Yeadon, was coming out of her flat. I had known Mrs Yeadon virtually all my life. She and her late husband had moved in when I was only four. A kindly couple who had no children of their own, they had often brought me back sweets and presents from their numerous holidays over the years.

Mr Yeadon had died eleven years before but Mrs Yeadon had remained in her little flat. She felt safe there, she said, surrounded by the friendship of my family on both sides. She lived between Aunty Mary, Uncle Jack and me on one side, and Nana, Granddad and Uncle Louis on the other. Patch, the dog, was one of her greatest pals.

Mrs Yeadon's face lit up when she saw baby Anthony. He was a smiling cherub with the most enormous blue eyes and fair hair. The two of them gurgled to each other in delight, part of the mutual admiration society. When she could tear herself away from Anthony's charm for a moment, Mrs Yeadon said she would love it if I called round with him some evening if I ever found myself at a loose end.

I didn't need asking twice. Mark was frequently out on a night either practising with his band or playing gigs with them.

Anthony had turned into the child that never slept, so my nights were frequently long, lonely and frustrating. I spent every-day entertaining my little sweetheart, by evening he had got bored of my repertoire.

So, a pattern of calling round a couple of evenings a week emerged. Mrs Yeadon, who now became May to me, would make coffee and get out the biscuit tin, and we would chat about trivi-alities while Anthony stole the show with his antics. His increas-ing mobility meant we spent a lot of time chasing a crawling baby up and down the flat or taking it in turns to bounce him up and down on our knees.

May was particularly good at this, in her middle sixties she was a large, cuddly, grandmotherly figure, and Anthony adored her. He would repeatedly peek through her glasses that she wore on a chain round her neck and then, if he thought she and I were talk-ing to each other to his exclusion, he would reach up and pop his dummy into her unsuspecting mouth, much to her amusement.

May would occasionally ask how Uncle Jack liked his adven-tures in London and I would recount his latest escapades from my weekly correspondence.

"Remember me to him next time you write," May suggested, I said I certainly would.

I had already been telling Uncle Jack of the kindness of his old friend and next door neighbour. He'd been pleased to hear I had the extra support while Mark was out so frequently on a night. I sent May's kind regards in my next letter. Uncle Jack responded with delight to have been remembered, he sent back a jovial response and for the next few letters and meetings I conveyed friendly greetings between them.

Uncle Jack came up for a visit, stopping with Uncle Louis and Janet again for a week. He called round to see May for a chat and suggested she might like to go for a drink sometime.

"Fancy," May said to me, "I haven't been in a pub in over twelve years!"

Still, he managed to persuade her that a sweet sherry and a bag of crisps would do her the world of good. So off they went to paint the town red.

Uncle Jack went back down south but now he had gained another pen pal and he and May also took it in turns to ring each other once a week. I soon began to realise May was more abreast of his news than I was.

One night I had a dream about Aunty Mary. She looked well, I thought, for someone who'd been dead for almost two years by this time. After the delight of seeing each other again she told me she had something to discuss with me and asked me to sit down.

In that bizarre way dreams have we were in the bathroom of the flat at this point, so we both had to perch on the edge of the bath. Uncle Jack was going to marry May, she informed me. I was a little taken aback.

"No," I said, laughing, they were just really good friends. I reasoned to myself that perhaps Aunty Mary wasn't too happy with the development.

"No," Aunty Mary insisted, I was wrong, they would be getting married and she thought it was very important that I understood that not only was she extremely happy about this but she had been actively working towards it from the other side.

She impressed on me that she was not at all happy with Uncle Jack being on his own and lonely down in London. She wanted him to be back amongst friends and family and, as she had been good friends with May herself for many years, she couldn't think of anyone more perfect to be his new companion. Furthermore, she was entrusting me with the knowledge so that I wouldn't appear shocked when they told me and so I could help with the proceedings. A quick hug, and a loving smile and Aunty Mary was gone.

I woke up and pondered on my strange dream, then dismissed it as my overactive imagination and carried on with my business of the day.

A week or so passed and Uncle Jack was once again up on a

visit and one evening there was a knock at the door. I answered it, Anthony on my hip as usual; Uncle Jack and May stood there together.

"Come in," I said. delighted. They did, and fussed over Anthony as always, then Uncle Jack got to the point in his straight-talking soldierly way.

They had come to see me as they thought it was only right that I should be the first to know. They were going to get engaged and Uncle Jack would be moving back up north again. They hoped I was alright with this. I was thrilled for them both, and totally stunned.

"I already know," I wanted to say, but I didn't think it appropriate to say his deceased wife had already shown up to give her blessing while in the presence of his new wife to be.

I just gave Uncle Jack and (my soon to be Aunty) May a big hug and made us all a snowball to celebrate (we were all a bit partial to a drop of advocaat and lemonade!). Anthony kept dipping his dummy into Aunty May's glass when she wasn't looking, much to everyone's amusement.

A few weeks later Aunty May and I caught a coach down to London. We went to visit Uncle Jack at the Chelsea Pensioner's home, the Royal Hospital, and got to see his residence at last.

The building and gardens were lovely although the accommodation was little more than a cubicle the size of a shoebox with just room for a single bed, a small chest of drawers and a wardrobe. As Uncle Jack himself might have said, "There wasn't enough room to swing a cat in there."

We had a nice lunch in the great hall with the rest of the pensioners, then helped Uncle Jack to pack up the majority of his belongings to take back with us. We would be collecting the remainder of his things and Uncle Jack himself when he was discharged as a pensioner the following week. By this time I was thinking of Aunty May and myself as the "escape" committee.

All's well that ends well. Uncle Jack came home, married Aunty May, and they lived very happy and productive lives together for a further eight years, partly thanks to the help of some celestial matchmaking, and a little Earth Angel called Anthony.

Mama's blessing

If my belief in the unconditional love from the other side needed reinforcement I had another experience to help convince me.

My mum and dad had an almost perfect relationship built on mutual trust, respect, love and laughter (lots of it). I can rarely recall a cross word between them in all the years I knew them, and disagreements were always couched in terms of affectionate, gentle teasing until a resolution was reached.

My dad was an easygoing, generous, laid-back soul, with just a touch of devilment that brings to mind Jack Nicholson at times. It could be generally said that he always enjoyed life to the full. He rarely suffered ill health, never complained (apart from over poor service in restaurants, for some reason) and drifted through life as one charmed. (Both he and my brother Lee have kissed the Blarney Stone and I think there must be something to its claims of magical properties).

My mum was an equally easy-going, jovial, generous soul. They were both perfectly suited to the gregarious roles they played as "meine host" within the licensing trade. Mum had gorgeous titian-red hair and, on the occasions it flared, she had a temper to match it, but as a rule she was the life and soul of every party.

Never have I seen a couple with such a lust for life and all it entailed; every challenge was an adventure. They were inseparable, and as Mum reminded Dad would still be so, whoever crossed over first, so he had just better remember it!

Sadly, this glorious partnership came to an end after a brief spell of twenty years when my Mum made her departure at just forty-eight years old.

It has to be said that my family have always epitomised the famed English "stiff upper lip". Dad arranged the funeral, allowed himself to grieve quietly in the intervening period, and then, after we'd said our goodbyes, he picked up the pieces and started again.

For quite some time Dad had been out of work after a sudden recession in the British economy had hit our business with devastating effects.

Mum and Dad had been forced to declare themselves bankrupt

and give up the pub and career they loved, moving into rented accommodation and living off the state.

Although they couldn't have seen it at the time this was actually fortuitous in that it meant Dad was at least at home with Mum through her decline into ill health. There are always blessings in disguise if we look for them.

Now, though, Dad was at a loose end. Some friends, Roland and Bet, stepped in and gave him some work helping behind their bar, as much to keep him occupied as to help with his finances and self respect at that time. Dad always hated having to claim benefits and jumped at the chance to be in work again.

Tragically, Dad's friend committed suicide not six months after Mum had passed, and now Dad found his role reversed.From being the supported he became the supporter, helping his friend's shocked and grieving widow through all the practicalities of a funeral and keeping her business running smoothly, whilst she came to terms with her own loss.

A year passed and gradually I realised from subtle references made by my brother Lee (who was working temporarily behind the bar before he left for London polytechnic) that Dad and his friend Bet had become an item.

Mum must have decided it was time to put in an appearance.I had another of my lucid dreams. I found myself on a balcony in what appeared to be a very fancy restaurant. Seated at the other side of the table was my mother, looking splendid as always. She gestured over the balcony to a table far below.

I was surprised to see Dad and Bet there also eating and drinking but totally oblivious to us. Mum and I were always very direct with each other so I asked her straight out if she minded.

"Not at all," she reassured me. Then she said that although she knew Dad was her soul mate she had no intention of him being lonely until they were together again and besides, she reminded me, Bet was her friend and she approved.

My mother, I discovered, who whilst on this side would have smilingly choked the life out of anyone who looked at my father twice, had become obligingly altruistic now she was on the other side.

"Besides," she added, "he won't marry her. I've already told him he's allowed another partner, but never another wife!" (Yes, that sounded more like the Mother I knew and loved).

She had shown up, it seemed, to make sure I was okay with this and be assured that she was. She wanted me and Bet to be friends, so we were. I got to know and really like Bet over the years, and she had also become part of the "Anthony fan club".

I never mentioned my "dream" to Dad, I didn't think he believed in these things, although I noticed there was never any mention of Dad and Bet tying the knot either.

Bet also passed away a few years ago, but I know her and Mum get on just fine on the other side, they often make a point of showing up at readings together.

Endings and beginnings

Sometimes, the path to spiritual enlightenment is like one cautious step forward and two back.

At twenty I had perhaps achieved the most peaceful, accepting, all-giving, all loving phase of my life and nothing, I felt at that point, could shake my belief in God's love and my connection to the Universe.

Then, over a period of eighteen months, my closest and dearest relatives were taken from me. Nana, Mum, Aunty Mary and Granddad all crossed over in quick succession.

As if this wasn't enough, my brother Lee went down south to further his education, my Uncle Jack went to live with the Chelsea Pensioners, and two of my closest friends found jobs in London and Birmingham. Finally, to add to the confusion I was feeling, I discovered I was pregnant, and had to give up my job in order to bring up my baby.

I still had Mark, fortunately, but he was given a place at Huddersfield School of Music, which meant by six-thirty in the morning he left the flat and wasn't home until seven or eight in the evening, as it was a long journey by bus. He was still playing in a band (which was rapidly becoming a bone of contention between us) and on the weekends had a part-time job at the local Cricket Club in order to try and make ends meet. Admittedly student grants were far better than the loans people get nowadays, but they still didn't go very far when you were a young couple with a baby.

I think I would class this period as my "dark night of the soul". Everything I had believed in and that had sustained me before was stripped away and, although I hadn't exactly stopped believing in God, I was extremely angry at him – he and I, I decided, were no longer friends.

It's funny how, when I look back, I can see that, as bleak as it seemed at the time, from somewhere came all the help I required. People I hadn't previously been close to seemed to step into my life just as I needed them.

My cousin Lynda (young Lou's wife) helped enormously with all my maternity needs – from going to ante-natal classes with me to finding all the clothing and baby equipment from her friends and relatives for me.

My Aunty Margery was there to help out immediately following the birth of baby Anthony, coming everyday for a week to help us get a routine together and ensure I was able to rest.

Uncle Lou and Janet were always there for day to day support, of course, and young Lou came across to help decorate the living room and sort out any practicalities; things that needed fixing or a bit of brute strength.

My next door neighbour became a close friend and, in becoming so, recalled my beloved Uncle Jack from the Chelsea Hospital for me eventually ended up as my Aunty May. She introduced me to a new friend who also had a young son and who had moved into the flat opposite. This new friend in turn introduced me to the local playgroup (where Anthony and I made more friends) and we went swimming together each week.

I was contacted by the mother of my friend Bev, who had gone to Birmingham, and she (Aunty Muriel) encouraged me to visit her once a week for a coffee and a chat.

My Dad found a new partner (Bet) and I was invited to visit them each week and stay for tea.

A friend I hadn't seen in years bumped into me at one of Mark's gigs and we resumed contact, too. Another friend of Mark's turned out to be a decorator and he decorated Anthony's nursery just because he liked us and he liked children.

And then of course there was Dolly, Mark's Mum, who could be my best friend one day and worst enemy the next, but who was always there with a beaming smile on her face for her little cherubic grandson, Anthony.

Suddenly, I understood the saying "when God closes a door somewhere he opens a window," as one by one all of these people came flooding into my life to help fill the gaps created. However, I was still angry at God, and because I wouldn't open myself up to the spiritual side of life I was empty inside. This situation would persist for ten long years, until something happened to allow the floodgates on the two worlds to open again, and reawaken me to the truth at last.

Part Four

Alas, that spring should vanish with the Rose!
That youth's sweet scented manuscript should close;
The Nightingale that in the branches sang,
Ah whence, and whither flown again, who knows!

The Rubaiyat of Omar Khayyam

Chapter Eleven
The lean and hungry years

Out of the mouths of babes

Small children are particularly sensitive to the other side, not least because they haven't long since arrived from there, but also because they don't question things or look for a rational explanation as we do once we grow up, they just accept.

When I was eight months pregnant with our second child we were still living in the flats and I had decided that Anthony's nursery needed redecorating. It had been beautifully decorated just the year before courtesy of a friend of ours but Anthony had decided to half strip one wall from the security of his cot one night, so I decided I'd just paint the room instead.

Anthony, aged two, was in his cot surrounded by toys and books to keep him out of mischief. Mark was at college, and I had decided to commence work myself, as the new baby's arrival was imminent. Bright as ever, I was balancing precariously on a rickety chair in order to reach the ceiling. It was really hard work being so heavily pregnant and slow going as I had to keep climbing on and off the chair to change my vantage point.

Suddenly, I became aware that Anthony, who had been chattering away to himself in language typical for a two year old (loud, enthusiastic and rather nonsensical at times) was now remarkably silent. I thought he must have fallen asleep.

Carefully, I stepped down from the chair and turned to look. Anthony was actually still wide awake, but mysteriously silent. His huge blue eyes were fixed to a corner of the room in an alert and wondering kind of way. Every so often he would nod as if in agreement to some unheard question. I traced his gaze to the corner of the room. There was nothing at all to see, no little twinkles of light, no shadows, not even any pattern as I had painted the whole room plain white.

"What can you see Sweetie-pie?" I asked him, puzzled.

Without looking at me at all he smiled and nodded again, then, glancing my way just once, he pointed with a small chubby hand at the ceiling again. I stayed there looking for a moment or two, totally mystified by his behaviour. Anthony abrubtly turned away and went back to playing once more.

I decided to leave my painting for that day. Thankfully when Mark came home he finished the nursery off for me.

It only occurred to me later how stupid I was, balancing precariously on an old weak and wobbly chair while pregnant. What was I thinking of? The room we were decorating had previously been my Aunty Mary's. I sometimes wonder if it was she who had called in to keep an eye on me and, as luck would have it, had been spotted by her great nephew and stayed for a little chat with him.

Strange occurrences

My husband Mark is a musician. Primarily he plays the bass guitar but back in his music college days he was known to dabble with any instrument he could lay his hands on.

In those days we were extremely poor, trying to live on a student grant with Mark making a few pounds extra working at the local cricket club.

Unfortunately, not only were we poor, but Mark, bless his cotton socks, was also extremely gullible. Far be it from me to say "a fool and his money…" but honestly, they saw him coming every time.

On this occasion some so-called "friend" had persuaded Mark that what he really needed to make it in the music business was an electric piano and, guess what, his friend just happened to have for sale at the knock down bargain price of only twenty pounds. (Not much nowadays I know, but back then it was a small fortune to us).

"But it's a bargain!" Mark protested as he struggled through the door with the objectionable piano under his arm.

It was no use me protesting, the deal was done, the money was gone, and he'd had to fight the thing every step of the way home from Huddersfield to Bradford on numerous buses. So, eagerly, he set it up in pride of place in the living room, whilst I sat scowling at him and it from the settee.

Then came the moment of truth. He plugged in the piano and hit the keyboard. An almighty screech came from the confounded article, followed by a pop, a bang, and a smell of electrical components burning, sparks, smoke and then nothing at all. He hurriedly unplugged it.

Of course Mark would insist that he must have done something wrong in setting it up or in transporting it. Never let it be said that his dear old friend had sold him a turkey!

Several days of tampering and testing ensued, all to no avail. The electric piano remained as dead as a Dodo, cluttering up the living room as a reminder of his folly. Mark optimistically let it remain there, determined at some point to find someone or some way to fix it. I just used it as a place to put the ironing pile.

Months passed and then one night, in the wee small hours, Mark and I were awakened by the most awful sound. We sat up shaking and clutching each other, "What was that?"

The scary thing was, we knew. It sounded exactly like someone leaning both arms across every key of an electric piano and making it emit one strident, screeching, off-key tone that had startled us both from our sleep.

Being my usual brave self I sent Mark out to investigate (well isn't it the man's place to get eaten by the bogeyman first?). Once he had turned on every light in the flat I tiptoed after him. There were no intruders, there was nothing out of place, and the keyboard sat innocently silent as usual, untouched by human hands and still unplugged.

Mark and I could only assume we had been mistaken, although we couldn't imagine what else may have made the noise. The only reasonable explanation was that it was external.

The next morning Mark received some sad news. His mother's oldest and dearest friend, Mrs Brown, a lady he regarded as a grandmother figure from when he was very young, had been found dead of a heart attack. It was doubly upsetting as he received the news on the day of his twenty-second birthday, when he would usually have paid her a visit so she could give him his customary card. Instead we spent most of the day trying to console his mum, Dolly, and take in the sudden unexpected loss ourselves.

Almost another year passed and still the electric piano graced the front room with its presence. Mark had long since given up on the idea of trying to fix it. The intention was always to store it away at some point, we just hadn't seemed to get round to it.

One night in May, around the time of Anthony's second birthday, Mark and I were once again awakened at around two a.m. by the terrifying ghostly noise of a keyboard sounding out one long loud discordant note. Again we sat and shuddered in bed until, hearts racing, we crept into the living room to find nothing unusual, nothing out of place, the keyboard still as it was, and still unplugged.

This time we pounded on the keys but they emitted nothing more than a dull, dead sound. Perplexed and more than a little shaken we retreated to bed once more.

The next morning I bumped into Aunty May on the outside landing (this occurred just prior to her marriage to Uncle Jack, while he was still in Chelsea). She was in a shaken state.

"Come in for coffee," she urged me. She asked if I'd heard the noise the previous night. Oh, so she had heard it too had she?

"The piano or organ noise?" I enquired.

"No, no," she said.

It transpired that the young couple who lived above her had had an argument and the girl had taken their baby son and left the lad (about eighteen years old) all alone. She had been staying at her mum's for a couple of days but he had asked her to come back and talk it through. Apparently, things had gone from bad to worse and she had left again, declaring their engagement off and that she was leaving him for good.

Well, said Aunty May, that was it, from around three o'clock that afternoon the noise was horrendous. (I have to say Mark and I had not heard any of this as our flat was not directly beneath his, as hers was).

It appears the young lad had systematically taken his flat apart. He had smashed and trashed everything he could lay his hands

184

on, even sawing the settee up into pieces and scattering the stuffing all over the place. The noise went on and on late into the night. Around two a.m., thankfully, the noise stopped and poor Aunty May breathed a sigh of relief and finally fell asleep.

Yes, the noise had stopped at two a.m., around the time Mark and I were awakened by the horrific sound in our flat. It seems the young lad, having destroyed the entire contents of his home, had decided to hang himself.

I honestly don't know what the connection is between two tragic deaths and a defunct electrical piano, but I do know the departing soul consists of energy that can affect electrical items. There has been well documented evidence of spirit phenomena affecting lights and other electrical appliances. Though why they would focus in on our piano is a mystery, unless it is to do with proximity. On the one hand, the closeness of Mark's relationship to Mrs Brown, and on the other, the distance between the site of the suicide and the machine in our living room on the floor below.

Could these departing souls have emitted just enough energy to make our piano let out a sound like a banshee's wail before disappearing into the night?

Whatever the cause, two instances of paranormal activity attached to this instrument was enough for Mark (sceptic and atheist) and I to decide to get rid of the piano for good.

Whether you believe in the afterlife or not, a piano sounding out a death knell in the dead of night does nothing for your beauty sleep!

Spectres at the feast

Now, I know this sounds bizarre, but even though a lot of my nearest and dearest are residing on the other side of the veil they still have a habit of sending me presents. Perhaps the best example of this came in 1990.

Mark and I were about the poorest we had ever been. We had two young children; Anthony, aged two and a half, and our new baby, Daniel, born the previous November.

Daniel was blonde, chubby and with that familiar twinkle in

his eye from birth, that says here is one of life's comedians. Photos of him around this time bear more than a passing resemblance to Humpty Dumpty - small, round and looking curiously egg-shaped.

Mark had just finished college, and as he hadn't secured a job at that point we were living on state benefits (and anyone who's been there and done that will know it's not much fun). We were still living in the flat that had been Aunty Mary and Uncle Jack's and, apart from the few bits we'd managed to get new for the children, everything else was now well past its best as my Aunt and Uncle had had things for thirty years or more before they had passed down to us.

To top the misery off we had the worst neighbour imaginable now living below us. He didn't like children and had taken to harassing us, day and night, every time Anthony ran along the hall or Daniel crawled or toddled clumsily around. He would blare loud music at all hours of the night (to show us what it felt like – he declared to me, though how loud music compares to a child toddling about defies explanation) and bang loudly on the pipes.

He had even taken to banging his ceiling with a stick in the early hours of the morning to wake the children up. Now, I'm a patient woman, but when it comes to my children, I have a very short fuse. This guy was in danger of taking a trip over his balcony before long!

Life was not a bowl of cherries in any respect. However, crazily, Mark and I decided it would be a good time to get married at last.

Our fifth anniversary as a couple was coming up and we wanted to make it all official on that date. Bearing in mind that nowadays most people don't even consider planning a wedding for less than ten thousand pounds how we thought it might happen on thirty-one pounds a week (if it was even as much as that) I don't know. I suppose if I hadn't fallen out with God in a big way at that point I may have taken to praying for a miracle. As that wasn't an option, I just wished very hard.

There followed a chain of events that, looking back, could only have been Heaven sent. First of all I needed to find an open minded "man-of-the-cloth" to marry us, as I really didn't want a register office do. Who, I wondered, would be willing to marry an atheist and an un-christened woman of no particular religious conviction who had two children already? A friend had suggested someone and I rang what I thought was his church only to find I'd rung someone else entirely. This turned out to be a complete stroke of luck!

Pastor Andrew Fellows and his lovely wife Helen were newly arrived from Canada. They were the same age as us, had two young children like us, and had the same zany sense of humour. We went along to meet Andrew and hit it off immediately.

He didn't mind our circumstances or beliefs (or Mark's total lack of them), he just believed that if two people loved each other and wanted to commit to one another then that was good enough for him. Amazingly Mark the atheist and the evangelical minister were friends in an instant.

This was the most generous of souls. Andrew had never conducted a wedding before and was delighted that we were to be his first. He helped us plan out all the fine details, gave his services, time and church for free, and even had the church decorated with fresh flowers, free of charge, for the day.

Further to this, people seemed to come from everywhere to help out.

A friend's mother who was a florist made my bouquet and the three bridesmaids bouquets and our headdresses out of silk flowers for next to nothing (because I'd been kind to her son on some occasion in the past, she insisted).

My Aunty Kath (my Dad's sister, who I didn't see very often as she lived the opposite end of the country) paid her friend to make us the most beautiful three-tiered wedding cake as her gift to us. One of Mark's college friends played the piano for the wedding in the church.

My Dad, who had very little himself at this point, insisted on paying for all the catering and the car. Mark's parents bought his suit and paid for the hire of the venue.

Another friend and her parents volunteered to look after the children on the day and baby-sit so we could go out again at night. My bridesmaids insisted on paying for the hire of their own dresses. My cousin Matthew took the wedding photos and paid for the album and the developing. Both our families gave us money to buy new things for the home. Uncle Jack and Aunty May bought us a lovely new double-divan bed, to replace our dilapidated old one!

In the end all Mark and I had to find money for was the ring and my dress. My ring cost sixteen pounds for a plain gold band and I found the dress of my dreams, for hire, in a shop that insisted I need pay only thirty-five pounds at five pounds a week as it was old anyway.

So there we were, all set for our wedding, everyone pulling out all the stops to make it a great success, then as I mentioned earlier, arrived our present from the world of spirit.

Two weeks before our wedding a letter arrived for me. I opened it and started screaming for Mark to come quick. He came running. We had been to enquire about a council house that had come empty but as everyone seemed to be asking (they'd had eight enquiries that morning before we arrived and the housing office had only been open fifteen minutes) we passed it off as a long shot. Now we were offered the house and had moved into our first real family home just one week before our wedding.

To top this off the council officer re-assessed our rent and realised we had been overpaying, so we were given a cheque for four hundred and eighteen pounds in excess rent from the flat, perfect for re-carpeting and decorating our new home throughout.

From Mark's perspective this was all just lucky coincidence but, if you take the picture as a whole, looks to me like certain people on the other side just didn't want to be left out on the big day after all!

Wedding day

The big day arrived, heralded in at dawn by baby Dan's shrill cry. Daniel, ten months old, hardly ever cried, slept through every night, and was usually an amiable, smiley little chap. On the eve of my wedding he decided to wake at midnight, and cry continuously till four-thirty a.m.

I spent the night in Anthony's bed, from where I could wave

and coo at Dan in his cot. Anthony had gone to stop at his nana's with Mark; my bridesmaids shared the main bedroom. Daniel and I had two hours sleep, then it was time to get up. I had a hair-dressing appointment at eight – little Dan was not impressed.

My bridesmaids and I hastened to the hairdressers on foot, as there was no car at our disposal, a quick half a mile jog at seven in the morning with a screaming baby in tow.

We deposited Dan (very thankfully) with my friend Beverley (who, despite being rather child-phobic, had gamely offered to look after the little chap for the day, as everyone else was caught up in the wedding itself). Fortunately, her parents my "Aunty" Muriel and "Uncle" Mike, were also on hand to help.

Hair done, we hurried home, closely followed by Bev and a still screaming Daniel. There ensued a mad couple of hours where we all tried to soothe Dan, get our outfits on and do one another's make up.

At one point I was trying to wrap gifts for the bridesmaids while Bev held slices of toast to my lips, commanding "bite, chew," and "swallow," at regular intervals, just on the off chance that in all the excitement I'd actually forgotten how to masticate my food!

My cousin Matthew arrived, our official photographer for the day, he followed dishevelled bridesmaids round the house, try-ing to get candid natural shots. I eventually found more gainful employment for him, holding my wedding dress over my shoul-ders whilst I changed a squirmy, squealy, indignant baby, who had become soggy at both ends now.

Dad arrived with the bridal car and the bridesmaids were whisked away. Matt, Bev and Dan followed and I experienced the one quiet moment of the day.

Eleven a.m. The car came back and Dad and I set off to the church. As we arrived, Terence, my soon-to-be-brother-in-law, and Mark's best man, came running out.

"Go round again," he advised.

"Is Mark not here yet?" I asked, concerned.

"Mark's here, but your future mother-in-law's gone missing," he explained. So we trundled off up a side street and parked in a cul-de-sac.

"I thought it was the bride who's meant to be fashionably late?" Dad laughed.

"Don't worry, I will be," I sighed.

Meanwhile, at another church, half a mile or so away, my in-laws-to-be, Dolly and Dennis, and Mark's two sisters, Denise and Susan, were wondering where the rest of the family had gone, and why there appeared to be a jumble sale in full swing at the church they had assumed we were marrying in!

This was in the days before mobile phones, so it took a tour of the surrounding area before the right church was located (perhaps the fact that it was a converted supermarket had thrown them off the scent a bit).

Anyway, we got there in the end.

Andrew Fellows conducted the traditional service, while Bev listened in a room down the hall over loud speaker as poor Dan continued to wail. Dolly struggled to keep a wriggly three year old Anthony still in his seat as he had every intention of joining us at the front, just to see what was going on. The church was packed from end to end with smiling friends and relatives, some of them clutching treasured possessions bought at a jumble sale down the road.

The reception passed in a blur of endless photographs. Matthew keeping everyone in check. (My favourite photo of the day shows myself, Mark and my relatives all with tears of suppressed mirth rolling down our cheeks. I remember the moment as if it were yesterday; Uncle Jim ordering that all "the big tall fellas," line up at the back, and Aunty Margery, in the wrong spot again, ending up in the midst of them, Young Lou gently guiding her forward with a "come on now Marge, since when did you qualify as a big fella?" as everyone erupted into laughter and Matthew clicked the shutter.)

There were folk pressing glasses of wine into my hand (I got about a sip out of each one and left a trail of alcohol behind me round the room), off the cuff speeches by Dad, Mark and Terence, brief audiences with people that seemed to last a duration of two minutes each, before another photo call, Anthony swinging round my skirts, poor baby Dan still crying in the background (the bewildered little mite must have wondered what on earth was going on), I managed to eat a handful of crisps and half a mushroom vol-au-vent.

The three hours went in a breath.

It was the middle of the afternoon. Everyone departed. One of my bridesmaids, Jane, headed back home with my group of much-loved Huddersfield pals. The other bridesmaid, Tina, escorted all Mark's college friends back to hers; she had kindly volunteered to put them all up for the night.

Mark and I got a lift back to our new house along with Anthony, a finally calm and sleepy Daniel and my brother Lee, freshly arrived from London for the occasion.

We had not been home long before I realised how ravenously hungry I was. Mark dashed out to the chip shop in his wedding suit, to get fish and chips all round. So we sat in the undecorated, sparsely furnished kitchen, surrounded by brightly coloured boxes full of wedding gifts, eating the first real meal of the day, laughing, joking, and unwrapping wedding presents.It felt like Christmas morning, only better, because Lee was able to share the moment with us too.

At night Aunty Muriel and Uncle Mike (Bev's parents) had bravely volunteered to baby-sit. Luckily, by this time, Daniel and Anthony were so exhausted they went off to sleep without a whimper and remained so all night.

We had a get together in a local pub, everyone who hadn't been able to join us for the afternoon reception joined us for a drink or six. I was particularly thrilled to see my friends Stephen and Celia, as Celia had been very ill, and we weren't sure she would be able to come.

At the end of the night I'd had several drinks but was just mildly tipsy. I swayed giggling into the ladies room and tried to repair my smudged eyeliner. As I gazed blurrily at my face in the mirror a strange thing happened, my features melted and morphed into those of my mother, my blonde curls darkened to red. I stood there laughing in delight.

"Well, fancy seeing you here!" The image smiled back and then transformed back into my own.

"Drunkard!" I hissed at myself, giggling again as I rejoined the party.

So that was the end of my wedding day. It was chaotic, a comedy of errors in some respects, done on a shoestring budget, and entirely magical, from beginning to end.

Living on the Edge

Looking back over those first early years together, right back before we even lived together I realise one thing; Mark and I were poor. My God we were so poor, but we were fortunate in many ways.

At first it was just Mark who was poor. When we first got together I had a good stable job working for the civil service, I had more disposable income than ever before, and I was carefully banking a set amount each month towards whatever the future held for me. Mark was an unemployed victim of Thatcher's Britain, one of several million who had left school to be placed on endless dead end schemes with no hope of a secure job at the end.

By the time we were a couple he was bouncing between work placements and stints of benefit. This did not faze him, as a young single guy he had become accustomed to this way of life.

His friends were all invariably in the same boat and, as they all got their benefits on different days, they shared what they had. It was constantly boom or bust. One day nothing to eat, the next day they were all in the pub, or more likely hanging around on street corners with bottles of cheap cider, eating takeaways or sloppy curries in some dubious back street establishment. This lifestyle didn't work for me; I tried to explain the merits of budgeting and making ends meet. Truth be told, there was very little to budget with. Mark did better than most, at least he managed to pay his utility bills on time.

As I said, we were fortunate. Mark's mum, Dolly, had managed to persuade the neighbourhood rent man to apportion a decent flat to Mark, who he'd known since childhood, so at least he had a roof over his head, even if he had no furniture to put in it.

I was still living with Aunty Mary and Uncle Jack at this stage. I would call to Mark's flat after work, bearing gifts, cast off curtains, portions of food (Aunty Mary swore she'd made too much dinner, again), odds and ends I'd purchased to brighten the place up.

One evening I turned up to discover Mark in the process of decorating. I use the term loosely, as what it appeared he was doing was gluing fluff to the wall!

"Look at this!" he exclaimed, proudly foisting a large cylindrical tube under my nose. I looked, but I was none the wiser. The outside of the box was covered in some foreign language that looked to be a cross between Urdu and Mandarin Chinese.

"What is it?" I wondered, bewilderedly.

"I bought it off some Asian guy for a quid, he had loads of these boxes in his shop, says it's the very latest thing in wallpaper."

His face was alight with enthusiasm as he scraped another handful of fluff out of the box and smeared it on the wall. I looked at Mark's delighted face, I looked at the large tub of fur, I found myself idly wondering if, assuming we had a cow to sell, he would find some little guy prepared to buy it for a handful of magic beans.

I took off my coat and got stuck in, almost literally, as it seemed that what we had here was in fact a tub full of glue and fur. We laboured for a further half an hour, and then stood back, as far as we could, to get a good look at our handiwork. It appeared as though several marmalade cats had been skinned and spread haphazardly across the living room wall. I looked at Mark's face; it was slightly less enthusiastic than when we had started,

"Do you think it will come off?" he asked me, wincing.

Fortunately for him, it did.

After Aunty Mary died and Uncle Jack retired to the Chelsea pensioners, leaving me the flat and all its contents, Mark moved in with me. We had Anthony, I gave up my job to be a fulltime Mum, Mark went to Music College, and we were living on his student grant. I found my savings were gone by half way through our first year together.

Now I also knew what it was like to be poor.

Friends of Mark's would drop round sometimes, usually hoping we could feed them. That was a joke; we were hardly able to feed ourselves by this point.

"Is there anything in to eat?" They'd ask, hopefully.

Sometimes the only person with food to spare was Anthony, but his baby milk didn't entice them.

One time two of Mark's friends scoured the deepest recesses of our pantry and discovered some two year old crackers, complete with resident weevils.

"Urgh, throw them out!" Mark and I declared.

To our astonishment they ate them all, even the weevils.

"Extra protein," they told us, cheerfully.

I realised they were even more desperately hungry than us.

Dad got wind of our plight and he started turning up with a bag full of meat every Sunday. This was great except for one small problem: Mark was a vegetarian. I was also the worst cook in the world. I managed to grill bits of sausage and bacon for Anthony, who was now a toddler and able to eat solids at last, but I didn't dare cook the chicken for fear of killing him off with salmonella poisoning.

Then I had a good idea. Chickens became a source of currency.

One of Mark's friends had a useful talent, he was a qualified (though sadly unemployed) decorator. In return for a chicken, (although he would have been kind enough to do so even without) he beautifully decorated Anthony's bedroom. I used the last of my savings on materials. No dead cat wallpaper for my firstborn, his room was resplendent with rainbows and Care Bears.

Mark and I lived on hand me downs, and were very grateful for them. His having two older sisters was very useful, as every so often a bag of clothes would wend its way to me.

Only Anthony and the new baby Daniel got to have anything new. I wasn't averse to people passing on things, though. Anthony's pram had carried fifteen babies before him, which would explain why one of the wheels was forever coming off and rolling down the hill whenever I was out with him. Good job I could keep it upright on three. Mark would often be seen running at breakneck speed from the top of the estate to the bottom chasing the errant wheel, while I crooned to baby Anthony, "Three wheels on my wagon, and I'm still rolling along!"

So, eventually, we got our lovely council house. We moved in the week before our wedding, which at the time we passed off as a lucky coincidence, although in hindsight I see more mysterious forces at work during that time.

Mark got a job, and so did I, part time for a large supermarket, working in the store and petrol station. For the first time in years we were able to stand on our own two feet. We lived in the middle of a large council estate, the one where we had both grown up, Thorpe Edge. Living in the flats I had always remained curiously removed from the estate. But now, we were in the thick of it.

To be fair, it wasn't all grinding poverty. Our immediate neighbours were good solid working-class folk who had bought their own house and had it immaculately done up. However, when you know what it's like to be hungry, to wear clothes and shoes till they virtually fall off your back and feet, you get a sense for who is genuinely in need.

We had a third child, a daughter this time, born in the May of 1992, her birthday five days after Anthony's. We named her Jessica Anne. Mark was the first to hold her. It was a tradition, I always insisted he get first hold of the baby. I figured I'd carried it around long enough, within the space of five minutes she had urinated down his front and been sick down his back.

"That's my girl," Mark quipped "I hope she's not setting a precedent for later in life!"

Over the next few years as the children grew older our home became a refuge for the hungry and heart weary. Every meal time would see us laying extra spaces at the table in anticipation of whoever the children would bring home this time.

Daniel was particularly good at finding children in need of a decent meal and coercing them back for breakfast, dinner or tea; sometimes all three. Jessica was well intentioned but indiscriminate. She would roll in with a variety of well healed, rotund, little people and try to explain why they needed to stay for tea.

"But Mum, they're starving!" She would plead, whilst I smiled and waved them out the door with a compensatory biscuit, knowing full well they were heading home to a three course meal and a bag of chocolate treats.

I don't think Mark and I were in any way unusual in doing this. There was this sense of community on the estate which meant the "haves" tried to look after the "have nots". We were painfully aware that we hadn't climbed so far up the ladder that we couldn't fall back off again.

There were hard times aplenty over our first few years together. I'd lost any vestige of spirituality I once possessed, so I no longer even bothered to pray for help. What got us through was a sense of humour, an ability to count our blessings (and despite what you may think there were in fact a great many), and the support of a large loving family on both sides.

With hindsight I realise that, hard though it was, Mark, the children and I learnt many important lessons in life during those poverty stricken years. Sometimes we cannot understand why it seems to be our lot in life to struggle, but the things we all experienced helped us learn compassion, resilience, and how to go with the flow and just laugh.

In every great adventure our hero or heroine has to spend some time in the wilderness, without a doubt, this had been that time.

Chapter Twelve
Faces at the window

Wuthering Heights

Mark was a musician, as I've said. Over the years he played in many bands, from punk to jazz to rock, his instrument being primarily the bass guitar, although he liked to dabble with other things given the chance.

Of all the bands he played with my absolute favourite was a group called Western Dance. Apart from Mark being in it this had the added attraction of my cousin Matthew on drums and our friends Stephen and Liam as lead guitar and singer. I spent many happy evenings following the band around Bradford and occasionally further afield. Even when Mark left the band (misguidedly, I thought) to be part of a jazz band and they gained a new bassist Ade, it was still Western Dance that I felt loyalty to. I would happily go to their gigs while Mark played his jazz in some smoke filled rooms to an audience of old men dozing over their pipes.

Apart from the band, there was the merry band of hangers on, great guys with bizarre sounding nicknames such as Fon, Skinny and Trog, who would happily act as roadies for the price of a free ticket. Then there were the girls, myself, Liam's wife, Ade and Matt's girlfriends, and Stephens's wife, Celia.

Celia was one of those people that the first time you meet you just know you're going to get on with. She was pretty, like an elf I thought with her huge eyes and pixie style haircut, vivacious and funny. We would watch the band and shout over the music to one another, dance and leap about together, then wait around sleepily while the endless task of dismantling all the equipment was going on. We never had the chance to really get to know each other well, but we had the easy friendship of two people united in their love and devotion to something. At every gig I attended I would look for her smiling face in the crowd.

We had something else in common; both Celia and I had our first child the same year, Anthony being a mere eight months older than her daughter Eva. We both had that exhausted look of new mothers let out on the town for a few hours. We would swap baby stories in the interval, sporting matching baby spit upon our shoulders from where we'd gone to say goodnight before leaving for the gig.

I went on to have two more children whereas, tragically, Celia went on to develop an aggressive form of cancer. It seemed terribly unfair to see the life and vitality of such a lovely young woman being sapped before my very eyes. Celia was optimistic as ever, whenever Mark or I ran into her she would tell us how she intended to beat the cancer. We fervently hoped she'd be proved right.

I had just come out of hospital following the birth of my daughter Jessica; Mark and I were delighted to have a baby girl as we already had Anthony and Daniel. Celia's husband Stephen had called to see us with my cousin Matthew. Celia sent her good wishes, he said, she was pleased to hear of the new arrival. Celia was in a hospice at the time and was unable to visit me, as I was her, so soon after the birth, but she sent the message she was delighted I'd had a little girl at last, and was hoping to get well enough to see her soon.

Jessica's cradle was placed alongside our bed on my side so that I could easily attend to her through the night. I usually woke several times and would place my hand on her to feel her breathing. One particular night I awoke as usual and turned towards Jessica, but instead of looking at the cot, I realised someone appeared to be sitting between myself and the cradle. There, sort of on the bed, yet not quite, was my friend Celia. I decided I was still asleep. She smiled a beautiful radiant smile at me and then "spoke" with her mind. She told me she'd just died.

"What are you doing here?" I wondered wordlessly in response. She replied, again by thought, that she had wanted to see the baby and say goodbye. She hoped I'd be a good friend to her husband Stephen and their little girl in the hard times ahead. I responded that of course I would, she smiled again, I blinked and she was gone. I was half propped up in bed looking at Jessica's cot again. I got up and fed Jessica, then went back to bed. I told myself this was obviously just a dream as I was aware Celia was so seriously ill and I was concerned about her.

Around teatime that same day as Mark and I were showing Jessica off to my sister-in-law, Sue, my cousin Matthew turned up. He asked me if it would be possible for Mark to go out that night, then added swiftly that a few of them thought Stephen needed company. Celia had passed away in the early hours of the morning as he sat by her side.

One sunny morning in June found Mark, Matthew and I, along with many other friends, attending the funeral of our dear friend Celia. Celia had always loved the story of Wuthering Heights, and a passage was read from the book, along with Kate Bush's haunting song playing us out.

I never did find the right time to tell Stephen what had happened that night, when someone has lost a loved one and you don't know what they believe, it's not easy to find the words, particularly when you only half believe it yourself. I still had a lot to learn. I do remember one thing though. At the funeral the vicar had said Celia didn't believe in anything and had seen him, looking for reassurances. She hoped, he said, that there was something else to come. Perhaps she had appeared to me, not as a tormented ghost at the window, but as a serene and gentle spirit come to say goodbye, so that we would know she had found that there was the "something else" she had hoped for, and was going to be alright now.

You wouldn't like her when she's angry

The first time I recall hearing my mother's voice again was eight years after her passing. In retrospect I can see evidence that my loved ones had never really been far from me, but, in my determination to be strong and self-reliant, I had decided that as they no longer existed in the physical sense, I would be deluding myself to search on a spiritual level. Besides, I have to confess I was a little miffed; I'd had three children and a wedding with not so much as an impression that they had attended. And, as for God, whether he was some omnipresent old chap with a flowing beard or all pervading source of goodness in the universe, he'd still marked his cards in my book, and we weren't on speaking terms anymore. I was incommunicado with the heavens and it looked likely to remain that way.

One evening, after a long hard day chasing after my three little angels, never ending housework and other wifely/motherly duties, I was ready to flop down exhausted, looking forward to some quality time with Mark, who'd been at work all day too. I felt tired and drained and starved of adult companionship as only another person who has spent the best part of their lives having conversations with children aged six, three, and one can understand. Don't get me wrong, it's a delightful time, but it doesn't always stimulate the grey matter and on that particular evening I really longed to be stimulated. This was the point at which Mark decided to announce that he thought he would just pop up to his local pub for a couple of hours, as he'd had a hard day. Now, call me unreasonable if you like, but this announcement did not go well. True, Mark was working to support us, but he was also playing in bands and practising most evenings too, with the result being that I barely saw him. To say I was going a little stir-crazy is an understatement.

After a heated discussion Mark did what was probably the worst thing he could have done at that point, he stropped off to the pub anyway, knowing full well I couldn't follow as I had three young children tucked up in bed upstairs and no-one to leave with them.

I was furious and upset, and totally at a loss as to how to resolve what I was feeling. I still desperately wanted to talk to someone, but my only chance at conversation had just exited stage left, so to speak, and on past experience would probably not now return till the early hours. My "unreasonableness" would provide him with the justification he needed to stay out drinking with friends 'til the wee small hours, I felt sure. So I focused my mind on the one person who would have been one hundred percent on my side, and whose temper would have matched my own. Mum. Never mind I couldn't see her, pouring out my troubles would be therapeutic, I decided, so I did. Boy, did I pour out my grievances! All those little things that niggled me in our relationship, all the real or imagined slights, disappointments, broken promises, shattered dreams… I hadn't realised what a trauma I'd been living through.

For about an hour I raged on and on, sniffling into my hanky, eyes red, throat sore, I have to say it was an Oscar winning performance. In my mind's eye I could see Mum there, nodding and agreeing, joining in with righteous indignation, lets face it – I had a lot to fill her in on over an eight year period. Then suddenly a voice in my head seemed to override my own.

"Oh, I've heard enough!" it shouted, and right before my eyes, unbidden, came an image, Mark crossing the stream, and from out of nowhere an almighty shove that sent him flying.

"No, Mum…!" I shouted, but she'd gone. Everything had gone, the tears, the anger, the feeling of another presence in my living room.

I felt unbelievably cheerful, and a little foolish for getting into such a state. Well, it must have done me good, I surmised, getting everything off my chest like that, still, it was a bit odd how abruptly it had ended. I felt much better, made a nice cup of tea, put on my Abba video, and within minutes I was singing away with not a care in the world.

About half an hour later a sudden knock at the door made me jump. I wasn't expecting a visitor at this time of night, and Mark had his key.

I approached the door cautiously.

"Who's there?"

Mark's voice, gruff and disgruntled, "It's me, let me in,"

Well, well, he was early, I started to open the door - "Where's your key?" - then I stopped, dumbfounded. Mark's key, I expected, was still in his pocket, but he obviously couldn't get it out. His pockets were oozing mud, in fact from his head to his toes he stood there resembling some strange swamp beast.

"Wait there, I'll have to put some newspaper down," I declared, somehow getting him into the living room without trailing too much mud on the carpet. He had to stand like a child with his arms out whilst I peeled the soggy layers of clothing off him, running back and forth to the washing machine with them.

"So, what happened?" I finally asked, but I had a feeling I knew exactly what was coming next.

"I fell in the stream, I don't know how, I always cross at that point and I didn't even feel myself slipping. Just one moment I was standing up and the next I was in the mud."

Fancy that. I didn't bother to tell him my theory. Firstly, he would never have believed me and, secondly, I wasn't sure if I could really believe it myself. But I do now.

A warning voice

Mark had just acquired a second hand car. My mother-in-law, Dolly, had purchased it for him for two hundred pounds, an absolute fortune to us in those days. We had been without a car for a year or so and Mark was thrilled with the novelty of having one again.

We had gone for a drive after work the previous couple of evenings and now he wanted to give it another spin. Something niggled at me deep down and I told him I wasn't keen on going out that night, but he looked really disappointed.

"I wanted to take Mum out, she's not had chance to go in it yet," he cajoled.

"Ok," I agreed. I didn't want to appear mean when she had bought the car in the first place.

I sat in the back with Anthony at one end, Daniel in the middle and Jessica, who was barely two, on my knee. Dolly sat in the front passenger seat with Mark driving.

Admittedly it was a lovely evening for a drive, warm and sunny, the sort of evening that stays bright till nearly ten o'clock. Mark headed out towards Haworth first. As the car climbed the winding roads up to the moors I found myself thinking of my friend Celia, who always loved Haworth; she had been dead for just over two years now. Suddenly I felt her presence.

"Turn round and go back Jane," her voice in my head instructed. I looked around, bewildered. The roads were quiet, everyone was enjoying themselves, and there was certainly no immediate cause for concern.

"Are we going much further out?" I ventured to ask.

Mark looked over his shoulder, puzzled. "Why, aren't you enjoying this?"

"Yes, I just wondered," I said lamely. We continued on our drive. A little further on we came to a roundabout.

"Go home, there's going to be a crash," said another voice inside, not Celia this time. That niggling feeling in my stomach was beginning to turn to butterflies, but still we drove on, everything on the roads was quiet and calm. I told myself to stop being silly. We stopped at a level crossing for a train to go past.

"Look Daniel, Thomas and his troublesome trucks," I pointed, determined to get into the spirit of the evening out, although by now the warning voices were chorusing together loud and strong, at least half a dozen of them. My stomach was churning over and over.

We were back on familiar roads now. "Are we going home?" I asked. Dolly looked at me,

"Why are you so impatient to be home, are you missing something on television, you needn't have come you know. I thought it would be nice if we stopped off for a drink somewhere?"

"Ok," I reluctantly agreed, I saw no point in telling my mother-in-law that I had a head full of dead people telling me there was danger up ahead.

We pulled into the car park of The Fox and Mark obligingly got crisps and pop for us all.

"Maybe this has changed the path of fate," I consoled myself. I had to force the drink down, I was so anxious to be home by now.

Down through Guiseley and Yeadon we travelled, coming to another roundabout that would lead us on the last leg of the journey home.

"Thank goodness," I thought.

Then inexplicably Mark turned off at the wrong junction "What are you doing, where are you going?" I practically shouted at him.

"Oh, I know I've gone wrong, but its ok, I can still get back this way too," Mark advised in a "what's wrong with you tonight?" tone of voice.

We reached a crossroads with traffic lights. By now my heart was hammering in my chest and my stomach was flipping over so badly I felt I could be sick. I looked down.

"If we get past here it will all be ok," I found myself thinking. Instinctively I clutched little Jessica tightly to me. Mark pulled out as the lights changed and I found myself closing my eyes and holding my breath as we crossed the junction.

Suddenly, Dolly shouted out, "Oh my God, that car!"

I threw my head up again and looked out of my window. A car had jumped the lights at red and was heading straight towards my side of our car, I could see the headlights looming closer.

"This is it," I thought. I tucked Jessica under my right arm and threw my left arm across the two boys huddling them close to me, bracing myself for the impact. The other vehicle collided with us sideways on. My side of the car crumpled in, throwing me towards the children, I clutched them to me as tightly as I could.

Then the moment had passed. Mark managed to pull the car to the side of the road and turn the engine off.

I sat up and inspected the children. They were frightened and crying in shock, Anthony had bumped his head slightly with mine, but they were otherwise unhurt.

"Are you ok, Mark?" I asked. He just sat with his head in his hands.

"I'm never driving again," he announced.

"Dolly, are you ok?" I enquired. She didn't respond. "Dolly?" I asked again and she let out a low, rather dramatic moan.

I felt cold fingers of fear clutch me, "Oh God, what's happened to Dolly?" I twittered to myself.

"Now, just get a grip of yourself!" A commanding, no nonsense voice took charge.

Instantly, I felt calm. I tried to open the door but it was stuck fast. Mark, seeing what I was trying to do, got out and ran round the car to my side. My door was crumpled in and stuck fast but, as Mark told me later, he somehow found strength far greater than his allowed him to rip it open and let myself and the children out. I passed the kids, still crying, to Mark and ran to Dolly's window; she slumped still moaning in her seat.

A man appeared at my side, he thrust a mobile phone into my hand, still something very rare in those days. I rang my father-in-law Dennis and hastily explained the situation, then I passed the phone back to its owner and asked if he would please call an ambulance. This roused my mother-in-law somewhat.

"No, no," she protested weakly.

After that things got a little silly. Two ambulances showed up, along with the police and the fire brigade (who had to cut Dolly's door off).

The children and I were taken in one ambulance with my father-in-law in pursuit. My mother-in-law went in the second ambulance, which must have been called by another witness, which also departed. Mark was in the police car giving a statement when an emergency call came through to them. Mark ended up in a high speed chase through the now darkened streets that culminated in a breach of the peace outside a Chinese Takeaway, where two enraged Chinese chefs danced around waving meat cleavers at each other.

I arrived at Leeds General Hospital with the now tired and bewildered children, closely followed by my frantic father-in-law. There was no trace of Dolly.

A quick check over by the doctor revealed the children were all fine. I had a small cut to my eyebrow, and bruises from my thigh to ankle. I'd been far too busy to even notice.

Dolly was still missing. The police showed up and deposited a somewhat shell-shocked Mark. The hospital informed us they had managed to locate my mother-in-law; she was in Bradford Royal Infirmary, where apparently the other ambulance had come from.

Trust us to crash the car on the border between two cities! So we sped off again (if speeding is how you can describe three adults and three children in a Reliant Robin). Dennis dropped us at his house and dashed off to rescue Dolly.

Dolly didn't like hospitals. She was more than a little annoyed to be taken to one, and even more annoyed when no-one else showed up there.

"They left me on a trolley in a corridor!" she told us indignantly, later. So she did a runner. Dennis was driving past the hospital when he saw a forlorn little character sitting shivering on the wall outside. She refused to be taken in again, so he brought her back home instead.

"Once she'd got her voice back I knew she was going to live," he explained with a wry smile.

The next day her own doctor examined her. She had bruised ribs caused by the seatbelt whipping her back into the crumpled wing of the car, thus winding her, hence all the dramatics!

When I told Mark later about my premonition of the oncoming crash he confirmed he'd sensed it coming too.

"So why didn't you come straight home?" I started to ask. Oh, I forgot, he doesn't believe in things like that!

Chapter Thirteen
Rays of light

In my father's house are many mansions

The strange thing about the spirit world is this; if you studiously ignore it for long enough, eventually it comes knocking at your door.

As I've said before, for a long time following the deaths of my mother, aunt and grandparents I was spiritually numb. I found myself unable to grieve on some level, because when you have spent months and years watching people suffer, logic dictates you should be relieved for them, and on no account should you wish to call them back. To think of them would be to summon up the pain of loss, and that would be selfish and counter productive, so I didn't think of them. Or so I told myself.

Of course I did think of them, every moment, of every hour, of every day, there they'd be, drifting in and out of my thoughts. I just never followed it up, never traced the memory back to see where it would lead. It was as if they were waving to me from a window high up, and I'd give a brief salutation then turn my attention back to the task in hand.

Ten years passed, one child became three. I had assimilated my new role and we became slowly more affluent, moved to a house, got jobs, and got on with each other the best we could. Progression was slow but steady. Somewhere along the way I had forgotten who I was and where I came from, but that was ok.

It wasn't until Uncle Jack became ill that I realised how spiritually detached I'd become. The doctor's diagnosis was cold and clinical, he had cancer, there wasn't a lot to be done, but they would experiment a bit anyway and see what happened.

So, there we were again, Uncle Jack being stoical and brave, me being overly cheerful and optimistic, Aunty May being secretly tearful and afraid. I watched as the endless rounds of hospital visits, operations, drugs and radiation took their toll. I was there every step of the way to support him, but I sometimes wondered where I could turn, who would be there to support me?

So, after ten years of silence, I decided to reach out to the heavens once again. My prayers were clumsy, rusty from lack of practise, a bit apologetic even.

"Hello God, I know you haven't heard from me in a long, long time, but I thought I might ask a favour of you anyway…"

So I asked and I asked. I promised anything and everything if I could just buy Uncle Jack another five or ten years or so and I waited for my answer.

Then the dreams started.

Night after night in the run up to his death I would find myself in a house, or a flat, or a skyscraper. Uncle Jack would be with me, then Aunty Mary would suddenly appear from one of the rooms. She would proceed to escort us round, showing us the view, the beautiful gardens, the spacious rooms, the luxurious furniture. It was like taking a tour with God's estate agent. I didn't understand the dreams, but they were uplifting and comforting all the same.

Uncle Jack, however, continued to deteriorate.

It had been many years since Aunty Mary's passing. It was only when it was time for Uncle Jack to join her that I got to hear my Aunty Mary's voice again (other than in dreams).

Uncle Jack was losing his battle with cancer of the oesophagus. I had spent a long night time vigil at his bedside, while Aunty May (his second wife) paced up and down, crying at times and wringing her hands. We were joined by Aunty May's close friend Heather, who was a nurse, and my cousin Young Lou, who was equally close to Uncle Jack (my aunt and uncle had given Lou a home for many years up to the time he married Lynda, when I was five).

I remember thinking that if anyone was going to collect Uncle Jack from the other side it would be my Aunty Mary who had been his beloved wife for forty-three years. In my mind's eye I could picture her holding the opposite hand to me as I waited to give him over to her care.

As the first rays of dawn came through the window, Uncle Jack finally let go and slipped away. Aunty May started to sob inconsolably. Lou led her from the room soothingly suggesting that a cup of tea might just be in order, Heather busied herself with tidying round.

I just sat looking at Uncle Jack's face, sad, yet relieved that his struggle was finally over. I felt a large sob start to well up in my throat, after months of holding everything in it felt as if a dam was about to break.

And then I heard my name "Jane!" as if shouted across a great distance. Not in my head, but actually in my ear. It was strange and distorted, as if through an electronic voice box with an accompaniment of white noise in the background, and yet unmistakeably Aunty Mary's. The sob, the sadness, everything I was feeling was swept away in that moment. I felt her presence alongside my uncles' so clearly for one fleeting moment, and then they were gone.

In the wake of this experience I felt unbelievably calm and serene, and elated. Yet there I sat, my hand still holding on to my Uncle's not yet cold one. I looked across at Heather, certain she must have heard something, but she showed no sign she had, just gave me a sad and sympathetic smile.

I will never have any doubts now that we do not pass alone. Be assured, when your time comes, you too will find yourself collected by those you loved best and who made the journey before you.

On the night after Uncle Jack crossed over, I had another dream, a very different dream. I was in a rowing boat with Uncle Jack and Aunty Mary, someone (a dark shadowy figure in a black cloak) was taking us across dark waters to the other shore. When we got there, and Uncle Jack and Aunty Mary got out, I got up also, but they wouldn't let me alight.

"You can't come with us any further," Aunty Mary told me, "Someone needs to take care of Aunty May now." The boat turned round, transporting me back across the still, dark water.

I woke up, puzzling over the dream, then suddenly I realised what I had been allowed to see; Aunty Mary had been preparing for Uncle Jack's arrival. She had shown us the beautiful places he could choose to reside ("In my father's house there are many mansions," Jesus said – I had never taken the words literally before). I had also been allowed to take Uncle Jack's final journey with him, across the river Styx (where else could it have been) to see him delivered safe on the other side.

Prayers aren't always answered the way you hope they will be, but at least I felt an acceptance now that this was how it was meant to be, it was just Uncle Jack's time to depart. I realised where we go wrong is in viewing death as a punishment, when actually it is the final reward for a life well-lived. We do not die, we simply return home.

More importantly, I was no longer angry with the universe; I was back on speaking terms with God. I just needed help in translation. Somewhere a door between the two worlds had been re-opened, and as I was to discover, they would not allow me time to close it ever again.

Attention grabbing

For many years I had had premonitions. For a long time I passed these off as dreams until I began to realise their peculiar accuracy. I was slow on the uptake as always though, so the spirits used to have to really labour the point with me.

For quite some time after Uncle Jack passed over it became my obsession to look after Aunty May. I would call to see her every morning and we would have breakfast together. I'd help her with shopping and paying bills and appointments, I'd take her out for lunch or round to my house, I'd cook a meal and take it across for tea, I'd go round with buns for supper and watch television till she felt ready to go to bed.

This went on for weeks. Needless to say Mark and the kids had to muddle along without me for a while, Aunty May's need at that time was greater than theirs, I reasoned, and, bless their hearts, they were happy for me to be at her beck and call.

"It's ok Mum, you look after Aunty May, we don't want her to be lonely," they would say.

A couple of weeks after Uncle Jack's passing I started to get recurring dreams of Aunty May constantly falling. Whether I was in bed at night or just dozing in a chair I'd close my eyes and there she'd be, toppling off ladders, out of windows, down stairs, with me ever running to catch her and failing miserably. Awake, I analysed it as a refection of my concern for her welfare now that Uncle Jack had gone. But each time I woke up I'd be so relieved. At least it was just a dream, I'd think.

Anthony and Daniel were now eight and six and had both joined the cubs. It was the end of the summer and they were having their annual rounders match. I invited Aunty May along, thinking an evening out in the sunshine, plus some tea, biscuits and company other than me, might do her good.

So, off we trekked down to the field. Several adults, including myself, Aunty May and my friend Liz as well as a troop of cubs including my boys and Liz's two sons. We spent a pleasant hour and then headed back to the scout hut.

There was just one little problem I hadn't foreseen. The way back was downhill, quite steep, and the long grass was mossy and treacherous underfoot. Poor Aunty May, her feet shot out from under her and she toppled sideways. I made a grab for her but, as she was of a larger frame than me, we both went flying into the grass. I was absolutely fine, but Aunty May wrenched her knee badly and ended up in casualty for half the night.

For the remainder of her life she walked with a stick.

Yes, I know - they had told me, they had kept showing me she'd fall but, as I've pointed out in recent years to them, in all the dreams I had, never once did they make her fall over in a field and surround her with cub scouts.

The stranger on the bridge

My cousin Lynda has always been well known for having "a good head on her shoulders". Calm, unruffled by daily life, despite the rigours of running a home and catering for the needs of four children, practical, a good cook, fantastic with a needle and thread, diligent housewife, warm and loving wife, mother daughter, sister, and in my case cousin. Lynda is one of those people who is on the go from morning to night, and usually for someone else's benefit. She just gets on with things and doesn't grumble at her lot, always happy with the simple pleasures in life; her greatest concerns have always been the welfare of everyone else.

Lynda and (Young) Lou had married and had their children young by today's standards. Heath, the oldest, co-conspirator of my childhood days, Brad, sensible, quiet and sensitive, Rachel, the girl, bright and bubbly, twinkling eyes full of mischief, and Graham, the baby, just two years older than my Anthony, a golden haired cherub growing into a humorous, level-headed young man.

Lynda's husband, my cousin Young Lou was a typical hard working, good natured, northern lad, also more than happy with a simple existence; devoted to his family and well liked by his friends. Together they ran one of those homes that should have been chaotic, given the number of people living in it, but wasn't, everyone muddling along in a good-humoured, good-natured way.

Lynda and Lou both worked, the older children looked after the younger ones, and somehow everything rubbed along merrily. It could be said that they didn't have a lot but they made the most of everything that they did have, and seemed richer for it.

Theirs was the sort of home where you'd stop by to drop in a birthday card and end up staying for the evening, lured by the warmth and cosiness, only evinced at the heart of the most loving families. Bribed to stay by the promise of copious cups of tea, and epic story telling by the fireside, I'd call round for ten minutes and end up happily staying for several hours. It was on an occasion such as this that Lynda recounted the following tale to me.

One summer evening, after a long shift at the local factory, Lynda was trudging home tiredly across the bridge near home. Lost in thought, she vaguely recognised the pleasant looking elderly chap who tipped his hat at her and flashed an engaging grin. She smiled back absentmindedly and continued on her way. It was only as she reached the far side of the bridge that she recalled who she had just acknowledged; Uncle Jack.

This would not have been so surprising, as he had lived just up the road, except for one small detail; Uncle Jack had been dead for over three months now.

She turned on her heel and ran back over the bridge. The road ahead lay straight, there were no turn-offs ahead, and yet, perhaps not unsurprisingly, the old chap had vanished, as if into thin air.

Why had Uncle Jack chosen that particular night to make an appearance? None of us could say, Lynda wasn't thinking of him, or anything in particular beyond how tired she was and what to prepare for tea. It seems they catch us best at times like these however, just when we are relaxed, tired and mainly unfocused.

I suspect our loved ones are around us far more than we know, we're generally just too preoccupied to see them.

The exploding tin of beans

Growing up, one of my husband Mark's favourite relatives was his Mum's brother, Uncle John. Uncle John had been a soldier and, from his photographs, quite a good looking chap in his day. Jet black hair slicked back, tall and straight as a die, with a flashing smile and the same blue eyes as his mother and sisters. A real hit with the ladies. He came back from the Second World War a changed man, his left leg shattered by exploding dumb dumb bullets, saved only by a quick-thinking surgeon, who had encased maggots in the wound, which fortunately ate the gangrenous tissue, and saved the remainder of the leg.

His confidence destroyed along with his leg, Uncle John walked for the rest of his life with the aid of a stick. Now, happiest only in the company of his family, he mainly kept himself to himself. Little Mark, however, seemed to bring the best out of him.

"Come on," Uncle John would say, and together they would go off adventuring, Mark measuring his childish steps to his Uncle John's halting lame ones.

"Uncle John, what happened to your leg?" Mark and his siblings would ask. For this Uncle John had a stock of answers, the most common one being how a tin of beans exploded on his camp fire and left him forever with a limp.

One day Uncle John had a fall out with his younger sister Dolly and for ten years or more no-one saw him. I heard tales of the much loved, mysterious uncle, but I never got to meet him until Mark and I were in our mid-twenties.

Fences mended between them, Uncle John and Dolly picked

up exactly where they left off. The years had changed Uncle John still further, now he was a virtual recluse, living alone in his little flat on the far side of Bradford. He had a mistrust of strangers and neighbours alike.

"Tell 'em nowt," he'd say, tapping his nose. "They're all as wide as hell!"

I wasn't totally sure what the expression meant, but I got the gist of it. Uncle John would watch me giggle.

"See that Jane," he'd wink at Dolly, "She's wide too, ate all me biscuits while my back was turned, you keep an eye on her!"

Uncle John would house-sit for Dolly and Dennis while they went away on holiday over the summer. This was no mean feat to arrange, due to Uncle John's cloak and dagger lifestyle. Dennis had to take a note and post it through Uncle John's door, as no amount of knocking would induce him to open it to anyone unarranged. The note would specify the time and date that Dennis would call back and collect him (usually a weeks notice was given). I suspect "collecting" involved a lot of synchronising watches, and probably a secret hand shake or two and a password, before Dennis could get the old soldier securely strapped into the front seat of his trusty Reliant Robin and brought home safely for Dolly to fuss over.

Once Uncle John even house-sat for me and Mark.

"Ooh you live in the lap of luxury," he declared. "I'll enjoy this, it's a little palace."

I decided this must be another of Uncle John's jests as I looked around my home with the thread bare carpets, Mark's dodgy DIY, second hand furniture, and dubious wallpapering attempts. Still, when we came back, after a week away at my Dad's chalet in Withernsea, kindly transported there and back by Mark's nephew Lee (we were car-less at that point) Uncle John assured us that he'd had a whale of a time and Dolly confirmed he had loved every minute. She had called in on him every day, just as Mark and I did when he house-sat for her.

I used to bake him jam tarts and buns to make up for all his biscuits I'd supposedly eaten, he probably suspected I was trying to finish him off.

"You have one as well," he'd urge, and watch to see if I survived, before dunking a jam tart in his tea and eating it.

One summer Mark rang me from his Mum's house because he wanted me to take a look at Uncle John who had been a bit unwell during the night. I dashed straight there, trailing small children behind me.

From what we could make out it sounded as if Uncle John may have had a minor stroke. He was a bit shaken by the experience, which had involved some slight numbness and tingling in his arm and a vague dizziness which he assured us had already passed. He was absolutely adamant he wouldn't see a doctor.

"You just try ringing one and I'll pack up and leave before they get here!" he declared.

We knew it wasn't an idle threat, it was rumoured that Uncle John lived without the benefit of gas or electricity, as he didn't trust anyone to come in and read the meter! He seemed ok, so Mark and I just kept an extra close eye on him for the remainder of Dolly's holiday. I had to do a lot more baking!

When Dolly came back we told her what we suspected. She and Dennis tried to inveigle him to stay longer, but Uncle John was adamant. He was ready to go back to his own little world and there was no stopping him. Deep down we knew that he was afraid that if anything else occurred there would be no getting round the indomitable Dolly if she took it in her head to ring a doctor or, horror of horrors, call an ambulance.

Winter came. Dennis dropped a note round as usual for Uncle John to come and stay a few weeks over the Christmas period. A week later he went to collect him, but strangely there was no sign of Uncle John, whereas he would usually have been waiting on the doorstep with his case packed, eager for his visit. Poor Uncle John couldn't answer the door; he'd been dead three weeks already.

Mark and his family were devastated. No amount of reassuring them that the ingrained old hermit would probably not have had it any other way could console them.

The spartan, damp living conditions confirmed what they had suspected; he had been accustomed to living without the benefit of heat or lighting. Dolly, Dennis, Mark and his sisters, Denise and Sue, took on the painful task of clearing out his flat. Mark found himself drawn to where all the official documents had been stashed away. Dolly was the only one to find parcel after parcel of tightly wrapped bundles of cash, hidden in water proof bags, secreted all over the flat. It was as if, she declared, someone was guiding her to it.

Christmas came.

On Christmas Eve I was at Dolly's house helping her with a bit of last minute wrapping. She hadn't the heart to do it herself, so I was trying to keep her spirits up with an endless diatribe about the children and how excited they were (all now hopefully tucked up in bed by Mark).

Job done, she and I retired to the kitchen for a last coffee before I went home. Dennis was due back from the club any moment, so I was waiting until he got in, rather than leaving her alone with her thoughts.

As we stood in the kitchen, waiting for the kettle to boil, I heard a sound in the hall. Dennis must have come home, I mused. Footsteps traversed the hallway but, instead of entering the kitchen, they started to go up the stairs. Clop-thud-clop-thud-clop-thud; the unmistakable sound of someone with a shattered leg, hobbling up the stairs with the aid of a stick. I turned to look at Dolly; she was following the sound up the stairs with her eyes, as if she could see through the kitchen wall.

"Do you hear it too?" She whispered. I nodded.

We cautiously went to the kitchen door, pulled it open and went out into the hall. The sound stopped immediately. There was no-one there. Dolly and I went back into the kitchen, she shakily poured the coffee, but a smile split her face from ear to ear.

"John's come home for Christmas after all," was all she said.

Treasured memories

My children were growing up fast. I was so busy working at the supermarket, petrol station, and as a school governor, that looking back the time passed so quickly the memories start to merge together. I'd like to give you a brief snapshot of their characters, because in a book about magic and wonder, nothing in my life has been more wonderful, or magical, than being mother to these three curious individuals.

Anthony, the boy, still had the same enormous blue eyes that dwarfed his other features, tall, slender, and full of a nervous energy that meant he was never still, even in sleep. As is often the case with the eldest, he was the one with the most serious side to his nature. In fact, as a small child he would often look at Mark and me with the eyes of a much older soul, as if we were errant children, and he the adult.

He took charge of the younger children, and frequently their friends, with a natural sense of leadership, trailing about leaning on a large stick as if it were some magical staff, looking like a wizard leading a band of unruly hobbits off on an adventure.

His nature was kind (extremely), sensible (mostly) wise (at times) and stubborn (very). He was trustworthy if left in charge of his younger siblings, but his curious nature often led him into trouble.

Often an idea would pop into Anthony's head and he'd run with it, without thinking of the consequences – shades of his Uncle Lee coming through there, I fear. For instance, at school they had been learning about Romans carrying flaming torches, which for some reason excited his imagination. I was at work one day and Mark was in the kitchen preparing tea for the kids. Anthony was in and out of the house, as six year olds often are, and Mark wasn't really paying much attention. Suddenly a strange smell of burning assailed his nostrils.

"Anthony?" He called, "What's going on?"

Peering into the hall he just saw Anthony's heels flying up the stairs, a strange trail of smoke wafting behind him. Alerted to some possible danger he decided he better pursue Anthony, only to find him loitering outside his room on the landing with a carefully studied expression of innocence on his face. The air around him was acrid with smoke.

"Anthony, what are you up to? What's burning?" Mark demanded.

Anthony raised his eyebrows and shrugged his shoulders in a "what Dad, me Dad? I don't know what you mean Dad!" gesture.

Mark barged past him into the bedroom. The smoke seemed to be coming from under the bed. Reaching under Mark plucked a smouldering branch from under the bed; Anthony had managed to light it by plunging it into the gas fire. Fortunately, it hadn't caught fully alight.

"Oh," said Anthony, "that's a Roman torch."

I will leave you to draw your own conclusions as to the end of this scene.

Anthony and his Nana Dolly were inseparable. During the school holidays, when he was older, he would often go into town for lunch with her and two of her friends.

Most young lads of his age would run a mile before giving up an afternoon to travel around town with three elderly ladies, but Anthony liked their company, was quite happy to help carry his Nana's shopping, and usually came back with some kind of gift for his trouble. Not that this was a mercenary act, Anthony has always had a genuine respect and interest in people both young and old.

On one occasion he had gone out with the three old ladies and they had stopped off in a café for a coffee and a chat, and perhaps a bun or two. It was Mother's Day and Dolly and one of her friends were exclaiming over all the lovely gifts they'd received from their families. Dolly's other friend remarked a little sadly that, as she had never had children, she had never received a Mother's Day present. Her friends commiserated with her.

"Where has that boy gone now?" Dolly wondered as they prepared to move on. He had finished his bun and had been wandering about the café getting under peoples feet, but now, just as they were preparing to go, he seemed to have vanished altogether. Just as they were about to form a search party he reappeared, like a rabbit out of a hat.

"Oh there you are…" Dolly was about to remonstrate with him, but before she could he was grinning from ear to ear and thrusting a pretty bunch of flowers into the hands of her elderly, childless, friend.

"Happy Mother's Day!" He announced cheerily, having spent all his pocket money on the present. The old lady's eyes filled with tears, and he was rewarded with a big hug that probably made him go red; he hadn't seen that coming.

"What a lovely, lovely boy!" She enthused to Dolly, and Dolly, bursting with pride at her grandson's thoughtfulness, had to agree that he was.

Thoughtful, yes, and occasionally thoughtless; Anthony meant well, and was generally sensible, but sometimes acted, as we have already seen, without thinking.

Uncle Louis still laughs at the time he heard a loud knock at the door but as he was descending the stairs was just in time to see something like brown gloopy mud being shoved through his letterbox.

Outraged he hastened to the door, throwing it open to shout "Come back you vandal!" only to see Anthony scurrying away. Hearing the door opening, Anthony spun round and gave a cheery wave.

"Hi Uncle Lou, I've posted some birthday cake for you and Janet," he announced, hurrying back for his ninth birthday party. Uncle Lou looked down at his feet, scooped up the sticky, gooey chocolate cake plastered to his door and carpet, then started to laugh. It wouldn't have occurred to anyone but Anthony to "post" birthday cake to somebody!

As they grew older Mark and I managed to raise the money for the children to attend certain activities like swimming lessons (I had learnt from Lee's experiences that it is wise to learn to swim when you are young) and karate (no-one was going to push my children about), but far and away their favourite thing was the Cub Scouts, or in Jessica's case, Rainbows and Brownies.

Here they learnt to appreciate the great outdoors, sleep under canvas, and become self-reliant.

Anthony took to it like a duck to water, lured especially by the camaraderie and campfires (we had started to call him "Anthony the arsonist" after his smouldering torch episode). They often went away on group camps and they all loved it.

The scout master would give out awards at the end of the camp, but no-one was more surprised than Mark and I when Anthony won the award for Most Organised Cub. We fell about laughing, as Anthony scowled at us. The Scout Master clearly didn't get the joke, but then he had never seen the state of Anthony's room!

Daniel, from almost day one, was the comedian of the family. Long before he could communicate in any other way he would have a big cheesy grin plastered across his chubby chops, his eyes permanently twinkling as if he knew a good joke, but he couldn't share it with us.

As Dan grew older it became apparent that he was also blessed with a "good imagination". He would play, enthralled, for hours with a crisp packet tied into a knot (which he said was an "Indian") or a couple of leaves that had fallen from the trees, dancing about his Nana's garden twirling them above his head.

"Tsk," his Nana would say, affectionately, "Look at that boy, is he right in his head?"

At three he would sit for hours and watch his Dad play computer games - sorry computer game, we only had the one, Super Mario - pointing his small chubby finger at the screen.

"Those are prats aren't they Dad?" He announced,

"What?" Said Mark, startled, and then he realised. Every time some little creature killed him off he would growl at the game, "Oh, you prat!"

Dan had been listening very attentively!

Dan liked to play too, and had an amazing aptitude for working out clues and puzzles and finding hidden doorways in the game. He had his own names for things,

"Look Mum" he said to me enthusiastically. "I have to get past the Ricky Tungs and Starican Beans!" I managed to figure out that a Ricky Tung meant Licky Tongue a small spherical creature with what appeared to be its tongue stuck out, but what a Staricon Bean was, was anybody's guess!

Dan loved to dress up, during the Super Mario phase he would often be seen running around outside with half a football (turned inside out) on his head and a raccoon puppet stuck down the back of his trousers (making a peculiar bulge) with its stripy tail stuck out. Somehow, in Dan's head, this turned him into Super Mario and made him able to fly.

We also had a phase of him dressed all in green with a green hood pulled up and a homemade orange mask on his eyes, plus his legs forced through the bottom corners of a carrier bag and the handles over his shoulders; he was a Ninja Turtle, and the bag was his "half shell".

Then there was the morning when Mark and I were rudely awakened to Dan, aged six and Jess aged three, running into our room, Dan with my tights on his head and Jess with some pink spotted pants on hers.

"Daadahh!" they announced "It's Rabbit Man and Super Knicker Woman!" (Don't know where Anthony was at this point...probably wandering round setting fire to the furniture with his magical staff, I expect!)

As a small boy we called him "Daniel (state the obvious) Cranmer". He loved to demonstrate his growing understanding of the world around him by pointing things out to us, "Those are cars, aren't they Mum?", "Cars can drive, can't they Dad?"

He would gaze up to the sky in wonder at where a plane had been, "That's a vapour trail, isn't Mum?" (I don't know how he knew such a large word). Or then there was my friend's favourite question, "Aunty Gina, why does a Butterfly?" (We are still figuring that one out).

Alongside his curiosity about the world around him Dan would inveigle us to try and see things with his eyes. As we were out walking it became apparent that Dan's landscape was full of wonderful castles way off in the distance, magical woods and mystical creatures.

"Look Mum," three year old Dan would pipe up. "See that castle?" I would strain my eyes into the distance,

"What castle, Dan?" I would ask, puzzled, and he would launch into a fantastical description of crenulated walls and turrets with flags waving, Dragons guarding moats, and rainbows you could ride on to get there, lighting up the sky. I would just be looking at the park and the dilapidated tennis court at the bottom of it. Naturally, I agreed with Dan anyway, I knew all about having "a good imagination".

Dan would draw all the time. He excelled at copying cartoon characters from being really tiny and, just as I had once declared that one day I would write books, he always declared that when he grew up he would make cartoons.

Anthony, Dan and Dan's best friend Lee had their own little stories to tell. They were about three naughty little boys, all called James. From somewhere they had acquired three identical baby dolls, or they were originally, now they were Dan's "James without an arm", Anthony's "James without a body" (in other words, just a dolls head) and Lee's "James without a head". I would hear them laughing hysterically out in the garden, all caught up in some wildly inventive tale of the "James's" it was lovely to see.

Dan used to love "Thomas the Tank Engine". From being a tot he would wander round humming the tune under his breath, either that or "The Mister Men". One afternoon I was half dozing on the settee and Anthony was watching TV, I knew where Dan was as he was driving trains up and down my back, humming his little tune, and Jess, still a baby at this point, was having her nap.

I was startled awake by a sudden knock at the door. Bleary-eyed I stumbled to my feet and went to answer it. To my annoyance a salesman stood there ready to start his spiel. I told him bluntly I really wasn't interested and was mildly surprised at how readily he wished me good day and hurried off.

As I turned to close the door I caught a glimpse of myself in the hallway mirror and, after a closer look, started to laugh... No wonder he'd left in such a hurry, he had been confronted on the doorstep by a woman whose waist length hair had Thomas, Percy, some troublesome trucks and Harold the Helicopter all neatly entwined in it. So that's what my little monster had been up to!

Jess, the baby, had to hold her own in the fight for position as the youngest and only girl in the family. Easy going and placid as a baby she would contentedly sit and gurgle at her brothers as they played. Anthony, the doting elder brother, would tickle her and gurgle back, Dan would regard her with a sinister smile on his face, that said, "You watch out, little imposter, usurping my place as baby of the family..."

When she was only a few days old I nipped out of the room for a few seconds only to come back and find Jess gone.

"Where's the baby?" I cried in alarm

"It's gone," said two year old Daniel.

I looked down in horror and saw a pile of cushions where the newborn should have been. On closer inspection she was unharmed, under them. After that I learned to watch the two of them like a hawk, or make sure sensible five year old Anthony was in charge for a moment.

Jess didn't talk for quite some time as her brothers would translate her nonsensical ramblings for her, but she understood a lot from being tiny.

One day Mark and I were tearing the place apart looking for a pound coin; it was the last of the money we had and we needed milk. As we scurried round the room wittering at each other as to who was responsible for losing it, Jessica, just one years old, followed us round, patting us on the arm, or leg, or whatever she could reach. Eventually, feeling mean, I paused to tickle her tummy and ruffle her hair. She giggled, then seeing me start to look away again grabbed my hand and put it on her tummy again, I gave her another tickle, she laughed again and lay down on the floor.

"What's the matter Jessie?" I asked, still distracted. "Do you want your nappy changing?"

She didn't smell at all, but maybe she was a bit wet, I wondered. Jess smiled and patted her tummy again. I quickly unfastened her all in one vest and undid the nappy, it was bone dry but there, at the bottom of it, was the missing pound coin! She had dropped it into her vest and it had slid down into her nappy but what a clever girl for realising what we were looking for and coming to our aid. I never underestimated what she could understand after that!

Jess was blonde, blue-eyed and bright as a button. I used to tie her fringe up on her head in a style we called a tree, it was very cute. Her brothers would give it a playful tug on passing, Dan somewhat harder than Anthony!

One day I was out in the garden pegging out the washing. Anthony and Daniel appeared next to me, running round my legs and tripping me up.

"Boys, you've left Jess on her own!" I admonished them. We all hurried round to the front door. Whoops, too late, it had shut and locked behind them. Now we were all locked out in the front garden and Jess, nearly two, was locked in the house alone. I told myself not to panic.

I knocked on the door and peered through the letterbox, Jess appeared, slowly, because she was trying to walk in my four inch high heels! She waved at me through the letterbox, I waved back.

"Jess, go and get Mummy's handbag," I begged, hoping she knew what I meant. She shuffled off in my shoes again; this was going to be a long wait.

Moments later she returned, trailing my bag behind her, it was open and assorted rubbish was being left in a stream behind her.

"Good girl," I said encouragingly, "Look in Mummy's bag and find my keys."

She looked at me for a moment while I held my breath. Then plonked herself on the floor and started rifling through the bag obligingly. Finally, she rattled the keys at me triumphantly. Clattering across in the high heels she thrust the keys through the letterbox into my waiting hands. I was relieved once again to be blessed with such a clever child.

Jess finally found her voice aged two and a half. Her brothers were tormenting her and she was trying to wrestle a stuffed bear off of them. Suddenly, she stopped, placed her hands on her hips and declared slowly and deliberately, "It's my Jecca's"

Mark and I fell about laughing.

"Oh, so that's what you call yourself is it?" Mark said.

She remained as "Jecca" for many years to come!

Animal attraction

Poor old Patch, he was old and confused. Walking home from the supermarket, via the park, I would often find Uncle Lou and Patch there. Uncle Lou standing talking to Patch, a little exasperatedly, Patch more often than not with his head in a bush.

"What's he looking for?" I asked

Uncle Lou laughed. "He doesn't know."

Uncle Lou explained that Patch had always been a very clean dog and, long before the advent of the "pooper scooper" and "dog toilets", Patch had always "made his deposits" in the depth of the bushes and buried them there. Now the poor thing knew there was something he wanted to do in the bush, but he no longer recalled which part of his anatomy was supposed to be in there. Uncle Lou would stand for up to forty minutes at a time trying to coax Patch to remove his head from the bush.

It was no great surprise when a few weeks later Patch went to join Uncle Jack and Aunty Mary on the other side at last. Uncle Lou and Janet were devastated.

"No more pets!" Uncle Lou declared. Much as he loved animals, the pain of being parted from them was almost too much to bear. He didn't want to go through that ever again. Janet agreed.

The thing is, people who understand animals in the way Uncle Lou always has seem to attract them, wanted or not.

A month or so after Patch's demise, Uncle Lou was putting his rubbish out and "tutting" at an abandoned car that had been dumped at the side of his flat. (I must point out this was not the tower block where we had once all lived, but a block designated for pensioners that had doors opening out to the pavement. He had been offered one right next door to Aunty May and Uncle Jack, who had moved there straight after getting married. We in turn had been offered a house that backed right on to their complex, and Young Lou and family had a house just round the corner from us, near Marks parents, so there we were, all together again… a coincidence? I think not!). Uncle Lou was thinking that he had better report the car to the council so they could remove it before someone decided to set it alight when a sudden movement caught his eye. Bending to look under the car Uncle Lou saw what appeared to be a cat. The poor little thing was just skin and bones, he saw, its ribs showing pitifully through its sides. No coaxing would persuade the cat to come out from under the car where it was hiding so Uncle Lou filled Patch's old bowls with titbits from the kitchen and fresh water. He put it at the side of the car and retreated back to the flat.

That afternoon, and a trip to the supermarket later for several tins of cat food, Uncle Lou was gratified to see on his return that all the food had gone from the bowls.

Over a period of several days Uncle Lou put out bowls of food and drink, each time increasing the distance from the car and decreasing the distance from his flat, until eventually he left the flat door open and put the food in the hallway.

One afternoon, as Uncle Lou and Janet sat watching the TV, a little visitor popped her head hesitantly round the door at them.

"Now then, hello, come on in," they entreated, and she did.

Tiggy (as they named her) tentatively made herself at home over the next few weeks. She was never happier than when curled up next to Janet on the sofa, or sleeping across Uncle Lou's feet at night. She grew from a starving little kitten, to a fluffy and well rounded cat, (almost spherical to be precise).

Over time word must have got out amongst the cat community that there happened to be a very nice man and woman living in the flat and, one by one, the waifs and strays seemed to turn up on the doorstep. Uncle Lou developed a policy that no hungry or ill-treated cat should be turned away, so before long there became an almost constant stream of feline visitors.

Last time I called, although Tiggy has long since gone to the "Happy Cat Home in the Sky", I was amused to see a large selection of bowls filled to the brim with cat food and various tempting morsels lined up in the hallway and living room.

"Who do all these belong to?" I wondered.

Janet enlightened me, "That ones for when Emma comes calling, she likes Tuna, and this is Emily's bowl, Charlotte prefers rabbit, that's hers. This one is for Socks; he calls in now and again..."

A veritable cat's restaurant.

So Uncle Lou, with his Pied Piper like charms, and Janet, with her love of small furry creatures, live contentedly in their unofficial cat sanctuary. I wonder what Patch makes of that?

Troubled dreams

One night I had another strange dream. This one involved me riding a bicycle along a river, but not as myself. I felt in this dream that I was actually Diana (one-time Princess of Wales) and I was terribly worried for some unknown reason about Dodi Fayed. Behind me was a man on a bicycle trying desperately to catch up, and I/she became more and more frightened, cycling faster and faster to try to leave him behind. Mists swirled alongside me as in several of my previous dreams of many years before, and then up ahead I saw a tunnel looming. There was a sense of dread as I pedalled towards the darkness and the mists closed around me/her.

I awoke with a strange feeling. I couldn't shake off the dream all day but I didn't know why. I recall Mark, Dolly and I had taken the children on a daytrip to Bridlington, and it was lovely, bright and sunny. As I sat on the sand watching them make sandcastles and splash in the sea the dream kept replaying in my head – but I couldn't understand why. Everyone has bizarre dreams from time to time, but something about this one had really impressed itself upon my psyche.

Early the next morning I awoke with a start. It was still dark and for some unknown reason Mark had got up early. I groped my way downstairs to the kitchen and found him making cups of tea for us, the radio was on.

"Princess Diana and that new chap of hers, Dodi, have been in a car crash," he said.

At this point the news was just coming in and it didn't appear the crash had been fatal. We put the television on and I felt a shock of recognition at the circumstances. With the exception of the bicycle as her mode of transport, there were the elements of my strange dream – the river, the road, people pursuing causing them to travel faster and faster and the final date with destiny in the tunnel.

My dream had preceded the accident by twenty-four hours. I told Mark and as usual he was sceptical.

"What's the point of having premonitions if you can't do anything about them?" He wondered.

In his logical way Mark assumes you would be shown these things in order to prevent them, but I don't think that is always the case - sometimes I think we just tune into something unexplainable, get a sneak preview of the future. I'm just an ordinary working mother, just because strange things happen to and around me, sadly, it doesn't mean they come with ready made answers supplied.

I discovered I didn't necessarily have to be asleep to get bewildering visions however.

Next, I encountered the strange daytime images that came dancing inexplicably before my eyes. On several occasions I would get an image that clouded out my vision of wherever I was or whatever I was doing. I would see myself looking out through a large, glass window - again surrounded by the swirling mists - then suddenly, filling my vision, would appear a jet plane coming closer and closer.

"Its going to hit the building," I'd think.

"Where am I? Where am I?" I asked my unconscious mind. Then the revelation would come: I was in one of the twin tower buildings in New York. The image would replay a second time, bewilderingly, then as suddenly as it appeared it would clear, and there I'd be, half way through the washing up or something mundane like that.

These glimpses into the future happened at irregular intervals over a two year period. I couldn't understand why it kept happening and if, as I suspected, it was a premonition, I still had absolutely no idea of how it could be prevented. Surely this would be an accident?

One day after the kids had gone to school I was curling up with some toast and tea in front of the Kilroy show, a daily talk show that was on every weekday morning. That morning's programme was about psychics and premonitions so naturally I was interested. Suddenly one woman made me sit up and take notice – she was having repeated dreams of a plane flying into a skyscraper. I was fidgeting with amazement.

"I see that too! I see that too!" I shouted at the screen. How strange, here was someone else having the exact same vision as me. But I still didn't know what could be done about it.

Mark came home unexpectedly early one afternoon. "I've been listening to the radio on the way home," he said, "apparently a plane has flown into one of the twin towers."

There it was, suddenly I knew, even as I was turning on the television, I knew what was coming next – another plane had hit the second building. My vision had always repeated itself twice.

As we sat in stunned silence looking at the flames coming from the gaping holes in both skyscrapers I felt a certainty of what was to follow and, sure enough, just moments after I'd seen the towers crumble in my minds eye, the buildings went down one after another to the anguished cries of the reporters showing the breaking news.

It's a terrible thing to know something so horrendous is going to happen and be totally unable to pinpoint when or how. How can you prevent something like that? To start predicting death and destruction before it happens makes you sound crazed and deluded and, after it happens, well, sadly it's just too late.

The paranoid mother

I sometimes have premonitions about my children, and I hate to say I am just as hopeless at preventing things there too!

The problem with being a mother is that it makes you a little neurotic at the best of times, so it's hard to tell a genuine premonition from an overactive imagination. I swear, at times, it's a miracle I ever let them leave the house at all!

Once, I was dashing to get ready for work at the petrol station when Dan came pestering.

"Mum, Mum, can I go to the canal with my friend Lee and his parents, and can we take our bikes?" (Dan had just purchased a second hand bike with his birthday money and was still getting to grips with it). As I looked at him suddenly I saw Dan in the canal instead of riding alongside it.

"Not on your bike," I ventured, thinking that should prevent a tragedy. Then I gave him a quick hug and admonished him to be careful. I went off to work and forgot all about it. I had self-diagnosed that once again it was a case of overprotective mother syndrome.

When I got home that night Dan was safely back and all was as it should be. Then he said conversationally, "Guess what, I slipped into the canal today Mum."

"What?" I stopped what I was doing.

It transpired he and his friend had been paddling in the slipstream that ran down into the canal, but it was slimed with moss and Dan had lost his balance and just slid into the canal. Fortunately, he said he'd felt strangely calm, and although he couldn't get out as the sides were too high and his clothes were weighing him down, he just kept treading water. His friends parents scurried about panicking as neither of them were strong enough swimmers to go in after him. From out of nowhere a man appeared, jumped in, scooped Dan under one arm and swam with him to the side where he helped him out.

"Are you alright?" He checked, Dan said he was, and the man just smiled, nodded and ran off.

So there you are, when your would-be psychic mother is too dozy to believe in her own premonitions, it always helps to have the odd Guardian Angel in reserve.

"Don't be stupid Mother," Dan said when I told him, "The man had lost a shoe… whoever heard of an Angel wearing shoes, let alone losing one of them!"

Perhaps a lot of the things I have to recount people would pass off as feminine intuition. Flash forward a second to my time in a psychic circle, the leading medium pressed me as to who was telling me things.

"I don't always get the impression of who it is," I explained. "Somehow I just know things, it's like being told something by somebody, but I don't always get an introduction."

I was in the kitchen, just minding my business and making tea, when a voice said quite distinctly in my head, "A wall has fallen on Jessica," and then, as an afterthought, "Don't panic."

My first reaction was "What?" but then I found myself moving instinctively out of the front door, down the back garden steps, through the gate, across the field, and down the alleyway between the pensioners flats. It was only at this point that the wailing of several little girls could be heard in the distance, I hurried my pace somewhat. Along the row of back gardens I ran until I came to a house further up the street.

Four or five of Jessica's little friends were crying hysterically, standing around a pile of rubble that had been a wall only moments before. Jessica's friend's father had Jess on his knee, wiping her eyes.

"The wall collapsed and fell on her," he said apologetically, "but I don't think she's hurt." I ran into the garden and gave her a quick inspection, although clearly shaken by the event; there wasn't a scratch or a mark on Jessica anywhere.

When she saw me she stopped crying and explained. Four of them were sitting on the wall when it started to wobble. Her three friends had jumped one way but Jess was sitting the opposite way round, so she jumped in the other direction and the wall had toppled onto her. Jessica's friends appeared to be more upset than she was. She'd had a fright but she was totally unharmed, as if protected by something invisible.

This wasn't the first time Jess was protected by an invisible source. I was at work in the petrol station and my brother-in-law James had just called in to fill up. As he was paying me the telephone at my side rang.

"Hold on a second," I said, knowing James wouldn't mind if I quickly took the call. It was Mark on the other end.

"Jessica's been knocked down," he said. I dropped the phone in its cradle, left my startled colleague to take over the reigns, and raced out to James's car with him.

When we got to my house Jess was resting on the settee in the living room. As luck would have it Mark had become certificated in first aid just two days before, he had checked Jess over before moving her out of the road.

"She seems fine, but we'd better take her to casualty and get her properly assessed," he decided.

On the way up to the hospital Jess told me what had happened. Some girls had waved to her from across the street, shouting that they wanted to show her something.

Overcome by curiosity Jess had stepped out from behind a parked car and had been struck by a car coming down the hill, which had instantly braked. Jess said the impact was strange, just a feeling like being pushed and then, as she fell, she recalled it felt almost as if she landed on a cushion, though in fact it was the middle of the road. Dan and his friend Lee, who were nearby, witnessed this and went running down to Mark, who ran straight back with them.

"Jess seemed fine," he said. "It was the poor chap who ran into her that was in shock." After speaking to Mark he just abandoned his car at the side of the road and walked home. He only lived down the road.

At the hospital they confirmed what we suspected already, Jess was unharmed, and apart from a gentle talking to from the doctor to be more careful when crossing the road in future, we were able to take her home without so much as a sticking plaster.

What struck me later was how everything had fallen together so neatly. My brother-in-law coming into my workplace just as Mark rang me, so I had instant transport home, the fact that Mark had just completed a first aid course, so he could check Jessica over instantly. Most amazing of all, the way Jess described the sensation of being hit by a car and knocked flying into the road as being pushed into a cushion. I feel certain someone was watching over her that day.

"I'm still here"

In life my father-in-law was often accused (usually by Dolly) of being heavy-handed and clumsy. He was famed for well-intentioned but generally ham-fisted attempts at DIY and home repairs. Dennis took all the ribbing with good grace, his usually good-humoured self unruffled despite the hilarity his "home improvements" caused amongst the family.

Death does not change us; apparently we can still blunder around causing unintentional mayhem from the other side of the veil. When my dear father-in-law Dennis passed he made his presence felt for quite a few days prior to the funeral. The day after he died Mark's little niece, who was only two, appeared to be able to see him still around Mark's mum, Dolly. She was talking and gesturing to someone who wasn't there, agreeing she would "take care of Nana."

Then there were the unusual electrical disturbances. Light bulbs blowing in everyone's houses, a sure sign of heightened spirit activity.

One night, I walked into the children's bedroom to find Ant, Dan and Jess very agitated. They were trying to watch television but as we all watched in amazement it flicked independently from channel to channel rapidly; the remote control lying untouched on a nearby bedside cabinet.

My mother-in-law had told me of the exact same occurrence the day before when she had been babysitting her nieces.

"Dennis," I thought, "just behave yourself will you?" obligingly the television stopped rolling. The energy then seemed to transfer itself downstairs, Mark's computer took to turning itself on and off independently. I tried to reassure Mark it was just his Dad paying a visit, needless to say he just looked at me as if I'd lost my marbles. However, once we had held Dennis's funeral the electrical disturbances seemed to calm down at last. This fits in with everything I've read and researched since. It seems it is quite usual for the spirit to "hang around" out of concern and curiosity in the intervening time between physical death and the funeral. This is an attempt to console loved ones and reach out to let them know everything is alright. Also there is a desire in some cases to see what happens to their human remains. It gives them a sense of completion, I suppose.

I must stress, from what I've learnt, that whether it's a quick trip to the crematorium or an interment underground, this does not unduly concern our loved ones in spirit. Rather, they are interested in who turns out on the day, how people cope, and how well the proceedings go. They are usually casual participants at their own send off. Because the spirit is comprised of energy, this explains the way they often affect electrical equipment when they draw close. Usually, following the funeral, this ceases, possibly because once they ascend to the higher realms their vibration also rises, to a point where they no longer affect things so clumsily when they visit.

Final farewells

When I was a little girl we used to have a lot of Ladybird Books at school depicting bible stories. I was as happy to read biblical stories as I was fairy stories, as I was a voracious reader. I still remember one book depicting a tale of a little boy called Samuel who had a recurring dream. Three nights God spoke to him, and each time he took no notice and referred to the master of the temple instead, who eventually persuaded him that instead of being afraid perhaps it might be a good idea to listen.

You would think I'd have learned something from that story wouldn't you. I certainly read it often enough over the years. Also, given my previous experience of dreams and visits you would expect me to be on high alert for messages from the great beyond. So, when my Mum showed up one night in a dream, and told me very kindly but firmly that they were preparing to receive Uncle Ace on the other side, naturally I acted on that straight away didn't I? No, actually I went to work as usual, pondering over the fact I'd had this dream, and what a shame I hadn't seen Uncle Ace for a while, and I didn't expect I would now.

I came home again and I waited expectantly for the phone call, and when it didn't come I thought, "Mother, you got that wrong!"

A week or two later Mum turned up again. This time she was a little more insistent that they were preparing for Uncle Ace and in the background there was the suggestion of a lot of excitement and scurrying about in preparation (I had the impression of people hanging bunting "Welcome to the other side" and laying out trestle tables... no... I'm joking, it was just that type of feeling). She gave me a hug, and a "now don't you forget I told you so," kind of look.

And I didn't forget, I went to work again and waited all day to hear the sad news. When it didn't come I thought, "Well, you're just making it up now, Mother."

For a third time she turned up in my dream, and she was getting really exasperated with me by now. She suggested perhaps Mark and I should pay a call on Young Lou (Uncle Ace's son) and take him for a visit, as we lived quite a distance away and Lou doesn't drive.

I went to work, I was beginning to think there was something wrong with me and this obsession with killing off poor old Uncle Ace, who was no doubt sitting at home right at that moment, happy as Larry, and the last thing he would want was a car load of relatives turning up on his doorstep unannounced in the middle of Coronation Street declaring, "Oh good, you're still here!"

Of course the call didn't come again and I'd got quite good at dismissing this as some warped twist of my imagination by this time.

A week later Dad rang, he had some sad news for me. Uncle Horace had passed away, fortunately with his three daughters round him. It dawned on me that perhaps Mum was letting me know while there was still time to visit, not just to say his passing was imminent. I said sorry in my head. At least I knew there was one heck of a party going on at the other side!

Mark has this theory that if you are psychic you must know everything. Not so. Being psychic is fine, it's being human that's the problem.

The constant questioning and doubt casting of the conscious mind is what often gets in the way of intuition. I think the rationalisation of everything is what stops the scientific mind from progressing in this area. If I had gone with my instincts, instead of awaiting evidence that my dream was correct, I would have got a last chance to make my goodbyes, whereas now I'll just have to catch up with Uncle Ace later.

Between this world and the other, I think an awful lot of messages get lost in translation.

Part Five

So when the Angel of the darker drink,
At last shall find you on the river brink,
And offering his cup, invite your soul
Forth to your lips to quaff...you shall not shrink.

The Rubaiyat of Omar Khayyam

Chapter Fourteen
Experiments and evidence

Transport has been arranged

After thirteen years Mark and I took the plunge and moved to a new house (on the same street as our old friend Diane and her husband Andy). It was the first time either of us had not lived on a council estate, by comparison the silence was deafening, and the peace remarkable. Mark and I embraced this tranquillity, but the kids were a little bored, our new neighbours refrained from streaking up and down the street whilst playing "Spin the Bottle" and we hadn't seen a burnt out car blazing like a beacon on the hill for weeks.

A strange incident occurred not long after we had moved into our new home. The kids, now in their teens, were all out with different groups of friends, leaving Mark and I free to get on with wallpapering the living room. I was standing on the ladder measuring the drop for the wallpaper, when conversationally a voice in my head announced, "Dan's had an accident."

"What?" I stopped what I was doing in order to tune in better. "He's just taken a tumble off his skateboard," the voice clarified.

"Is he hurt?" I asked. "No, its ok," I was reassured. "Don't worry, someone will bring him home, don't stop decorating." Convinced I was losing my marbles I carried on decorating as instructed.

About ten minutes later there was a knock at the door. Mark answered it as I came wobbling down the ladder, I could hear him talking to someone in the hall. I joined him to find Dan limping in carrying his skateboard.

"I came off my skateboard, Mum," he explained, "but I'm ok, I've just banged my elbow and twisted my ankle a bit. Johnny's Mum was just leaving for work so she gave me a lift 'round because I was limping."

The lady in the doorway gave me a cheery smile. "He'll be ok," she said, I gave my thanks and she gave a little "it's nothing" sort of wave and left.

The voice from nowhere was right again, and furthermore it had arranged Dan some transport home. Not bad for something I'd kept dismissing as a figment of my imagination.

Spirits and Spiritualists

Being interested in all things spiritual, naturally I sometimes attend my local spiritualist church. I first went with my friend Diane, her parents and my Aunty Mary when I was about fifteen. It was at the time when Doris Stokes was at her height of popularity and seeing a medium was the latest craze. My friend's parents had attended a few times, so we persuaded them to let us go along as we were curious as to what happened there.

I don't remember being overly impressed by the medium that night, there was a lot of "fishing" going on and it seemed to be the elderly ladies who were targeted, the suggestion that they might know a man, or woman, who had passed over seemed highly probable. Nonetheless, the people were very friendly and welcoming and there was an extremely nice atmosphere to the place. Diane and I went on a few occasions after that but, being fifteen, of course we had other things to think about – boys, make up, and dancing mostly, so eventually our visits petered out.

Many years later another close friend's sister died unexpectedly. Strangely, at the time it happened I was preparing to go out for the evening with Mark, as it was his birthday, when suddenly my head was filled with my friend's name being called over and over again and an overwhelming compulsion to go to her. I couldn't justify why I was feeling that way as I had seen her just the night before and she had been fine, so Mark and I just went out as planned. Nonetheless, the evening was doomed to failure as I couldn't shake the feeling of overwhelming sorrow pressing inexplicably down on me. We came home early, almost stopping off at my friend's house on route but I stopped myself, thinking we would be silly to disturb her at that hour just for "a feeling".

The next day I heard from my friend. At around the time I had first started to hear her name being called in my head her sister had died instantly of a heart attack.

I pondered the strange coincidence for several days. I was

becoming increasingly drawn towards the world of spirit but I was still sceptical on many fronts.

On an impulse I bought a book by Rita Rogers, a famous English medium. I knew very little about her but I was drawn to her smiling face on the book cover. I read her book from end to end one afternoon, astounded by many similarities between her experiences and mine. There was an address to write to her directly, so I did, wondering if she still held one to one readings.

I was very excited when I got a reply, unfortunately it said that Rita could only now be contacted through a magazine, and sometimes a lucky reader was chosen for a reading. I understood but I felt very disappointed. There was a nice poem tucked in with the letter and I kept that. Well, I thought, sitting at the table in the kitchen (this was in our previous house, at a time when I was just starting to accept there was something strange going on), I had thought someone was trying to get through to me but clearly I was mistaken, I might as well give up on this "talking to the dead" malarkey. I pushed the letter to one side and started drinking my cup of tea. A glass that was on the draining board drying suddenly shot off and landed unbroken in front of me, spinning several times before it stopped. The kids jumped and slopped their cornflakes all over. Everyone looked at Mark accusingly, as he was washing up.

"Don't look at me!" He declared, "I didn't do anything!"

It was as if someone had taken exception to my defeatist stance. "Ok, ok," I thought, "You lead me to whatever comes next then!"

My friend had been plunged into a deep depression following her sister's demise. We were out for lunch one day and fell to discussing the strange compulsion I'd felt to call her on that tragic evening. This led to a discussion of the paranormal. She told me one of the things that had lifted her spirits a little was watching the programme "Crossing Over" with an American medium called John Edwards. I hadn't seen it but promised I would look out for it.

From there the discussion turned to mediums in general and somewhere at the back of my mind a memory came knocking. I told my friend about the local Spiritualist Church I had attended over twenty years before and she was intrigued. I said I'd go along with her if she liked. So we started attending, a little tentatively at first, not sure what to expect, but we were made very welcome.

Over time I came to understand how the medium works. It is a three way communication system with the spirit on one side, you on the other and the medium acting like a complex radio receiver in the middle. The clarity of the messages received varies a lot, depending on the skill of interpretation of the medium, the strength of the vibration emitted from the spirit and your own willingness to open up and receive. I found it a fascinating process, and, in case you have never been and were wondering, not at all scary!

One of our regular mediums at my local church is a fantastic chap called Michael. He brings things across so distinctly and with such humour that he often has us all practically rolling in the aisles.

I recall one time he declared to a member of the congregation, "Can you tell me why a pig has just wandered past me... and another one?" The poor woman could hardly speak for laughing.

"Oh, they were my Uncle's!" She declared, "They were his pets – they lived in the house with him."

"Well, just so you know," said Michael, "the pigs are doing fine!"

We were all hysterical with laughter.

On one occasion I was sitting listening to him give a message to someone at the front. The back of my hair was tickling as if it was being pulled or blown. Then I remembered Mum once saying that if she ever got chance to contact me from the other side she'd blow on my hair so I'd know it was her.

"Mother," I said (inside my head). "If that's you, stop messing about with my hair and get up front and introduce yourself to Michael the medium."

Michael finished with the lady in front and took a drink of water. "Now," he said, "I'm being told that the person I need to speak to has a ring with three stones in it."

I looked down. There I was, twisting my engagement ring, with its three stones, 'round and 'round my finger. I put my hand up alongside four other women in the congregation.

"Ok," said Michael, "let's narrow this down a bit – this lady's mother has passed over."

Now there were only three of us with our arms raised.

"For goodness sake, Mother," I thought. "If this is you then just tell him your name!"

"Ah," said Michael, "January... no, no, it's Jan."

The other two women put their hands down.

"My mother's name was Jan," I told him.

From there things came thick and fast. Jan was there with Bet or Betty (my Dad's partner after Mum had passed, who was now also on the other side) and another lady (perfect physical description of Aunty Mary given) who also had a mother feel to her (which she would, as I'd lived with her my entire life) and a good description of what each woman had passed with.

Then came an amazing revelation; he knew my mother had been in a coma for several weeks before she died. The last time I had seen her I had "thought" things to her, rather than saying them out loud, as I felt self conscious in a room full of people. Michael told me that my mother had indeed heard me in her mind. He then relayed back the entire message, word for word.

Next he brought through two soldiers and went on to describe Uncle Jack and Granddad accurately. He said how they got on much better now than in life, which made me laugh. Then he told me my mother wanted to validate that she had been watching over me and mine and went on to tell me I'd been up and about at three that morning, also the younger female to my side (my daughter Jess) had been sewing. I laughed at that, never in a million years had my daughter been sewing, but you could forgive him the odd mistake in such an excellent reading, I suppose (he was right about me being up in the small hours though). He asked why he was being shown eight rose bushes in all different colours. I pointed out that just that weekend gone I had planted eight rose bushes (all different, as he said) for family members that had passed.

"Well, they like them very much," Michael said, "but Bet wants Daffodils for her, please."

Then I realised I hadn't planted anything for Bet and that, yes, she had always said Daffodils were her favourite flowers. I resolved to plant bulbs in the front garden straight away.

"One more thing," he said. "The other gentleman who has just passed has arrived safely."

That was my Uncle Ace who had died just two weeks previously.

Finally, just as they were drawing their energy back, Michael said, "Oh, I'm sure you won't know this name as it's really unusual but someone just shouted out Cordelia!"

I shrugged my shoulders and said I would take it with me.

All the way home in the car I mused over the strange name. It didn't strike a chord on my side of the family at all, I knew my grandparents' and great grandparents' names. Just as my friend dropped me off at home a thought occurred. I ran into the dining room where Mark was sitting reading.

"What was the name of your Grandmother?" I asked.

"Cordelia," he said. I started dancing about with joy. Jess came in to see what all the fuss was about and so I reiterated everything to her and Mark.

"It all makes sense apart from one thing," I said. "Mum said she'd been watching Jess sew and Jess doesn't sew."

Then it was Jessica's turn to get excited.

"I do" she declared. "I had a needlepoint lesson today at school."

So there it was, everything absolutely perfect, even the things I couldn't have known about (which, for the cynics amongst us, discounts cold reading and the idea that a medium somehow reads the sitters mind).

This is what a medium means when they ask that we take the evidence away with us. It has to be said that I've had readings before and since and they can be a bit hit and miss, but when you get the perfect connection, like I did on that occasion, the experience is truly mind blowing.

So, if your experience with mediums isn't too good up to press, try not to be disheartened. It's a bit like Chinese Whispers, remember, so stay as open as you can and someday you too may be lucky enough to get an exceptional message that just blows you away. If that's not proof of life after death I don't know what is!

The Developing Circle

As my interest in the paranormal grew, I found further opportunities for advancement began to present themselves quite naturally (as the saying goes, "when the student is ready the teacher will appear").

Through our occasional visits to the Spiritualist Church my friend and I were invited to join a development circle. Now, I have to say that at this point, intrigued though I was, and despite my strange experiences and interesting childhood, it had never seriously crossed my mind that I had anything beyond the most basic psychic ability, but I was flattered to be invited and far too curious to turn the offer down. I'm so glad I didn't!

During my time in the psychic development circle I had many strange, wonderful and uplifting experiences. We began with the basics, learning how to feel and see auras (the energetic field around the body), opening and closing chakras (the bodies energy centres), simple healing techniques, and learning how to trust our intuition. Every week brought new things to explore and discuss. We had a treasure trove of new experiences and sensations to discover. Perhaps my favourite experience was this one…

Several weeks into our circle we had all convened as usual, said an opening prayer, opened up our chakras, and had our inspirational talk from the medium leading the circle.

"Today," she declared, "we have some visitors. They have been waiting for you to arrive."

We all looked expectantly round the room. I must admit, I was generally quite sceptical about being able to see anything on these occasions, but the room did appear a little misty.

"I want you all to stand up and walk around the room and, well, we'll just see what happens," she said with a smile.

"Oh no!" I thought, what was I expected to do now, wander round the room looking as if something was happening, just to be polite?

Still, I stood up obediently, took a couple of steps around the outside of the circle, feeling foolish, although everyone else seemed perfectly at ease with this exercise.

Then, suddenly, a hand slid into mine. I let out an involuntary gasp, looked down, and of course there was nothing to see. Then another hand grasped mine on the opposite side. I was stunned.

Now I know how bizarre this sounds but, believe me, I was not expecting anything to happen, so I was startled and amazed myself. Spirit hands feel solid, yet tingling, like having a mild electrical vibration, and similar to the resistance you would feel if pushing against water when swimming. I could probably have closed my hands if I had wanted (but that would have been incredibly rude) so I just stood there transfixed till a gentle tugging made me walk.

So, slowly we circled the room, my two mysterious companions and I, my entire focus was on the incredible sensation of holding hands with people I could not see.

Every so often we'd stop for a moment or two and I'd ask, "Who are you?" But there was no response. Maybe I was trying too hard to pick up on their names.

Eventually, as we had almost traversed the entire outside of the circle, I asked again, "Please, tell me who this is?"

Suddenly I was greeted by an exasperated laugh.

"Well, for goodness sake, who do you think it is?" In that instance I recognised the presence of my mother and my Aunty Mary, both holding tight to my hands, laughing at my confusion. I was back at my seat and, before I could converse any further, the medium requested we all say our goodbyes and sit down. I felt the strange sensation of hands releasing mine and the sudden emptiness once more.

Everyone sat down and the medium asked for people to volunteer their experiences. Some people had felt enveloped in a hug, parents, friends and loved ones had all come forward, and in one case a delighted couple had found their daughter waiting for them in a corner of the room, they were in tears of joy.

Even now I cannot really begin to describe the euphoria felt by everybody. I try hard to remain open minded to everything that happens but I retain a healthy scepticism for most things until proved otherwise. I hadn't expected to feel what I did, because I had never heard at this point that it was possible to feel spirit contact in that way. My mother's voice was in my head, heard over the top of my own internal ramblings. It is a strange but entirely wonderful thing to have physical contact with someone (or even better two someones) you haven't touched in over twenty years.

So now when my husband Mark pours scorn on my experiences I take no notice whatsoever because, whether he chooses to believe or not, I know beyond a shadow of a doubt that we continue to exist after physical death. When you've held hands, walked and talked with two people who died (supposedly) twenty years before, what more evidence do you need?

A toe in the water

After a few weeks more of attending the development circle our leading medium suggested it might be a good idea for us to try our own psychic abilities and mediumistic powers out for ourselves. There was an instant tension within the group. What she wanted us to do was go round the circle one at a time and just explain whatever came into our heads. How hard could that be, right?

I was relieved that I was about halfway round the circle, which meant that a few people had to go before me but there were also enough people going after me that we wouldn't be left dwelling on what I had to say. (Which I didn't expect would be very much!). All too soon however it passed to me.

I did my best to clear my mind although, despite Mark's insistence that I'm a bit empty-headed, it's amazing how much stuff gets cluttered up in there the moment you want to think of nothing at all. I tried to focus on just a wall of colour, a pale blue, hoping that at some point something was going to pop up that hadn't been generated from my own consciousness.

"Just say whatever you see," the medium prompted.

Great, all I could see was the blue wall I'd constructed to stop me seeing things! I took a deep breath and told myself to relax. Suddenly, a garden gate appeared before me. It was aging before my eyes, someone was painting it a rather lurid green, it was swinging back and forth, there was the impression of time spent talking across it, and then it started to age and decay. Flecks of the paint were chipping off, it was becoming more and more weathered, the hinges were becoming rusty.

I described what I was seeing as it happened.

"Good, good," the medium said. "Do you see anything else?"

I could see daffodils. "Not because of spring though," a voice in my head said. I relayed this to the group, then I heard the voice again, a little muffled.

"I'm not sure," I said, "if I'm hearing "let's be frank" or if I'm being told this is Frank."

I was shown briefly an elderly gentleman, just as a flash, and the words "tell them he's arrived safely," so I explained that apparently an elderly gentleman had arrived safely over the other side. (I was beginning to see why some mediums are accused of being vague!). That was all, I was back to my blue wall again. I opened my eyes.

"Can anyone take that message?" Our medium asked.

The lady next to me put up her hand, lovely Myra, the healer. I was intrigued as to what it could possibly have meant to her as it made absolutely no sense to me whatsoever.

"The garden gate is my sister's," she said. "She bought the house from our next door neighbour. We'd lived next to them for years, and we'd swung on the gate as children and talked across it as adults. It is green, and yes, she has let it fall into a state of disrepair," she laughed.

Then she pulled back the lapel of her jacket and, pinned to the underside, hidden from sight till that moment, was a daffodil.

"I'm wearing this today and my sister who owns the gate will be too, as a token of remembrance to our father. Today's the anniversary of his death and daffodils were his favourite flower. Also, the old gentleman who has arrived safely was my sister's father-in-law, he passed away two days ago."

Finally, she turned to me with a smile and passed me something. I looked down and it was a crystal (some people like to use them in psychic work as somehow they help to concentrate the energy). She turned it over in my hand while explaining to everyone what she was doing. I could see the back of it had a name inscribed, "Frank".

"The crystal was given to me by Frank," she explained. "Not only was he the neighbour my sister bought the house and accompanying gate from, he was friends with my father, knew my sister's father-in-law, and he was the one who introduced my family to this Spiritualist Church."

I think the expression is "you could have knocked me down with a feather". There was I thinking I was spouting a load of gibberish and yet here, sitting right next to me, was someone to whom it made perfect sense. I really couldn't have dreamt it up if I'd tried. I knew nothing about Myra and her family other than she was a trained healer and a member of the church.

It's amazing what you can do if you try.

Suspicious circumstances

My second attempt at receiving an impression from the other side was slightly more dramatic.

Once again we followed the same format of working round the circle and taking it in turns to describe exactly what we were receiving.

When it was my turn I focused on the pale blue wall again and slowly an image started to form. I tried to reject it three times as I thought it was a retrieved memory of something that had happened to a friend's father many years before, but it was the only thing that kept appearing in my head so I thought I had better just get on with it before everyone got impatient with the delay. Once I started to describe what I was seeing, instead of distorted images, this time it played like a reel of film, including soundtrack.

I had the impression of stumbling alongside the canal, I was a youngish male. "I'd had a drop too many," a voice in my head explained. I looked down at my hands and I was carrying fish and chips wrapped in newspaper. Suddenly, I tripped slightly and I saw the newspaper package being dropped towards the edge of the canal. I walked unsteadily down the side of the bank with the intention of retrieving the package, then I had the impression of falling and it all went black.

I opened my eyes pulling back from the scene, guessing that perhaps the man had fallen in.

Opposite me a nice young woman called Suzanne was crying her eyes out. Our leading medium came to my side.

"Clearly you can take this," she said to Suzanne.

A voice spoke abruptly in my head, "Tell her I'm really sorry for all the trouble I caused," then he was gone. I relayed the message quickly. After Suzanne composed herself she explained that I had just described exactly the circumstances of her twenty-one year old nephew's death. He hadn't gone in the water as I'd assumed, the moment when it went black was the moment that he had hit his head after slipping on the muddy bank. Apparently, he had been found dead by the canal the next day, with head injuries. They had never known about the fish and chips, which must have long since sunk to the bottom, and for a long time foul play had been suspected. Suzanne's older sister had been torturing herself over the exact circumstances for the past few years, she told me.

I was overwhelmed with the realisation of what this meant to Suzanne and her family and yet I had come so close to dismissing it, thinking it was the product of an over-active imagination.

Sometime later I asked my Uncle Lou about the circumstances of our family friend who had died at the canal. It turned out that he had removed all his clothes, folded them neatly and dived in. A rather bizarre suicide, or a skinny dip that went tragically wrong? Either way, totally unlike the vision I had been shown after all. I was beginning to think I needed to start taking this seriously!

Healing

Although it has only recently been diagnosed, for as long as I can remember I have had recurring flare ups of Rheumatoid Arthritis.

Even as a child I can recall waking on particularly cold mornings so stiff that I could barely move. In college I used to virtually freeze to my chair because our room was so cold in winter. It was not unheard of for friends to have to drag me manually from my seat after a lecture and manipulate me to standing upright. Bits of me would just lock into the sitting position. I would describe myself as feeling like the tin man from "The Wizard of Oz" begging "oil my joints."

I know I'm slow on the uptake, look how long it took me to figure out I wasn't just an odd-ball, I was actually psychic (yes, I can hear my friends saying, but you're still an odd-ball as well). It didn't even occur to me to query why I got so stiff and my joints were painful until I hit my mid thirties, despite the fact that my mother was almost crippled by Rheumatoid Arthritis by her early forties (they were about to install a stair lift and had delivered a wheel chair just weeks before she died). I just assumed that everyone got stiff joints and ran a fever every time they exerted themselves, in the same way that as a child I assumed everybody had imaginary friends, could see one scene superimposed over another if they visited places of historical interest and would just "know" things that were going to happen in the future.

It was only when my cousins Nick and Matthew were diagnosed with Ankylosing Spondylitis that it dawned on me to ask. My doctor confirmed that Ankylosing Spondylitis is more common in males, whereas Rheumatoid Arthritis tends to develop in females; both are auto immune diseases, where an overzealous system attacks itself, most commonly the joints and soft tissues. Over time this can cause excessive damage. On the plus side, however, my cousins and I do have a strong resistance to everyday ailments.

I'm not one to dwell on this type of thing so rather than resorting to painkillers and medication of any sort I try to ease flare ups with rest and warm baths. I find that if I can infuse my system with a sensation of well-being it tends to "stand down" its defences and I can get on with life.

While I was part of the Development Circle I had a particularly nasty flare up. It was January and really cold, the condition had attacked my hip joints and my left leg so painfully I could barely walk. My ankle, knee, and all the muscles in between had been affected. Nevertheless, I was determined to attend the circle; it is deemed the height of bad manners to miss a session as you are breaking an appointment not only with the other members but with friends on the other side.

The lady I sat next to was the church's healer, so I thought perhaps I may get chance to have a word with her. However, we were

251

so busy with several things that evening I never got round to mentioning it, and I didn't want to make a fuss, so I put it to the back of my mind and tried my best not to reveal the discomfort I was experiencing. Still, it was a relief to get home that night. I thought I would just get a warm drink and have an early night.

I was hobbling through to the kitchen when my leg gave a painful twinge. I thought, half jokingly, to the spirit world, "Well, a fat lot of good you've been tonight, you seat me next to a healer and then you don't even give her a prod in my direction."

The thought was no sooner out of my head than an incredible thing happened. I had the most bizarre sensation of several hands physically touching my bad leg. It was almost like an intensive massage not just on top of my skin but beneath it as well and it made me stop completely in my tracks. I looked down but, naturally, there was nothing to see.

I was so taken aback I gave up entirely on the idea of heading to the kitchen (and believe me, it takes a lot to distract me from putting the kettle on!). I just made my way to the settee and lay down. No sooner had my head touched the cushion than I fell into a deep and very restful sleep.

I woke an hour later, aware that the sensation of being massaged and pummelled had gone completely and so, to my utter delight had the pain and stiffness. I got up cautiously and discovered that I felt as good as new, supple and flexible. This feeling generally takes several days to come back after a flare up and is a gradual rather than an instantaneous thing. I sent a heartfelt thank you to my unseen therapists.

That was six years ago, I have not had a bad flare up in all that time and I find I can maintain my good health by visualising a green healing light flowing in through my crown chakra (on the top of my head) and bathing all my joints.

My healer friend always explained that healing came through her as a conduit rather than from her personally. It appears that all I needed was to ask and because I was receptive I tapped directly into the source of healing energy. I know this sounds far fetched and I would have been entirely sceptical had I not experienced it first hand (several of them actually) so to speak.

Chapter Fifteen
The Dreamtime

Visits beyond the veil

From being small I have always had the most amazing dreams. Some of previous existences, some of travelling, flying at high speed across different landscapes, seeing the world from above, some precognitive, occasionally involving family members returning to pass on information to me. Now it seems I was ready to cross the divide for myself.

One of the first times I had the feeling that I actually had visited the other side rather than having a visitor from there involved my Aunty Mary. She had been gone from this side of life for about a year and, much as you would expect me to dream of her often, up to that point there was nothing I could recall. In my dream I was standing outside a door, someone unknown to me opened it and said I could go in now. I didn't question this, I just entered the room.

The room was quite dim. There were wooden walls, similar to a log cabin effect, but at the other side I could just glimpse another door part-way open, the most beautiful sunlight was glowing around the edges of it.

Sitting next to this door, on a plain wooden bench, was my Aunty Mary. She looked much better than when I had last seen her, though not completely well. Her hair was thicker and browner, all the grey had disappeared, and her face looked more youthful. I could tell she was happy to see me once again.

I found myself sitting on a bench opposite her. She seemed to speak with her mind rather than her lips and I was invited to ask questions.

"Where is this place?" was the first thing that came to mind.

Aunty Mary described it as the "Waiting Room" but I didn't understand what she meant. She explained to me that sometimes when a person has had a particularly hard life, a sudden, shocking exit or a traumatic illness (as in her own case) they arrived at the other side still suffering the ill effects in some way. A period of rest and relaxation is prescribed and slowly and gently the returned spirit is healed. It is as if everything goes into reverse and not only do the physical ailments begin to recede but the spirit also rejuvenates to whatever age in their life they feel most comfortable (often mid twenties to early thirties). A child arriving would progress upwards in age in much the same way as if they were still on the material plane.

Aunty Mary explained that this is why, after a person's funeral, there is frequently a "silent," period, where we have no contact from them. They need to have this period of readjustment to the other side again.

"I've almost completed this now," she thought to me with a lovely smile. I had the impression she had requested our meeting and that as part of her healing process she needed to reassure loved ones of her soul's survival on the other side.

It was important for us to move forward from the grieving process on both sides of the veil. Sometimes we do not realise that by grieving too deeply in the material world we impede the process of the spirit advancing on the other side, as they are called back to us again and again. (This is not the same as thinking of them, sending out messages and loving thoughts. It is more when we wallow in the depths of despair that we unwittingly trap the energy of our loved ones to this plane, and stop them from moving on freely).

I was permitted a brief hug by persons/spirits unknown, then Aunty Mary exited through the other door into the radiant light and I found myself in bed, wide awake.

You have to understand that this was a strange concept for me at that point in time. When I did consider an afterlife I had always supposed that you arrived on the other side perfect, healthy and ready to hop onto your cloud with your harp. I was intrigued by the idea of aging backwards; it had never occurred to me that you would be any different from how you were when you departed.

It was only years later when I started investigating further that I came across many pieces of literature from mediums and inter-life regression papers that I found this is reported several times. Once again it was validated that this was not purely the workings of a fertile imagination.

As if I needed further evidence Mark had a similar experience many years later, several months after his father, Dennis, had passed away. He described the wooden walled room to me and the plain benches they had sat upon. I told him it was the "Waiting Room".

He looked at me cynically.

"It was a dream, Jane," was all he said.

The three wise babies

I have had three visitations that each time followed the same pattern. The main criteria seemed to be that I had to be pregnant at the time. In each supposed dream I found myself in a room somewhere, in the presence of what I have come to term as a "wise baby". This is, to all intents and purposes, a baby in appearance but with the eyes of a very old soul.

In each dream this baby has telepathically communicated to my unconscious mind who it really is and what we have agreed prior to its (and indeed my own) birth. Sadly, I can't consciously retrieve this information.

This dream has recurred three times, just prior to the birth of my three children. It leads me to believe that I have had a contract with each of them for a long time in which I agreed to be their mother in this lifetime. Again, this is something that happened long before I started to get really interested in the spirit world and prior to my reading any well known texts, which explain that before we accept another incarnation we plan a life chart and co-ordinate it with everyone who will play a major role with us in this lifetime. This includes family members, partners, close friends and in some cases enemies, as each person's task is to spark a new challenge, support or hinder progress in some way.

Just as I recognised Mark as my soul mate and the person I would eventually marry on first meeting (and boy, have we provided each other with challenges) I felt a similar instant recognition with a variety of friends. It is no coincidence that one of my closest lifelong companions is my cousin Matthew, born just one month after me. Like Mark he is inclined to dismiss all this as my delusional mind, yet has remained a staunch supporter and ally throughout my life in anything I ever decided to do. He doesn't believe in God, but I am sure he would acknowledge that somehow there has always been an ancient connection between us.

Before each of my children was born I felt incredibly broody. It was less the need to have a baby than the urgent imperative from somewhere that a baby was waiting to make its appearance. Even before I found out I was pregnant with Anthony, and let's face it I certainly wasn't planning on becoming an unmarried mother at that stage in my life, I just had a feeling that something momentous was about to happen. When I discovered I was pregnant it was a kind of "Aha, so this is what happens next," kind of feeling. Mark was taken slightly more by surprise than I was, and twenty-three years later you could say he's still in shock.

In case you're wondering, the babies in my dreams didn't in any way resemble the ones that arrived; they were androgynous for one thing. I had no inkling of whether they would be male or female when they were born and they each had identical mops of dark brown hair and huge brown eyes. My children were all blonde/fair and had blue/grey eyes. They were representative of the old souls about to be reborn as opposed to the children they would become this time round.

It's an interesting concept that not only is it possible to be reunited with loved ones on the other side through dreams and astral travel, it is also possible to meet with souls not incarnated with you this time round and still feel that easy familiarity you have with friends and family in the material world.

The Summerland

Gradually, over time I have found myself visiting the other side more and more frequently in my dreams. How can I tell it's the other side? For one thing the dreams are incredibly lucid. I can always remember every detail on waking, they make sense, unlike your average dream (which is just the mind's way of downloading all the junk it's encountered), and there is a certain uplifting quality to the experience. Waking from a visit to the spirit world leaves you with a feeling of being revitalised, refreshed and rejuvenated.

For another thing there is the daylight there which is unlike anything encountered on the material plane. It is the sunniest, warmest and most tranquil atmosphere you can imagine but with ten times the intensity. The sky is a blue too beautiful to imagine and the whole place engenders a thrill like embarking on the voyage of a lifetime, Christmas Eve when you were a child, or falling in love for the very first time. From the moment I arrive there until I leave again I feel a tingle of anticipatory excitement. Whether I encounter someone I know or not, just being there is uplifting enough.

The place I find myself returning to is like an old-fashioned seaside town. The sea is a crystal clear blue, reflecting the magnificent sky. I spend a lot of time in a little harbour there, just looking at the boats and the water. There are streets and streets of quaint little shops, the type with many paned windows. Every shop is painted a different bright colour and sells intriguing objects and beautiful artefacts. It is like a child's version of fairyland.

There are several tearooms and restaurants, these are frequently the places I encounter my relatives. (Mark would probably remark that I've gone to bed hungry, once again).

Now let me explain this as best as I have come to understand it. We don't actually need to eat on the other side. Our physical bodies are gone but we are capable of experiencing any pleasurable sensation we wish and so many spirits still enjoy the sociable aspects of eating and drinking. Likewise, we no longer have any need for money but many of us still like the experience of shopping, purely for pleasure.

I know from many of the descriptions I have read that there are many different aspects to the spirit world and this is just a small part of it that I seem to access quite easily. I believe that everyone has different perceptions depending on what represents Heaven to them but the one constant in every instance I've heard of is the luminous, radiant, uplifting quality of the light. That, for me, defines where I've been once I wake up and recall it.

Interestingly, I discovered not so long ago that another name for the astral plane is "The Summerland" and, having been there, I know why!

The not so old soldier

It was on one of these trips to the "other side" that I encountered Uncle Jack again for the first time in months.

In this dream I had Aunty May along with me. This is quite unusual in itself, as I generally seem to make these visits alone. We had been looking in the windows and exploring the pretty little shops together when Aunty May expressed the desire to have a cream bun and a pot of tea.

She and I chose one of the many tearooms and seated ourselves by a table quite near the door. It had a pretty white lace tablecloth and a vase with some flowers of a variety I've never seen before, but they were beautiful with bright vivid colours.

As we waited for our tea and buns to arrive I gazed around the café. From a table at the far side came much merriment and laughter. I looked across and there were three soldiers, dressed in World War Two khaki uniforms. One of them seemed quite familiar somehow.

As I caught the eye of this soldier he suddenly scrambled to his feet, excused himself to his colleagues and made his way through the tables towards us. Now to my delight I could see it was Uncle Jack. However, not poor eighty year old Uncle Jack as I had last seen him. This was a much younger and more vibrant version, tanned, healthy, at the most in his late thirties, I would have guessed.

"Well, well, fancy seeing you here!" He declared, obviously delighted to find I'd stumbled across his hideout on the other side.

"You look better, a lot younger too," I told him.

He smiled.

"Best of all I can eat now, I'm having fish and chips again," he informed me, he nodded towards Aunty May, who was seemingly oblivious to his presence, or maybe she just didn't recognise him.

"Tell Aunty May about the fish and chips, she'll be pleased," he added.

With that he gave a grin and a wink and made his way back to his companions. I found myself at home in bed once more, but feeling extremely happy to have seen him.

The next time I saw Aunty May I made a point of telling her about my "dream". She was very pleased about the fish and chips as he'd predicted. Uncle Jack had passed over due to cancer of the oesophagus. As part of the attempt to keep him alive as long as possible the doctors had to put a plastic tube down his throat. Not only was this incredibly unpleasant, it meant he could no longer eat solid food at all. Uncle Jack's only remark on the subject was a heartfelt sigh.

"No more fish and chips," he'd said.

Brief encounter

The more I recount these experiences to you the more I realise just how much time I spend in eating establishments on the other side. No wonder I'm putting on weight, I'm eating through the night as well as the day!

So, there I was, on the other side again, this time in what appeared to be a food mall of some kind. The kind of place where there are lots of different stalls selling a variety of tempting dishes of every type imaginable. I was seated in some sort of a booth and I had a pushchair with me; Jessica was in it (she was just a tot at that time in reality). I have found that although the children accompany me from time to time Mark never, ever does. I was in the process of feeding Jess and myself, a spoonful for Jess, a spoonful for mummy, a bit of mopping up between mouthfuls, typical lunchtime with a toddler type scenario.

I became aware of a middle aged woman in the next booth. She seemed very familiar but I couldn't place her, somehow. She was impeccably dressed and had thick dark brown wavy hair, set under a small pillbox hat reminiscent of the forties or fifties style. She seemed to be regarding me on and off too, in a contemplative way, but neither of us spoke. When she had finished her cup of tea she picked up her handbag and walked purposely towards me.

"What a lovely little girl," she remarked, tickling Jess under the chin. Jess laughed up at her, blue eyes twinkling.

"I know you from somewhere, don't I?" She smiled, then shook her head. "I'm sure it will come to me later," and with a smile to us both she left.

I was still trying to figure out who she was several days later. As I was looking through an old box of photographs the answer came to me. This attractive, elegant lady in her mid-thirties was actually my Nana. The last time I'd seen her she had been eighty-six, little and bent by the years, with steel-grey hair. I had been nineteen, still young, slim and childless. No wonder we had struggled to recognise each other in our current guises. Once again, this reinforced to me the belief that on the other side we age in reverse and also far more rapidly than in the material world. If it was just a dream, as Mark insists, why would I consistently see family members getting ever younger, stronger and healthier; to the point that I now only recognise some relatives from photos taken before I was born?

A fragrant spirit

I dreamt of my mother not so long ago. We sat and talked for a long time. Once again it was one of those experiences where her words were some guidance for my unconscious mind and I couldn't recall the discussion when I awoke. The one thing I did take with me, much to my delight, was a scent I hadn't recalled since her passing. Just as I was about to leave she caught me in a hug, laughing and resting her head on my shoulder as she used to do at the end of our late night chats when I was a teenager. As I woke up I could still smell the scent of her perfume, hair, and skin. It lingered on my shoulder and pillow.

I heard of people smelling fragrances of loved ones that had passed before, but this was a new and very pleasant experience for me, and further evidence that these night time visits were so much more than dreams.

The Dark Side

There is another place I have visited on my nocturnal travels. I never go there alone. At first I was aware of my guide as little more than a protective shadow by my side but more recently I have been able to look upon him properly.

Dressed in a black robe from head to foot, this is a dark angel; protector of the darker realms, the lowest dimension, and the place where souls whose vibration is too dense to reach the higher realms above, abide.

I have no doubt that this is where the image of the Grim Reaper evolved from, but I feel nothing but strength and infinite compassion emanating from this being, and I am never afraid to travel with him.

This realm is what people of a religious background would determine as Hell, but it is not hot and fiery, and people are not cast down there by an angry God. I am told that this realm is inhabited by souls who through their own life choices caused pain and misery to others. Now it is their own guilt that holds them prisoner here.

It is a widely held belief that the soul reverberates faster the more advanced the being is. Acts of love, kindness and compassion raise the vibration, while cruel, malicious, evil deeds lower it. At the point of physical death our spirits go to the level we have achieved. An advanced soul can visit spirits in the lower realms but in order to visit a higher realm the spirit would have to work to raise their vibration by acts of kindness and compassion, possibly through another incarnation, hence the idea of karma.

In life these tormented souls have never lifted their vibration. They do not reach out to the light because they are unaware that it exists. This place is dark, it is like the loneliest parts of a city unlit by street lamps, and it is cold.

I have been allowed to walk these streets in order to have a better understanding of how the other side works. My dark companion gives me a feeling of safety and security but he does not shield me from sensing the despair inherent in this place. I have never seen anyone, yet I know they are there, closeted behind those dark, blank, windows. It is the stillest, most silent place I have ever encountered. I am always relieved to return home from there.

I do not believe that the souls that inhabit that plane have to stay there forever; I think eventually there is a chance for them to reincarnate and try to rectify past mistakes.

This much I have realised from my research and exploration;

God, or the Universe, depending on how you view the eternal source of light, does not punish us, we raise or diminish ourselves by our own thoughts and deeds.

There is one belief of several religions which I absolutely dispute. That is the idea that suicide casts a person's soul down to this region. I must stress that this is absolutely untrue. Someone who takes their own life breaks a contract because they have set themselves too hard a task in this existence. They are greeted on the other side with unconditional love and compassion by their friends and guides. Ultimately they have to face the realisation of the pain they have caused to loved ones on this side of the veil and that in itself is punishment enough. They will still need to return at some point and face up to the challenges that were too much for them this time round but they will try a different strategy and take on board more support next time.

The other misconception is that non-believers will also find their souls condemned to this dark place. I would again say that this is untrue. My Granddad was a lifelong atheist and he has shown up in dreams and through mediums on several occasions. I know many atheists who are of the highest-minded, humanitarian, loving spirit imaginable. Lack of any religious belief does not lower the vibration of these souls.

At the end, it does not matter if you believe in God, only that he believes in you. I fully expect that the worst that my disbelieving husband will experience on the other side is my greeting him with an "I told you so!" This will really annoy him; he so hates to be wrong.

Chapter Sixteen
Close encounters

Drawing closer

Our loved ones on the other side don't experience the pain of separation in the same way that we do. There are several reasons for this. For one thing they are wiser than us, in that they know for a fact that they are only apart from us temporarily. They are able to see us when they like, so do not miss us like we do them. They are in a place where there is no negativity and all they experience is peace, love and laughter. There is no time as we understand it on the other side; it is not linear, so to them they will be with us again in the blink of an eye.

How do I know these things? From things I have been told by them, dreamed, and read over and over again reiterated by some of the finest mediums the world has to offer.

I do not worry about my departed loved ones at all, I know they are fine. This doesn't mean they aren't concerned for our welfare. When we are upset they draw close and once their energy field connects with ours they are able once again to feel the strength of human emotions.

If you watch some of our well-loved televised mediums at work you will often see them asking a spirit to draw back and give just the words not the emotions. This is because the spirit has drawn close to their loved one and connected with the emotion again.

When they communicate to the medium they transfer this emotional energy as well, a clairsentient medium (one who connects by feeling) will pick up on this and can be equally overwhelmed by the surge of emotion.

It is not just sorrow that they sense though. They are often drawn to us at the happiest times and they love to feel our joy and laughter. If you are having a wonderful family celebration you can guarantee there are several extra unseen guests at the occasion.

Many well-known mediums say they struggle to receive messages personal to themselves. This is probably because they are afraid that things they pick up for themselves are a product of their own imagination and they are far more comfortable reading for other people.

I have found over time that it is quite easy for me to sense when loved ones in spirit draw close, and have become adept at differentiating between them, although I can't always grasp what they are trying to tell me.

My mum's presence usually makes herself felt by a prickling, tickling sensation on the back of my neck and hair. As she draws closer I feel an excited, overjoyed emotion start to surface, like someone bubbling over with laughter at the thrill of seeing you again. If I keep very still I can sometimes make out a phrase or message or get a visual impression of what she wants me to know. Though, often, it is just that she is coming near purely to say hello.

Aunty Mary's energy is much subtler. It is more like someone wrapping a warm blanket round your shoulders, soothing and comforting. I know when she is there, but I can't generally discern a message. She is still as quiet and gentle as in life.

Uncle Jack's presence feels more like someone standing behind me and politely clearing their throat. Once he has my attention I will get a strong visual image of the message he wishes to convey, or sometimes a short phrase. Uncle Jack's is the voice most likely to take charge when there is a crisis looming; he goes into his army sergeant mode and barks out helpful instructions. Uncle Jack is often perceived as the voice of reason and authority, much as in life, similarly Aunty Mary offers gentle strength and comfort, and my mother is madcap mayhem and hilarity personified – she never changes.

I have been told by a few mediums that Uncle Jack is a good communicator. The first time he came through to me via a medium was a wonderful experience. I sat in her tiny reading room and suddenly became aware that the temperature around me had plummeted. I had a sensation like running water going up and down my spine.

This feeling dissipated as Uncle Jack transferred his energy to the medium. She told me that she had a man with her. He'd been rather excited that I was going to see her and had been hanging around a while with her. (Old habits die hard, excuse the pun, in life he was always early for appointments!) She then went on to describe the condition he had passed over with (cancer of the oesophagus) but reassured me that he was fine now.

I got many validations to confirm it was Uncle Jack. He expressed concern for Aunty May's bad knee, said he was pleased to see I was still keeping my diary (I had kept it from being seventeen and now had years worth of recorded memories – he obviously knew they'd come in very handy someday!), he finished off by saying, "And of course, we are looking out for the children," in a "what else do you expect?" kind of way. I had to laugh, as whenever I send out thoughts to my family in spirit I usually add that they are to "watch out for my children, whenever I'm unable to."

This was one of the things that later led me to the spiritualist church. I had purposely avoided mediums for many years as I wasn't entirely sure I believed in them but this woman's accuracy matched with the sensations I experienced in that room delighted me and convinced me there was definitely something worth pursuing further here.

Another time, a different medium, my friend had gone in first to be read, and I was left alone with the medium's girlfriend. She was really pleasant and explained to me that as she was also in training, could she possibly try and see if she got anything for me. I was fine with this, it was two for the price of one after all, but I wasn't expecting much as she had said she was just a beginner.

She said she had the impression of a soldier standing behind me and got the name of Jack or John (Uncle Jack was actually John, but called Jack all his life). I smiled and thought hello to Uncle Jack; I was far more used to him showing up by this point.

Then I had an idea.

"Do you remember the yomping?" I thought to him. (Uncle Jack used to meet me from my friend's house when I was a teenager and walk me safely home. Always full of fun he used to insist we had to "yomp" like soldiers did in jungle terrain. A kind of bizarre walk that involved lifting your knees to chest height and stamping them back down powerfully as you march, it looked like something straight out of Monty Python's "Ministry of silly walks" sketch. This was something entirely personal to our relationship, a joke between us).

She frowned for a moment.

"I don't know what he means by this," she said, "but I can see him stamping his foot down, he's saying something that sounds like stomp, stomp."

I was beside myself with happiness. Not only had she seen Uncle Jack, I had been able to communicate a request to him and he had been able to pass it back via this lovely girl, who admittedly was only practising her skills, though clearly she will make an excellent medium someday!

The main medium that night was rather hit and miss, but I had nothing to complain about, I had already had my contact for that evening and I was more than satisfied.

They show up when you least expect it

Sometimes it is apparent that we are being watched over and assisted by the other side. They cannot always prevent hard times and tragedy coming into our lives but there is often a sense of them trying to soften the blow.

There was a family wedding down in Surrey. We were all very excited and we were travelling south en masse for the nuptial celebrations. Aunty Margery and Uncle Jim weren't really up to the journey so they weren't going, but two of their sons and one daughter-in-law were expected. However, at the last moment something happened that meant unfortunately Martin and his wife Andrea had to stay at home which meant that Matthew was also unable to attend as he was going to travel down with them. The rest of us journeyed south and a good time was had by all (more of that later).

Back up north, as we were travelling south, the day began like any other. Aunty Margery got up first and went downstairs to make a cup of tea and turned the gas oven on low to warm up the kitchen. Uncle Jim in the meantime was slowly and steadily getting washed and dressed. He had suffered from a crumbling spine and poor mobility for years, so these things couldn't be rushed.

Aunty Margery was in the hallway just watering a plant when something caught her eye. The hallway leads on to the living room, and the kitchen in turn leads off from that. From her vantage point in the hall Aunty Margery looked in amazement as a number of flaming kitchen rolls bouncing off the top of the fridge and onto the kitchen floor. Hardly believing her eyes, she started into the living room from where she could see flames roaring up the back of the fridge and towards the kitchen ceiling. As their main exit was the outside door located in the kitchen she realised one escape route was effectively cut off. Courageously, she crossed the living room and closed the door between the kitchen and the living room to keep the fire at bay a little longer. Heading purposely back into the hall she started dialling 999 only pausing to call, "Jim dear, you better hurry, the house appears to be on fire!"

Now is probably a good time to explain that my Aunt and Uncle were both possessed of that stout English spirit that refuses to be ruffled in the face of famine, flood, pestilence or, as it happens, fire. None of that silly "Oh my God, we're all going to die!" attitude for them. If you're going to meet your maker prepare to face him with your boots polished and your cardigan properly fastened up!

Uncle Jim, fortuitously, by this time had mounted the stair lift, and it was trundling slowly down the stairs. He told me later that just at that moment he wished it had an accelerator on it. He arrived at the bottom of the stairs just as Aunty Margery finished her 999 call.

Smoke was starting to billow across the ceiling, time was running out. Uncle Jim was trying to open the Yale lock on the front door which was seldom used and prone to sticking. From the other side a host of well-intentioned neighbours were attempting to shoulder barge the door.

"Stop banging the bloody door!" Uncle Jim commanded through the letterbox. "I can't get this bloody lock to open with you lot pushing on it!"

The neighbours drew back respectfully, and with one last surge of energy Uncle Jim managed to get the lock to open. The door opened and the next-door-neighbour and his friend managed to carry Uncle Jim through the door and down the steps in his wheel chair, which was luckily stored in the hallway.

They were out into the fresh air. The kind woman from across the street took them in for tea and biscuits and they were able to make a phone call to Matthew. How fortunate that he was now on hand to help out instead of being hundreds of miles away at Lee's wedding!

It transpired that a gas pipe had fractured and been leaking slowly behind the fridge. Strange as it may seem it was actually lucky that when Aunty Margery lit the gas oven the gas ignited, otherwise it may have continued to build to the point where an explosion became inevitable.

The fire had occurred a year to the day after a small burglary. An opportunist thief had managed to break into their kitchen and steal Aunty Marge's new radio cassette recorder. Uncle Jim had been outraged that after forty years of paying insurance he still had to pay excess that cancelled out the cost of the radio and was about to cancel his policy. Fortunately, Mark and I had called round to commiserate and managed to talk him out of it. So now the insurers had to house Aunty Margery and Uncle Jim in a hotel for a few months. Matthew oversaw the repairs to the property, including a new kitchen, and saw to all the paperwork. The hotel was just round the corner from our house, so ideally placed for Mark, the kids, and I to call in and visit.

My first day back at work after the wedding, I got a phone call from Matthew to tell me what had happened. We both agreed it seemed like fate had conspired to keep him at home where he would be needed. Five minutes after I'd put the phone down the fire alarm went off at work. We all traipsed outside for half an hour. It turned out it hadn't been a practise, yet there was no fire either, the alarm had mysteriously gone off by itself! I had a feeling someone was just letting me know they were aware, and they had the situation all under control.

Northerners head South

Mum has her hands full; she must spend her time flitting back and forth between Dad, my brother and his family, and me and mine. Mark the kids and I drove down south for my brother Lee's wedding. Dad travelled down by plane, and there was another car-load with my cousins; Young Lou (not so young by this time), his sons Brad, Graham, Heath (more commonly referred to, in recent years, as George, Herbert and Ted) and Heath's wife Emma. It being November, the journey was particularly long and arduous, with erratic weather conditions and poor visibility, still everyone was in high spirits and the kids were excited to be seeing their Uncle Lee get married. It was to be Jessica's first time as a brides-maid and she had been dying to see her dress for weeks.

We made reasonable time until we hit the legendary M25 in the rush hour on a Friday afternoon. This is a total contradiction in terms, nothing rushes anywhere on the M25 during the rush hour!

I rang Lou: "Ey up," came the familiar gruff northern voice. After a bit of friendly banter we ascertained we had all roughly hit the M25 at the same time

"It's been a long journey," Lou commented, "our Herbert started asking if we were "nearly there yet?" forty minutes into the expe-dition. We'd only just got past Sheffield; then again, furthest he's been is the far side of Greengates Park."

It turns out we were going the opposite way round the M25 to each other.

"It'll take you hours!" I told Lou. "Good luck!"

The phone clicked off on some good-natured expletives from the other end.

We crawled and crawled. Two hours in traffic to move only eight miles. Luckily we were just coming up on Heathrow Air-port; a chance to point at aeroplanes close up!

Eventually we got to our hotel, seven hours after we set off, tired, hungry, but still in high spirits. Lou and co. walked in right behind us… I couldn't believe it. Apparently, although they had a lot further to travel, driving away from Epsom to begin with, bizarrely their side of the motorway had been virtually empty, and Emma had sped round like a bat out of Hell, pulling up behind us in the car park only minutes later!

We all dumped our cases and met up in the restaurant for a

hearty meal and several drinks all round.

The morning of the wedding arrived. We dropped Jess at Lee's house as she was one of the bridesmaids and would be getting ready there. Mark, the boys and I returned to our hotel and proceeded to get our outfits on.

I should learn to engage my brain before I put my mouth in gear, because Mark was all dressed up and ready to go when I decided to say that I didn't think the tie he had brought was a good match with the shirt and suit. Mark looked in the mirror and agreed with me.

"Never mind," he said, he thought he had seen a gentleman's outfitters near where we had dropped Jess off, it would be a ten minute job to nip out and buy a new tie. I've learned over the years that once Mark has a bee in his bonnet about something it's best to just let him get on with it. Plus we still had an hour, plenty of time, he persuaded me, so off he went.

An hour later the boys and I were standing in the foyer, still looking out for him. Lou and the others had apologetically said they had better set off, but they would let Lee know why I wasn't there.

Just as I was about to tear my hair out Mark appeared, he had got a bit lost he said, but the good news was his tie now matched his suit. I refrained from strangling him with it because he was the only one amongst us able to drive!

We set off, someone (naturally we all blamed Lee) had written out the directions, sadly not from our hotel, but from a starting point in the middle of Epsom. There was one small problem with this; the Chinese restaurant he had chosen as our marker had the smallest, most well-hidden sign I've ever seen, or in this case almost didn't see!

Around and around Epsom we went, dementedly. I rang Lou for inspiration, however, they were also lost and doing the same loop as us over and over again.

There was much hysterical laughter as we despaired of ever getting to this wedding. As luck would have it, as we passed the place for the fifth time round Mark caught sight of the restaurant's sign at last.

I rang Lou and tried to explain where we were, then we were off, speeding down little country lanes. At this point torrential rain started to pour down. I felt certain we had already missed the wedding, as we were very late, and kept telling Mark he'd be as well to slow down, there was no point in him killing us all when chances were it was halfway through the ceremony by now.

In the midst of all this chaos Mum arrived, suddenly she was cackling in my ear like the witch from "The Wizard of Oz".

"Excuse me Mother," I thought to her, "but I don't quite see the hilarity in travelling over two hundred miles to see my one and only brother get married and then missing it!" More laughter in my head, I was beginning to wonder if maybe it wasn't her at all and I'd finally gone insane.

"Don't worry, you wont miss it," came the reassuring thought. There was something distinctly mischievous in that reply.

"Mother, what have you done now?" I asked. She vanished without deigning to respond.

In a flurry of mud and churning tyres we pulled into the church yard. To my surprise two ushers with enormous umbrellas appeared to escort us inside.

"Hurry," they said. "The bride's nearly here."

Nearly here, I'd expected the ceremony to be half over! I rang Lou; sadly, they were still doing the "Epsom Tour" trying to find the starting block for the map. Mark, the boys and I rushed down the aisle and collapsed in a heap on the seat next to Dad. He raised an eyebrow.

"Talk about cutting it fine, what kept you?" he asked.

Lee turned around. "Nice of you to make an appearance," he grinned.

"I was going to ring you, but your phone's turned off," I explained.

"Yes, I thought you might ring," he said, "that's precisely why my phone is turned off!"

For some reason he'd envisaged me calling just as he was making his vows, I don't know what he takes me for!

Suddenly the bridal march began, the long awaited bride had arrived. We scrambled to our feet and tried to look presentable.

I peered down the aisle to see Jessica walking proudly with the other bridesmaids; she looked lovely.

Mum was back, this time she had wedged herself between Dad and me.

"Told you you'd make it," she laughed.

I spent the entire ceremony with one ear on the service, and the other tuned in to Mum's exclamations of pride; how smart Lee looked, how adorable Jessica was in her bridesmaid dress, didn't Dad look well, weren't the boys growing tall. She was having a wonderful time and, as I was the only one aware of her presence, I was the sole recipient of her very loud and vocal glee.

At some point I could hear her sniffling loudly.

"Do you have a handkerchief on the other side, Mother?" I wondered. There was a trumpeting as she blew her nose, rather loudly in my ear. I told you they only get emotional when they get close, well I reckon she was sitting in my lap at this point. Now and again she would zip off for a moment or two, I'm guessing to get in closer to the action. But as she had established contact with me she would be back in a flash to continue her soliloquy. It was only after the ceremony that Mum went quiet at last. Presumably she was now checking out the rest of the guests.

Much later I managed to catch up with Lee and offer my congratulations. I explained the ordeal we'd had getting there (poor Lou and co. arrived so late they daren't come in and had sat out the ceremony in the local pub). Jessica told me that the deluge of rain started just as the bridesmaids had set off and, wouldn't you know it, the windscreen wipers had decided to stop working that morning. The driver had to keep stopping the car, leaping out and wiping the windscreen. They had crawled all the way to the church. He then had to make a second trip with the bride. Fortunately she had intended to be fashionably late, which was just as well!

Mum's maniacal laughter sprang to mind. I shook my head; she had clearly known something we didn't. If you don't buy into that, then, as Mark would say, it was quite a coincidence, wasn't it?

Somehow, we all managed to arrive at the reception without

getting lost. I was relieved to see Lou and the northern contingent already arrived, looking tall and splendid in their suits and ties, if a little ill at ease in the manner of fellas more used to jeans and t-shirts.

Emma looked lovely, Mark and the boys smart (all with impeccably matching ties) and Jess floated about in her bridesmaid dress. Even I had managed to find a suitable outfit for the occasion, we had all scrubbed up well, you might say.

Dad joined us briefly. His sister, my Aunty Kath, and her husband, Uncle John, where there, along with their five grown-up children and respective partners. One of these being my cousin, Anne Daniels, the record-breaking polar explorer. It struck me as funny that she can navigate across frozen waste lands with only a compass and the light of the sun and stars while I couldn't navigate round Epsom with the aid of some instructions and a road map!

Dad was gravitating between the two groups, in between photo calls and being introduced to the bride's family.

Eventually, we were shown into the main dining room for a lavish sit down meal. Mark, the kids and I were pleased to find our table large enough to seat Lou and the Webster clan as well. Anthony had been given the task of recording the speeches on our camcorder, which he dutifully did, all with the lens cap on, so we might as well have taken a tape recorder!

The speeches were well thought out and witty, but I often wish we had recorded the discussion round the dinner table. Musings over where the gravy was and what was this drizzled congealed goo (jus), why we were having a pudding in the middle of the meal (the champagne sorbet palette cleanser) and, my personal favourite, when being served the chocolate dessert and raspberry coulis our Herbert demanding, "What's with this red sauce shit?"

"Hark at Egon Ronay there," said Lou, laughing.

It was a fine meal, but if someone had borne in a platter of pork pies and a bottle of "Daddy's Sauce" it would have been no less appreciated!

The day wore on, dancing and drinking (except for poor Mark, who doesn't dance and couldn't drink as he was the driver) until eventually, around two in the morning, we were able to give the newlywed's a congratulatory kiss, make our excuses and leave.

So, there we were, let loose on the roads of Surrey again. Lost. We kept following the signs back to Epsom but the weird thing was, no matter what route we took, we always ended up in a place called Reigate, and there the trail went cold.

Mark was playing a CD by "The Stranglers", a strange track that breaks out into diabolical laughter over what sounds a bit like distorted Wurlitzer music in the background (Waltz in Black), a fitting soundtrack to our aimless meanderings down the back roads and by ways of Surrey.

Eventually I had a brainwave.

"Let's stop trying to get to Epsom, lets follow the roads to Dorking instead," I suggested.

Lee had lived in Dorking a few years before; it was the only other place I knew. So we did, and wouldn't you know it, we found Epsom while looking for Dorking. I maintain to this day that down south, after dark, all roads lead to Reigate!

The next day we packed up and headed home. A big cheer went up as we passed Watford gap. We were heading north and we knew which way to go for the first time in days!

Back in Bradford, as we stumbled wearily from the car, I understood the whole "Pope kissing the ground" thing, on landing in a country. It was all I could do to keep from falling to my knees, Yorkshire, blessed Yorkshire.

As Dorothy once said, "There's no place like home!"

Wishes granted

Although she has now been dead (in the physical, bodily sense) over twenty years, my mum still likes to put in an appearance every so often. Generally, what I feel is her presence. With all spirits it feels much the same way as if you were sitting in a room and someone you were close to just walked in. You would probably sense them even if you didn't hear their footsteps and before you turned and saw them. As they draw closer still their personality starts to make itself felt more strongly.

Sometimes I would just be sitting at work tapping away on my computer, with nothing in my head but mortgages, and all of a sudden there she would be beside me. Often a memory will pop unbidden into my head, as if someone is saying, "Hey, do you remember when we did this?"

I frequently get the physical sensation of fingers twiddling with my hair, something she suggested she would try and do by way of contact when she passed over; obviously she has now mastered this. Then every so often I'll hear a burst of infectious laughter in my head, frequently teamed with a favourite quote or expression she used a lot; it's like someone reminding you to lighten up.

A few years ago Mark and I were pleased to hear our eldest son, Anthony, had been offered a place at university. On the one hand this was a cause for celebration, on the other a cause for consternation. Because Mark's and my combined salaries came above a certain threshold Anthony would get no help with his fees, which came to more than a thousand pounds. The assumption is that if you earn above a certain amount you must therefore be able to pay for your child's education, except at eighteen Anthony was not a child, he was an adult, but had no means of paying the fees himself until he started earning.

Mark and I had struggled for many years to get to where we were and part of that meant amassing loans for cars, furniture and other necessities that we were now in the process of paying back. Spare cash was, as ever, hard to come by.

I was in the bathroom, pondering over the dilemma as I got dressed for work, pleased, but also wondering how we would manage to pay the fees. Characteristically, at this point my mother "showed up". The feeling was one of overwhelming exuberance, I could tell she was chuffed to bits that her first grandchild was going to university (she had always aspired for me to do this, but I'd never got round to it). The impression I had was of someone laughing and saying, "Isn't it wonderful? Isn't it brilliant? I'm so proud, I'm so excited!".

"Mother," I said, "I don't want to dampen your enthusiasm, but how on Earth are we going to pay for this; wonderful news, though it is?"

More elated feelings abounded, a feeling of "what the Hell, its only money," and then her favourite phrase from the film "Mame"; "Life is a banquet and most poor sons of bitches are starving to death!" For anyone not familiar with the phrase, it doesn't mean literally starving, but depriving themselves of all the wonderful experiences life has to offer.

It was Mum's way of telling me and Lee to just get out in the world and "Live!" Lee was pretty good at this, I was far more cautious, once upon a time.

"Yes," I thought wryly, "and we'll be starving with them if you have your way." Then a thought occurred. "Hold on a minute," I said to her, "you're so clever, you find a way for us to pay these fees!"

It was like "poof" and she was gone. Her essence vanished from the bathroom without a trace, just me, alone again, staring at my frown lines in the mirror.

"Ha, that shut you up fast!" I thought. Out on the landing folk were braying on the door to get into the bathroom. You can picture the scene, "Oy, stop arguing with the dead people and let us in!"

I arrived at work and just as I was getting seated my manager called me over. Wondering what I'd done to warrant this attention so early in the day I followed her out of the office and into one of our training rooms. She passed me a pink envelope.

"Oh great," I thought. "Start the day off by getting my cards!"

"In view of all the hard work you've been doing recently I decided you were due a pay rise," she smiled.

I opened my envelope and there in black and white was my revised contract. My salary had been raised by just over a thousand pounds.

"Thank you," I spluttered, grinning from ear to ear. I wasn't sure who I was saying it to, my very generous boss, or my mother and her immaculate timing. She always was a show off!

Long distance call

Sadly Young Lou and his wife Lynda had divorced, amicably, after many years of marriage. After initial sadness, Lou was getting on with his life and had found a new partner. By strange coincidence an old girlfriend had signed up to "Friends Reunited" within an hour of Lou going on it for the first time. They were delighted to make contact again, but meeting in person would be easier said than done, as Pam now lived in Canada.

For a couple of years they spent all their spare cash and every bit of holiday entitlement flitting back and forth around the world.

On one of Pam's longer visits Lou suddenly got the urge for them to go on holiday abroad together; somewhere different to experience other than England or Canada.

The tale which follows is both strange and poignant; I thought I would let Lou recall it in his own words:

Hi Jane, Re Tale....

Dec 5th 2005, I was made redundant at art glass; Pam was due over from Canada for a few weeks over the Crimbo/ New Year period. I thought it would be a treat for the two of us to take a warm break... Lanzarote was first choice, our Alyson had recommended it. As I knew my old lass was living on Tenerife, Los Silos is the village name, I decided it might be a good idea to book for Los Christianos and pay the old girl a surprise visit during our stay.

So we flew out on Friday 6th Jan 06, got settled in the apartment and did what holiday makers do for a couple of days. We intended hiring a car for the Tuesday / Wednesday part of the stay and having a trip up to Los Silos on Tuesday.

Anyway plans change as they do sometimes and we decided to hire Monday / Tuesday instead. We travelled the mountainous route to Los Silos and after enquiring in the village as to the where-abouts of my mum's address we arrived at her flat, to be greeted by no answer at the door and a letterbox crammed with mail. CONCERN!!!

A nice Spanish resident in the block informed me that my mum was in hospital, and another Spanish lady very kindly invited me into her flat and made telephone inquiries as to which hospital / ward etc she was in. (thank you senorita) I was all English and they were all Spanish, bit of a kerfuffle to say the least, but we set off on route to the hospital.

We had been on the road since 10 in the morning and it was around 5 in the afternoon when, after numerous stops for directions, we arrived. We got to the ward and a nurse directed us to mum's

bed, in stuttering English the nurse gave us the bad news, "Eve fatal,"
they can't say Ivy (mum's name) in Spanish so the nearest is Eve.
Apparently she had been in dock since the 13th December. Lung
cancer was the diagnosis, (too many tabs.)

Mum never came round, although I swear I detected a flicker of
recognition in her closed eyes as we talked to her. Sadly she passed
away 25 minutes after we arrived. I will never know if she had hung
on in there or was it purely coincidence????........

I had not seen or heard from my old dear since I was 18 (1969)
when out of the blue she rang me in 2002, 33 years later. She told
me she had been living in Tenerife since 1982 and she wanted to put
her affairs in order. I asked if she was doing that because she was
ill, as you do. She assured me that she was ok and not to worry, but
on reflection she must have known her time was coming. We wrote
occasional letters and all was going great for about 6 months, when
all correspondence ceased. I tried to ring but the telephone system
over there is crap, and I had no further calls or letters from her, so I
decided she must have had second thoughts about keeping in touch
and let sleeping dogs lie, that is until we decided on Tenerife instead
of Lanzarote!!!!

There you have it in a nutshell Jane, if you need any more info let
me know and I'll do my best. Cheers Lou x.

So, after thirty three years Lou was finally reunited with his
Mum, literally just before she died! It begs the question who was
pulling what strings to bring them together just before time ran
out... I don't gamble, but I'd love to know the odds on it being a
pure coincidence!

Meeting my guides

Everyone has spirit guides, so I'm told. Some people have the
same one through many lifetimes, some have a team who advise
depending on the subject, some chop and change throughout
their life. Different things work for different people, but the good
news is none of us are ever on our own. (Not even my dear disbelieving husband although I suspect his guide has long given up
and spends most of his time with his feet up, drinking a cup of
Earl Grey tea and reading "The Guardian").

I always took it for granted that there was someone else there with me. From being really tiny I was very much aware of an older, sensible, dispassionate, reasonable voice in my head. I used to think it was the voice of my "conscience" because when I asked Aunty Mary who it was that was her explanation. Imagine, then, my surprise when I first saw "Pinocchio" and his conscience was a little green cricket called Jiminy! I never cared for insects at the best of times, much less one sitting permanently on my shoulder; I decided Walt Disney had definitely got it wrong!

I suppose the first guide I could put a name to would have been Jenny; the older girl who used to materialise next to me in my Nana's mirror. I didn't immediately connect her to the voice in my head. I thought she only appeared when I looked for her in the mirror, whereas the voice in my head was around a lot of the time. Not to confuse this with my own internal chatterbox that has been going on since as long as I can remember, my chatterbox always corresponds to the age I am at – when I was a child it raised the worries and questions of a child etc. The voice of my "conscience" has always been much more mature and totally reasonable.

The next guide I was introduced to was when I was around fourteen or fifteen; it was when I first experienced the spiritualist church.

For a few weeks I'd been having the compulsive urge to cross myself in the way the Catholics do. This was rather strange as I came from a non-religious family and I hadn't really come across people doing it in my daily life. It almost felt like a nervous tick, for no reason at all I would have to fight the urge to make the sign of the cross at any given opportunity. I also kept getting the name Maria whispered in my ear. It was all very odd.

One particular evening after the service, my friend, her family and I stopped back for tea and biscuits. Just as we were about to leave, the medium, a kindly old gentleman, came across and shook my hand.

"I just have to tell you," he said, "you have the most lovely nun with you, she's been sitting with you all evening, I have a feeling she must be your guide."

I thanked him politely and then as we left the church I asked my friend's mum what on earth he'd been talking about. She explained about spirit guides, to my satisfaction.

I was quite amazed to think anyone would consider me worth following around. Still, suddenly all the Catholic gesturing made sense – clearly Sister Maria was making quite an impression on me. I thanked her for her interest in me but pointed out, in that no-nonsense way that teenagers have, that I was not a Catholic, wouldn't be converting to one, and although I was quite happy for her to hang around if she wished she could keep all her crossing to herself thank you!

I found the urge to cross myself ceased from that moment on, but I do believe she hung around for several years, as between fifteen and nineteen I entered quite a spiritual phase. Reading and studying the bible, although as always reaching my own very definite conclusions as to the different texts, generally feeling much calmer and at peace with the world, and I took to wearing a cross, for no other reason than it really "felt good". I still had no desire to join any particular church or devote myself to any one religion, although Jesus became my hero insofar as anyone who could heal people and be so selfless and wise got my vote any day!

Throughout my twenties and early thirties I have no idea whose thankless task it became to guide me, I was far too angry at God, the Universe and everything to listen to or commune with anyone. I didn't really question whose voice it was I heard for some time. I assumed if it wasn't my own it must be one of my numerous relatives now residing on the other side – I had totally forgotten the concept of spirit guides.

It wasn't until I joined the psychic circle that the issue came up again. We had done our usual prayers, meditations, and opened up our chakras. Everyone was feeling nice and relaxed; as usual the room felt slightly chilled and was a little misty.

The leading medium announced that tonight we would get to know our spirit guide. She bade us all close our eyes, relax, and see who approached us. I must confess my inner sceptic piped up again at this. "Oh yeah, just who are you going to dream up for yourself now then?" I tried my best to shut it out and make my mind as empty as possible from any preconceived ideas – I wondered how many of us were going to end up with Chief Sitting Bull at this point!

I sat for about five minutes trying desperately not to let my mind drift off at a tangent, when slowly I became aware that I was now standing on sand, barefoot, with waves lapping around my toes. As I looked up a man dressed in blue robes with golden hair and beard and piercing blue eyes stood before me. He smiled.

"My name is Peter, I have been your guide for many years," I heard him say, although his lips never moved.

The medium called us back to the here and now; I was vaguely surprised to find myself still sitting in the circle with perfectly dry feet. Of course, being me, after the meeting I put my spirit guide to the back of my mind, that sceptical side trying as usual to convince me he was the product of an overactive imagination.

A few years passed and suddenly here I was trying to write this book. I found things flowing effortlessly at first, but when I came to the more technical side, like trying to organise all these random thoughts, stories, experiences into a format that made sense I began to struggle. I need to call in more help, I thought.

I had been reading about angels briefly one day, and I wondered if there were any around to assist me. As most of my introductions come whilst asleep I made a request before nodding off one night to be introduced to anyone who might be of service.

In the middle of the night I awoke as if shaken, as I was coming out of my slumber my eyes focused on two shining figures standing in the doorway.

"Our names are Uriel and Ariel," said a voice, then I was fully awake and they were gone. I must confess, even though I had requested an introduction, I was still surprised. I had expected something strange, dreamlike and surreal to occur, not a nice straight forward "here we are, how d'y do" scenario. Still, I was extremely impressed by the promptness with which they had shown up!

The next day I did a bit of research over the internet to see if I could find out anything about these co-creators of "the book".

Uriel (it turns out) is a patron of literature and music. He bestows on us the gift of creative fire, as well as the power of prophecy. He also helps in developing our psychic abilities and is an angel of transformation. He is the spirit of ministration and peace. Uriel is an archangel and his name means Light or Fire of God. I must say I felt very impressed and honoured to have him on board for the ride! Ariel, also spelt as Auriel sometimes, is just described as the "angel of destiny", which hopefully means he is guiding me along the right path!

Caught up in a wave of enthusiasm for this new way of meeting and greeting celestial folk I decided to ask for an introduction to my spirit guide the following night.

As before, I suddenly awakened in the middle of the night, yes, you might have guessed, to a smiling bearded chap who reminded me patiently that his name was Peter; he was far too gracious to add that he'd told me that already. At least I was now convinced that our previous encounter hadn't been a figment of my imagination.

So, with the assistance of my trusty companions, I soldiered on with "the book" until Christmas arrived with its numerous distractions. I set it aside temporarily, only to find on the return I was once more struggling to get back into the flow.

One day I was chatting, as you do, to Peter, now that I was totally convinced of his existence. I happened to mention that I was almost there but really struggling with this last bit and could he help a bit more, or if he was busy, perhaps he knew of someone else who could lend a hand.

I woke in the middle of that night to a song being sung loud and clear, and very beautifully, in my head. I lay there puzzled, then realised I recognised the song; it was from an old Olivia Newton John movie called Xanadu, and the song was called "Magic". I hadn't seen or heard the song in over twenty five years, in fact I'd totally forgotten its existence, yet here was someone singing it, word perfect, in my ear as I slept.

I won't trouble you with the entire song, but the message encapsulated in it is that you have to find your path, follow your dreams, and you will be guided every step along the way!

You can imagine that to have such clear confirmation of someone's intention to assist me was breathtaking. I was enraptured by this beautiful voice and uplifting promise.

As the singing came to a stop I enquired the name of my new assistant. Gold letters appeared in my mind – Alicia. As I started to fall asleep again I suddenly remembered the concept of the film, the character Olivia Newton John played was a muse!

Who better to help me finish this book, I thought as I fell into unconsciousness once more.

So there you have it, I now have an archangel, an angel, a spirit guide and a muse all aiding and abetting in this twisting, winding tale, not to mention my mother popping in every now and again saying in an exasperated voice, "Haven't you finished it yet?"

To be fair I did tell her I'd have my first book published by the time I was sixteen, so I am dragging my heels a little – sorry Mother!

Conclusion

Every life begins a journey, what we need to understand is that death is not necessarily the end of that journey.

I began this story with tales of those who had gone before, wonderful people, whose bloodline I am very privileged to share. When I began to unravel the threads of the past I learned a great many things I did not know, not only about them, but about myself.

I sometimes think I arrived on this planet a wiser soul than I will depart it, but hopefully this voyage of discovery I find myself on will rectify that.

Ancestors and Angels, the book, has gone through a great many incarnations to get to this final stage. Every time I thought I knew where I was going with it, it would twist away in another direction. My hands might have typed the final transcript but I sometimes think other minds than mine dictated the text.

Four long years have passed since I first scribbled rough ideas in a note book I would then discard and forget about. Three years since I left my job on a whim to write my first book. How time flies…it is almost a century since Mary Holdcroft came back to life in the mortuary and declared she'd been to the other side, and was allowed back to say goodbye one last time. (The women in my family are so stubborn!).

Of course, they have all come back, in their own way, and in their own time. I need you to know that I am not in any way special or unique, my family may be quite adept at cutting through the veil, but they are not alone in this.

We are all born with a sixth sense, but often it diminishes because the other five are less subtle. Animals still communicate telepathically but humans have learned to speak. We see with our eyes but we pay less attention to the visions in our heads.

There are so many things that we take for granted these days, mobile phones, televisions, satellite pictures from other continents beamed around the world in the blink of an eye. How far fetched would that have seemed once?

Our technology is based on vibrational frequencies. Our souls are likewise just vibrations on an even higher frequency. So many people can accept the one, but struggle with the other.

I am not a scientist, and I follow no religion. I have drawn the conclusions and formed the opinions espoused in this book through my own and others' experiences, through reading a vast quantity of texts, through experimenting and taking part in many weird and wonderful things.

It is not my job to convince you or persuade you to believe one way or another. I am here to entertain and intrigue and hopefully delight you. I am merely a writer, not some new age spiritual guru (anyway, don't you at least need to grow a beard for that?).

The universe is a vast expansive place full of miraculous things. I urge you to go out into it and experience life for yourself. If you should find anything weird or wonderful be sure to write and relate it to me.

I have many more stories to tell.

Epilogue

The quest continues…

I was working furiously on this book for the best part of three years and every question answered seemed to lead to more questions. Not that that bothered me, I was hungry to learn everything I could on this exciting journey… where would it lead next?

This was pretty much the question I would fall asleep asking my guides and angels each night…

What next? Tell me more!

Then for three consecutive nights I had the same bewildering dream. I was standing at the foot of a long table, around which sat men in frock coats, one woman, and a chap who looked remarkably like Abraham Lincoln (well, he was wearing a top hat at any rate) was sitting at the head.

Each night we held long discussions and this Lincoln look-a-like and a distinguished looking chap with a grey beard would confer, then give me further instructions. And every morning when I woke up I would have forgotten what they were!

So, on the third encounter, when I asked again what I was meant to be doing next, instead of telling me what it was, they made the word appear in gold letters hanging in the air.

"You must study…" said the grey bearded chap, and lo and behold there it was. The word THEOSOPHY.

I remembered that the next morning but I didn't know what it was, and neither did Mark. (Which is very unusual!)

So I looked it up; Theosophy is of Greek origin, and means "Wisdom of the Gods" It is a truth that must be discovered and experienced by each person for themselves. There is a Theosophical Society in England that is dedicated to the comparative study of religion, science and philosophy and practices the art of self-realisation. The society is comprised of many people from various religions and backgrounds and is based on a belief that mankind is a spiritual family and that mankind can have a glorious future through a compassionate and intelligent way of living.

I looked through several sources to get my head around this new idea and was taken by surprise to come across a photo of the grey bearded man in my dream. It turns out this chap was Henry Steel Olcott who alongside Madame Helena Blavatsky (presumably the only other female present in my dream) co-founded and established the Theosophical Society.

I was further intrigued to discover Olcott was one of the three men commissioned to investigate the assassination of Abraham Lincoln. It seems they have struck up a friendship on the other side!

So what does all this mean?

Well, for me, it means I still have a lot to learn in my quest for the meaning of life, the universe and everything, and for you, if you still want to come along for the ride, it means... you'll have to wait for the next instalment!

I've already started on the next two books, hope to see you all there!

Jane Cranmer, December 13th 2010,
just after tea, sitting in the dining room, drinking wine.

About the Author

Jane Cranmer is a fifty-some-thing mother of three grown-up children and devoted Nana to two grandsons.

Married to Mark for a very long time (in her words), she would describe her upbringing as Enid Blyton meets The Twilight Zone with a touch of Shameless thrown in for good measure.

Her hobbies are, unsurprisingly, the extensive study and research of all things paranormal, quantum physics, ancient and modern reli-gions, theosophy, reading and writing. She has lived most of her life in Yorkshire (God's own county, so they say) but in recent years has moved to Cornwall, lured away by the siren song of the sea - when you've had enough of the wildness of the moors and wallowed in the mists for a spell, it's nice to be amongst the Faerie folk occasionally.

Jane is currently researching all aspects of the paranormal and would love to hear your stories, you can contact her on Facebook on her Author page. Jane Cranmer Author of Ancestors & Angels.

Everyone has a book in them, or so they say... Do you?

If you are an artist, performance poet, musician or storyteller who aspires to see your work in print, contact us to discuss your project.

LS Arts is a Yorkshire-based independent publisher specialising in books with creative content. We publish titles of special interest:

- *Local histories and biographies*
- *Music histories and biographies*
- *Sports biographies*
- *Poetry books and plays*
- *Satirical postcards and calendars*
- *Books for schools and education*

Interested in working with us?

We offer a full in-house design service. We can take your work from a typed manuscript, through every aspect of the design process, to print and distribution.

Interested in stocking our products?

Indie bookshops, music shops, arts centres and coffee shops - contact us to receive complimentary copies.

info@leeds-streets.uk
www.leeds-streets.uk

Lightning Source UK Ltd.
Milton Keynes UK
UKHW010431090223
416681UK00003B/1046